INTEGRATED CIRCUITS

MOTOROLA

SERIES IN

SOLID-STATE

ELECTRONICS

The Engineering Staff, Motorola Inc., Semiconductor Products Division   INTEGRATED CIRCUITS

*Prepared by the Engineering Staff, MOTOROLA INC.
Semiconductor Products Division*

Contributors

JAMES R. BAUM

EUGENE A. BLANCHETTE

HOWARD K. DICKEN

JOSEPH C. GORDON

JACK C. HAENICHEN

DWAYNE S. KING

WALTER H. KORNFELD

I. ARNOLD LESK

GLEN R. MADLAND

JOHN E. McNAMARA

GEORGE C. ONODERA

REMO A. PELLIN

ALVIN B. PHILLIPS

RAYMOND M. WARNER, JR.

INTEGRATED CIRCUITS

Design Principles and Fabrication

EDITOR

Raymond M. Warner, Jr.

DIRECTOR OF ENGINEERING
MOTOROLA INC., SEMICONDUCTOR PRODUCTS DIVISION

ASSOCIATE EDITOR

James N. Fordemwalt

PROJECT MANAGER
MOTOROLA INC., SEMICONDUCTOR PRODUCTS DIVISION

ASSISTANT EDITORS

Charles S. Meyer
David K. Lynn
Michael J. Callahan
Lothar Stern

M c G R A W - H I L L   B O O K   C O M P A N Y

New York   San Francisco   Toronto   London   Sydney

43525

4 5 6 7 8 9 – M P – 9 8 7 6

Dedicated to Dr. Daniel E. Noble, Group Executive Vice President, Motorola Inc.,
whose vision and professional encouragement has contributed so much
to the practical realization of today's integrated circuit technology.

FOREWORD

The science of semiconductor technology had its beginning about 1930 with the theoretical work of F. Bloch, A. H. Wilson, and others. For the most part, however, this basic technology remained a pursuit of physicists for the next twenty years. Although many solid-state devices such as microwave detectors had found engineering application during World War II, it was not until the dramatic invention of the transistor in 1948 that the entire field of solid-state physics became, of necessity, a field of vigorous engineering activity. Since that time, the tremendous vigor of American industry has introduced one new device after another and one new process after another, until today, transistor technology has broken frequency, power, reliability, and cost barriers that were considered nearly impossible only five years ago. In addition, we now stand on the threshold of an entirely new technology—that of integrated circuits—which promises to have a greater impact upon electronic systems than did the transistor itself. Although the delay between research and development and between development and production usually seems interminably long to those most actively associated with the construction of engineering devices, it appears in retrospect that in this case the progress has been almost astounding. In fact, it is illuminating to go back to the beginning of the electronic era and look at the basic experiments which led to the development of the vacuum tube, in order to see how our technological timetable has been greatly compressed during the last fifty years.

Actually, as early as 1725 du Fay discovered that the region surrounding a red hot body was a conductor of electricity, but the first definitive experiments which showed conclusively that electrons could pass from a hot filament to a cold plate were performed by Edison in 1883 (158 years after du Fay's observation). Even so, it was not until 1905 that Fleming developed the diode; and DeForest added a third electrode known as the grid in 1907, twenty-four years after Edison's experiments. If the same timetables were in effect today, the first practical engineering device based upon the band theory of solids should not have been invented until approximately today; and this simple device should not have led to a new engineering technology until approximately 1980.

It is not my purpose here to account for the various factors which make this progress possible nor to anticipate the state of the art even twenty years from now if this rate of productivity continues to increase. Instead, it is sufficient merely to point out the tremendously rapid transition that has been made from fundamental physical research to engineering practice in this particular instance, and to contend that this example does not represent an isolated phenomenon, but more nearly describes typical creative engineering activity as it exists today. A natural result of this progress is that we as engineers and as managers find it difficult to accept the rapidity with which technological change is thrust upon us. We naturally draw upon our past experiences to help us judge what actions we should take to prepare for the future. Our problem is that there is no experience we can draw on from the past which will help us to anticipate the tremendous speed with which technological change will come in the future, because the pace of modern technology is always increasing.

Because we try hard to recognize this problem here at Motorola, we feel strongly that the era of integrated circuits is not something which will evolve slowly during the next decade; but it is an era that is already upon us. Those who are not designing equipment today using integrated circuits are already behind the main flow of American technology. It is this firm conviction on our part that led us into sponsoring last year the unprecedented course in integrated circuits which was given to 200 key engineers from all parts of the United States and Europe. Two books on integrated circuit design have evolved from this course. It is our hope that these books will give you the basic knowledge you need in order to apply this exciting and new technology.

None of us knows for certain where this new technology will lead us. It appears evident, however, that we are only at the beginning of a tremendous revolution in electronic system techniques, which has been made possible by mankind's increasing knowledge of the behavior of solid-state materials. We at Motorola think we are fortunate to be part of a profession that allows us to take part in this exciting progress.

Dr. C. Lester Hogan
Vice-president and General Manager
Motorola Inc.
Semiconductor Products Division

PREFACE

Integrated circuits constitute a very significant portion of the burgeoning domain of microelectronics; their interrelationship is described in the following Note on Terminology. This volume is the first of two on integrated circuits, both based on an intensive course presented to the electronics industry by Motorola's Semiconductor Products Division in order to accelerate the understanding and acceptance of this new art.

This volume is generally concerned with circuit design from the standpoint of device and process properties and limitations. It is divided into three parts which progress from theory and principles to a discussion of fabrication practice. At the heart of present-day integrated circuit technology is semiconductor technology, and Part 1 of this book is devoted to the fundamentals of this subject. Properties of bulk semiconductors are treated, and applicable junction theory, including that for the practically important case of diffused junctions. Part 1 concludes with a treatment of transistor engineering, since integrated circuits are built around the transistor. Part 2 takes up the design principles for monolithic and hybrid integrated circuit devices. Particular stress is placed upon the comparison of these approaches, upon the fundamental and state-of-the-art limitations on their capabilities, and upon the nature of the design compromises that are required. In Part 3, then, practical procedures are outlined and compared for actual integrated circuit fabrication.

The second volume based on the Motorola Integrated Circuits course will be concerned with integrated circuit analysis and design. That volume will address the subject of device and circuit models, will describe terminal parameter characterization of integrated circuits, and will outline actual design procedures for both digital and linear circuits. New techniques of analysis and design are introduced in order to handle the increased complexity of circuits in the integrated form.

Although integrated circuit technology is indeed based upon semiconductor technology, in motivation and approach it represents a break with the past of this discipline. The brief history of semiconductor device technology can be sketched rather completely in terms of the techniques—chiefly junction-forming techniques —available to the engineer. Some of these in the sequence of their exploitation were the pressure contact metal-semiconductor junction, the grown-from-the-melt-junction, the alloy-regrowth junction, the electrochemically deposited metal-semiconductor junction, the diffused junction, and most recently the epitaxially grown junction. Following each of these important developments, there was a rush to move into the new area thus opened. Sometimes a new device structure concept was intimately associated with the new technique, as was the mesa transistor with the diffusion process. More often each new technique was applied to the full range of known device possibilities, sometimes providing an advantage and sometimes not. The device designer has provided a reasonable number of new and unique device concepts, but these have had to wait for years (occasionally a decade) for the right process concept to come along. The device designer has been technique-limited.

There is no reason to think that the sequence of important process innovations is at an end, but at least the bag of tricks accessible to the device designer is now full enough so that he usually has more than one process choice open to him when he contemplates the fabrication of a new device. Consequently his work is now inclined to be a little more contemplative than before, and less a helter-skelter pursuit of the latest technique fashion. The new orientation on the part of the device designer is shared by the designer of compatible integrated circuits. Indeed, the latter has an even greater realm open to him—the full range of today's semiconductor technology coupled with thin-film techniques.

It is difficult to pinpoint the beginning of today's integrated circuit concept. Since junctions have capacitance, and semiconductor materials have resistance, it undoubtedly occurred to many people early in the transistor's history that it would be possible to fabricate entire circuits in and on semiconductor crystals. Indeed, limited efforts were made in this direction several years ago, again in the pioneer spirit—the spirit of exploring a new area. This new area of development was so spacious that motivation had to be strong indeed before it could be profitably mapped and investigated.

However, resolute motivation was not long in coming. It became apparent that ever more sophisticated systems with acceptable degrees of reliability cannot be achieved simply by assembling ever larger numbers of ever more sophisticated devices. Even though today's discrete devices exhibit levels of reliability far exceeding those of yesterday, the advances have not been great enough to offset the effect of growth in system complexity and size. Added to this is the problem of achieving ever more reliable interconnections, quite apart from internal device reliability. The relief offered by integrated circuits is primarily in the reduction of the number of separate pieces in a complex system. By-product advantages of circuit integration are smaller size, better temperature tracking and transistor matching, potentially lower cost, and higher speed in so far as speed is affected by the reduced propagation delay associated with smaller size. (There are of course difficulties too, stemming from the new proximity of the circuits and their elements.)

The cost factor just named deserves a further word. The cost per transistor in integrated circuits is quite low, whereas in the conventional circuit the cost of transistors may be a limiting factor in circuit design. The designer of conventional circuits may therefore have to make performance compromises in order to limit the number of transistors.

Beyond the pure reduction in piece count, important as that is, there is in contemporary integrated circuit practice an inherent tendency toward simplification. This tendency can be illustrated by a sequence of events, already a matter of record in our integrated circuits experience, which can be generally outlined as follows: A conventional circuit is designed and tested with conventional discrete components. A monolithic integrated version of the same circuit is designed on paper. It is realized that a design change is possible which would have a trivial effect on circuit performance but which would produce a major simplification in the monolithic structure. The monolithic circuit is fabricated according to the revised design and performs as expected.

In other words, we have opened the door to a new class of circuit refinements—those changes which have important simplifying consequences in the integrated circuit, but which would have no simplifying effect on the conventional progenitor. Further, this kind of simplification can be pursued through orderly procedures. It is too early to say how far integrated circuits, even at their present stage of evolution, will be able to go in raising the limit on system complexity. Perhaps totally new approaches to the large system problem will be devised. But at present the integrated circuit approach is certainly the most promising.

The Motorola Integrated Circuits course represented a substantial effort by a large number of people. The contributions were marshalled in a remarkably short time by the Motorola staff and were put in the form of voluminous loose leaf notebooks provided to each student, supplementing the spoken word. In preparing the present book, the editors began with the written and oral information thus assembled. Given this wealth of starting material, the editors have endeavored to provide unity, coherence, and accuracy, and have sought earnestly to achieve a uniformity of presentation level and style throughout, as well as uniformity in important details such as notation and graphical convention.

It is not possible to enumerate all those whose labors produced the information residing in this book, but at least we can list most of those who contributed directly to manuscript preparation, either at the lecture-note stage or subsequently. Unfortunately even this listing cannot be exhaustive.

Chapters 1 and 2 on basic semiconductor and junction theory were written by the Editor. They are based largely on a series of lectures he presented to Motorola engineers starting in 1960. In preparing the present material he profited from discussions with a number of Motorolans, and in the case of Chap. 1, from material prepared by A. B. Phillips for the Integrated Circuits course. J. E. McNamara wrote the treatise on impurity diffusion which was enlarged to include diffused junction properties, thus constituting Chap. 3. Chapter 4 on transistor engineering is based on lecture notes prepared by A. B. Phillips, which he had in turn derived from his book on this subject.

D. S. King prepared the original material on fundamentals of integrated circuit design, Chap. 5, which opens the discussion of design principles constituting Part 2 of this book. J. E. McNamara and D. S. King wrote Chap. 6 on the subject of multiphase monolithic circuits. Chapter 7 on the key subject of transistors and diodes for monolithic circuits is based on the material originally prepared by A. B. Phillips and E. A. Blanchette. The Editor and G. C. Onodera wrote Chap. 8 on field effect devices for integrated circuits. Chapter 9 on other active devices for integrated circuits was originally prepared by I. A. Lesk, and Chap. 10 on passive components, by H. K. Dicken.

In Part 3, which deals with actual integrated circuit fabrication, Chap. 11 on epitaxial growth was originally written by R. A. Pellin. J. C. Haenichen wrote the lecture notes on wafer processing and assembly processing which were the basis for Chaps. 12 and 14, respectively. Chapter 13 on the subject of thin films is based on material prepared by I. A. Lesk, G. R. Madland, and W. H. Kornfeld. Chapter 15 is derived from the material on packaging originally prepared by J. P. Gordon, and that on thermal design considerations prepared by J. R. Baum.

D. K. Lynn and C. S. Meyer critically and constructively reviewed the first seven chapters and contributed new material to Chaps. 4 and 7. M. J. Callahan reviewed the first four chapters and prepared Appendix A. Much of Parts 2 and 3 of this volume were adapted from original lecture notes by J. N. Fordemwalt. L. Stern reviewed the entire final manuscript for clarity and style.

The Editors wish to thank all the authors for their patience and their whole hearted cooperation. Also, we would like to thank our unusually competent repro-typist, Mrs. H. L. McKeown, who provided an indispensable degree of continuity throughout this long task. Finally, we are extremely grateful to the numerous anonymous Motorolans who made positive contributions to this project.

R. M. Warner, Jr.

CONTENTS

PART 1 SEMICONDUCTOR AND TRANSISTOR FUNDAMENTALS

xv

A NOTE ON TERMINOLOGY

Because different people mean different things when they talk about integrated circuits, the first step will be to define what *we* mean by integrated circuits in this book. Almost everyone agrees on the general principles involved, but the terminology actually may differ from organization to organization (or even from person to person within a given organization). A number of papers have been given on the subject of integrated circuit terminology, and a recommended set of definitions* has been published by the Electronic Industries Association.

One of the ways of categorizing the field of microelectronics is shown here in chart form (Fig. I). In this chart, the entire field of microelectronics is arbitrarily broken into three major categories: discrete components, integrated circuits, and a third, unlabeled box which has been called by a variety of names, including "functional devices," "integrated morphology," "molecular electronics," etc.

In the discrete components approach to microelectronics, small but otherwise conventional components are assembled in some orderly fashion in small, high-density assemblies, e.g., the micromodule. The third, unlabeled category includes solid-state entities which perform a particular circuit function, but in which individual components, *normally* identified with that circuit function, cannot be identified with any specific portion of the solid-state material. One of the best examples of this type of device is a quartz filter, which displays the circuit characteristics of a tuned circuit, although the inductance normally associated with a tuned circuit cannot be identified in the quartz.

Integrated circuits, the second category in Fig. I, can be further subdivided into two major categories, viz., thin-film circuits and semiconductor circuits. Two special cases of thin-film circuits are shown—cryogenic and magnetic—together with the thin-film circuits of more general circuit applicability involving passive and active components. In this latter approach, the passive components, such as resistors and capacitors, together with interconnections, are obtained by thin-film deposition techniques, and then active components, such as diodes and transistors, are added separately.

* Recommended Terminology in Microsystem Electronics, *Microsystem Electron. Bull.* 1, Electronic Industries Association, New York, December, 1962.

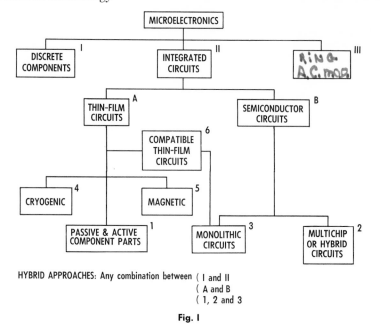

HYBRID APPROACHES: Any combination between (I and II
                                         (A and B
                                         (1, 2 and 3

Fig. I

Although thin-film circuits will be discussed, this book is primarily concerned with the second subdivision of integrated circuits, that of semiconductor circuits. This approach can be further subdivided into two categories. In the first of these categories, monolithic circuits, an entire circuit function is constructed in a single block of semiconductor material. The second category, which is a variation of the first, is sometimes called the "multichip circuit" approach, and in this book is called the "hybrid circuit" approach. In this approach, two or more semiconductor blocks, each containing circuit components, e.g., resistors, capacitors, transistors, and/or diodes, are interconnected to form a complete circuit, and assembled in a single package.

Finally, there are numerous variations of the approaches shown on the chart, which also may be called hybrid approaches, involving combinations of the various approaches shown. For example, thin-film techniques can be used to provide resistance and/or capacitance, while the remainder of the circuit functions are performed by multichip, hybrid circuits, and/or monolithic circuits. Only the more important of these hybrid approaches are shown in Fig. I as compatible thin-film circuits. In this case thin-film techniques are used to deposit passive elements, e.g., resistance and capacitance, directly on a silicon substrate, which includes other components, such as transistors and diodes, and possibly additional resistors and capacitors.

R. L. Pritchard

GLOSSARY OF SYMBOLS AND PHYSICAL CONSTANTS

A Area

$Å$ Angstrom unit $= 10^{-8}$ cm

A_E Emitter area

A_s Effective area of surface recombination

a Concentration gradient (grade constant)

a_c Half thickness of FET channel

α Current gain for common base operation

α_o Low-frequency small-signal current gain for common base configuration

α_i Inverted common base current gain

α_n Current gain of the p-n-p portion of a p-n-p-n diode or triode

α_p Current gain of the n-p-n portion of a p-n-p-n diode or triode

BV_{CBO} Breakdown voltage of the collector junction (emitter open-circuited)

BV_{CEO} Collector-emitter breakdown voltage (base open-circuited)

BV_{CES} Collector-emitter breakdown voltage (emitter junction short-circuited)

BV_{CS} Breakdown voltage of the collector-substrate junction

BV_{EBO} Breakdown voltage of the emitter junction (collector open-circuited)

BV_{GDS} Breakdown voltage gate to drain and source

β Common emitter current gain (h_{FE})

β_o Low-frequency small-signal common emitter current gain

C Capacitance

C_D Diode capacitance

C_P Parasitic capacitance

$C_T(0)$ Transition-region capacitance per unit area for a junction at equilibrium

C_T Junction transition-region capacitance per unit area

C_{TC} Collector junction transition-region capacitance (total)

C_{TE} Emitter junction transition-region capacitance (total)

C_{TS} Substrate junction transition-region capacitance (total)

γ Emitter efficiency

D	Diffusion coefficient
D_n	Electron diffusion constant
D_{nB}	Electron diffusion constant in the base
D_o	Pre-exponential factor in the general diffusion equation
D_p	Hole diffusion constant
D_{pE}	Hole diffusion constant in the emitter
d	Distance
d	Diameter
E	Energy
E_C	Conduction band lower-edge energy
E_F	Fermi-level energy
E_G	Energy gap between the valence and conduction bands
E_V	Valence band upper-edge energy
E_i	Impurity ionization energy
e	Base of the natural logarithm
$\mathscr{E}$	Electric field
$\mathscr{E}_m$	Maximum or peak electric field
ϵ_o	Permittivity of free space $= 8.85 \times 10^{-14}$ farad/cm
f	Rate of flow or flux
f	Frequency
f_C	Frequency at which Q equals unity
$f(E)$	Fermi distribution function
f_T	Common emitter current-gain-bandwidth product in cycles per second
$f_{\max}$	Maximum frequency of oscillation
f_o	Center frequency
f_p	Frequency at which Q peaks
f_α	Alpha cutoff frequency
f_β	Beta cutoff frequency
G	Conductance
G_e	Grounded-emitter power gain
G_o	Initial or low-voltage conductance of FET channel
g	Charge generation rate
g_m	Transconductance
g_{mo}	Initial or low-voltage transconductance
ΔH	Activation energy
h	Planck's constant $= 6.62 \times 10^{-27}$ erg sec
h_{FE}	See β
η	Unijunction transistor standoff ratio
θ	Phase angle for common base current
I	Current

I_B Base current

I_C Collector current

I_{CBO} Collector-base reverse current with open-circuited emitter

I_{CEO} Collector-emitter reverse current (open base)

I_{CO} Leakage current in a reverse-biased junction

I_D FET drain current

I_E Emitter current

I_{EBO} Emitter-base reverse current with open-circuited collector

I_F Forward current (through a junction)

I_H Hold current in a p-n-p-n diode or triode

I_J Current injected in a unijunction transistor by the junction

I_P FET pinch-off current

I_R Reverse current (through a junction)

I_{RE} Emitter recombination current

I_g Charge generation current

I_{nE} Emitter electron current

I_o Current through a p-n-p-n diode or triode in the ON or conducting state

I_p Tunnel diode peak current

I_{pE} Emitter hole current

I_{sB} Surface-recombination base current

I_v Tunnel diode valley current

I_{vB} Volume-recombination base current

J Current density

J_n Electron current density

J_p Hole current density

J_s Saturation current density

j Imaginary unit such that $j^2 = -1$

K Equilibrium distribution coefficient

K_t Thermal conductivity

k Boltzmann's constant $= 1.38 \times 10^{-16}$ erg/deg K

κ Dielectric constant, or relative dielectric permittivity

L_D Extrinsic Debye length

L_i Intrinsic Debye length

L_n Diffusion length for electrons

L_{nB} Diffusion length for electrons in the base

L_p Diffusion length for holes

L_{pE} Diffusion length for holes in emitter

l Quantum number indicating electron orbital angular momentum

l Length

l_C Length of the collector

l_E Length of the emitter

l_b Length of an edge of the collector-base junction

l_c Length of an inner edge of the collector stripe

λ An integration variable

M Avalanche-current multiplication factor

m Quantum number indicating spatial orientation of electron orbital angular momentum

m Excess phase

m Mass of the free electron

m_n Effective electron mass

m_p Effective hole mass

μ Carrier mobility

μ Amplification factor

$\bar{\mu}$ Average carrier mobility

μ_n Electron mobility

μ_p Hole mobility

N Net impurity concentration

N Total number of atoms in a system

$\bar{N}$ Average net density of the dominant impurity

N_A Acceptor impurity concentration

N_{BC} Background impurity concentration

N_B' Net impurity concentration in the base near the emitter junction

N_C Equivalent density of states in the conduction band

N_D Donor impurity concentration

$N(E)$ Number of states per unit energy interval and unit volume

N_M Maximum net donor concentration in FET channel

N_V Equivalent density of states in the valence band

N_c Net impurity in FET channel

N_g Impurity concentration in the gas phase

N_o Surface impurity concentration

$N(x)$ Impurity concentration as a function of distance

N_1, N_2 Net impurity concentrations on the two sides of an unsymmetrical step junction

n Exponent in the avalanche multiplication equation

n Quantum number indicating approximately the total energy of an electron

n Conduction electron concentration or density

n_{BE} Electron concentration in the base at the emitter junction

n_D Density of electrons bound to donors

n_i Intrinsic concentration of holes, electrons

n_n Electron concentration in n region

n_o Nonequilibrium electron concentration induced by external means

n_p Electron concentration in p region

n_{pB} Equilibrium concentration of electrons in p-type base

n^+ Heavily doped with n-type impurities

ξ Pinch-off point in FET

P Probability

P_t Total power dissipation

p Hole concentration or density

p_A Density of holes bound to acceptors

p_{BE} Hole concentration in the base at the emitter junction

p_n Hole concentration in n region

p_{nE} Equilibrium concentration of holes in n-type emitter

p_o Nonequilibrium hole concentration induced by external means

p_p Hole concentration in p region

p^+ Heavily doped with p-type impurities

Q Electrical charge

Q Total charge per unit area on one side of a junction

Q Surface impurity concentration per unit area

Q Quality factor for a reactive element

Q_p Value of a point charge

Q_v Charge per unit volume

q Charge on the electron $= 1.60 \times 10^{-19}$ coul

R Resistance

R Universal gas constant $= 1.987$ cal/deg mole

R_L Load resistance

R_S Sheet resistance

R_{SB} Sheet resistance of the base

R_{SC} Sheet resistance of the collector

R_{SE} Sheet resistance of the emitter

R_{cs} Case-to-surface thermal resistance

R_{in} Input resistance

R_{ju} Junction-to-ultimate-sink thermal resistance

R_{out} Output resistance

R_s Series resistance

R_{sa} Surface-to-atmosphere thermal resistance

r Distance from a position in question; radius vector magnitude

r_B' Base resistance

r_D FET drain radius

r_S FET source radius

r_{SC} Collector series (bulk) resistance

r_{SC}' Series resistance of the entire collector region over the area of the substrate capacitance

r_{SE} Emitter bulk resistance

r_e Dynamic emitter-junction resistance

r_o Radius of filamentary FET channel

ρ Resistivity

$\bar{\rho}$ Average resistivity

ρ_B Base resistivity

ρ_C Collector resistivity

ρ_E Emitter resistivity

s Quantum number indicating orientation in space of electron spin angular momentum

s Surface recombination velocity

s Complex frequency variable; the operator d/dt

s_p Spacing of four-point-probe points

σ Conductivity

σ Real part of the complex frequency variable s

$\bar{\sigma}$ Average conductivity

σ_i Conductivity of intrinsic silicon

T Temperature in degrees Kelvin (°K)

T_c Temperature at cube-center case

T_j Temperature at junction

T_s Temperature at surface

T_u Temperature at ultimate heat sink

t Time

t_{OFF} Turn-off time

t_{ON} Turn-on time

t_d Average collector depletion layer transit time

t_{dr} Diode recovery time

t_f Fall time

t_r Rise time

t_s Storage time

τ Carrier lifetime

τ_B Carrier lifetime in the base

τ_{nc} Electron lifetime in the collector

τ_s Storage time constant

V Voltage; applied voltage

V_B Breakdown voltage

V_{BE} Base-emitter voltage

$V_{BE(OFF)}$ Emitter reverse-bias voltage to turn transistor OFF

$V_{BE(ON)}$ Base-emitter voltage in the active region

V_{BO} Breakover voltage of a p-n-p-n diode or triode

$V_{B_1B_2}$ Voltage between base 1 and base 2 in a unijunction transistor

V_C Collector voltage

V_{CB} Collector-base voltage

V_{CC} Collector supply voltage

V_{CE} Collector-emitter voltage

$V_{CE(SAT)}$ Grounded-emitter saturation voltage (collector saturation voltage)

V_D FET drain voltage

V_E Emitter voltage

V_F Forward voltage (on a junction)

V_G Bandgap in volts

V_G FET gate voltage

V_{J_1} Potential at the junction edge closest to base 1 in a unijunction transistor

V_P FET pinch-off voltage

V_P Unijunction transistor peak voltage

V_{PT} Punch-through voltage

V_R Reverse voltage (on a junction)

V_S FET source voltage

V_b Bias voltage

V_o Voltage across a p-n-p-n diode or triode in the OFF or blocking state

V_p Tunnel diode peak voltage

V_t Total voltage

V_v Tunnel diode valley voltage

v_D Average drift velocity

v_s Signal voltage

v_{sc} Average scattering-limited velocity for carriers in an electric field

φ Fermi level in volts

φ_n Fermi level in n region

φ_p Fermi level in p region

X Distance for transition from nearly complete depletion to nearly complete neutrality

X Thickness of a layer

X_B Base thickness

X_C Collector thickness

X_j Diffused layer thickness; junction depth

X_m Total depletion layer thickness

X_1 Partial depletion layer thickness for a diffused junction; that portion lying toward the surface

X_2 Partial depletion layer thickness for a diffused junction; that portion lying toward the interior

x Distance

x_j Junction position; junction depth

ψ Electrostatic potential

ψ_n Electrostatic potential in n region

ψ_o Electrostatic contact potential barrier or "built-in voltage" for a junction

ψ_p Electrostatic potential in p region

z Lateral extent of FET channel

ω Angular frequency

ω_B Intrinsic cutoff angular frequency of a uniformly doped base

ω_C Reciprocal of the collector RC time constant

ω_E Reciprocal of the emitter RC time constant

ω_T Common emitter current-gain-bandwidth product in radians per second ($\omega_T = 2\pi f_T$)

ω_α Alpha cutoff angular frequency

ω_β Beta cutoff angular frequency

Part **1**

SEMICONDUCTOR AND TRANSISTOR FUNDAMENTALS

1

BASIC SEMICONDUCTOR PHYSICS

Today's integrated circuits have their roots firmly planted in semiconductor technology. Hence this chapter outlines the principles of semiconductor physics. The treatment is aimed at the man who is or who will become an integrated circuits engineer. The material is largely descriptive, but becomes quantitative at points where this will contribute to a basic grasp of the subject, or where the information is of a type that has everyday utility to the practicing engineer.

The ideas in this chapter are developed in what, it is hoped, is a logical sequence designed for straight-through reading. An upper division student in engineering or science should have no difficulty in reading it in this manner, and the graduate engineer may find that a reading of this chapter constitutes worthwhile review. The reader who seeks information in depth should consult the bibliography at the end of this chapter. Reference 3, in particular, is brief but comprehensive and has an extensive list of primary references.

Part 1 of this volume is mainly concerned with theory. It starts with the broad base of semiconductor bulk properties in this chapter, proceeds to the still broad subject of p-n junctions in Chap. 2, through diffused junctions in Chap. 3, and then to basic transistor theory. That such a large fraction of a book on integrated circuits should ostensibly be aimed at the junction transistor may at first be surprising. However, the bipolar junction transistor is clearly the heart of present-day integrated circuits. Further, the transistor embodies most of the properties and effects invoked by supporting elements in monolithic integrated circuits, so that a basic understanding of the transistor equips an engineer to begin a specialized study of these other elements.

1-1 Band Structure in Solids

The electrons in an isolated atom can exist only in certain well-defined energy states. These states or modes of motion are characterized by specific values of four quantum numbers.   These are n, a number which designates approximately the total energy of the electron; l, a number designating the magnitude of the orbital angular momentum; m, a number indicating the orientation in space of the orbital angular momentum; and s, a number indicating the orientation in space of the electron's spin angular momentum.   Further, according to the Pauli exclusion principle, each of these allowed states in a given system can accommodate only one electron.   (In the present case the "system" is an isolated atom.)   Thus, when a proper complement of electrons is added to an atom, these will fill the available states, starting at the lowest energy and proceeding upward in energy until all of the electrons are exhausted.

As two atoms approach each other and begin to interact, the corresponding energy levels in the two atoms, originally at the same energy, will begin to separate in energy.   This is sometimes termed energy level *splitting*.   The higher energy states corresponding to outer-shell electrons will split first as the two atoms are slowly brought together; on the other hand, splitting of the lowest energy states occupied by the innermost core electrons may require physically unrealizable proximity.   It is also true that the magnitude of the splitting, or the separation in energy of the two states produced from a single level, will increase as the strength of interaction increases.

Mechanical Oscillator Analogy.   These principles can be illustrated nicely by means of a mechanical analogy.   Figure 1-1 represents a pair of mechanical oscillators incorporating identical springs and masses and moving in frictionless slides. When they are completely independent, they each exhibit the same resonant frequency of vertical oscillation.   Then let them be coupled by a weak, massless spring as suggested in Fig. 1-1.   Now they can oscillate in unison with a frequency identical to that observed before, since the coupling spring contributes nothing to this motion.   But if they oscillate in opposition, the coupling spring lends stiffness to the system and the natural frequency of oscillation is raised.   That is, interaction of the oscillators through the coupling spring has led to a splitting of the natural frequency into two values corresponding to two different oscillation modes.   Oscillation frequency in this case is the analogue of electronic energy in the atomic case.   Thus the analogy is particularly appealing because in quantum mechanics, energy is proportional to frequency.

Though the analogy is crude, it can be pressed somewhat further: Increasing the strength of the coupling spring will clearly produce a larger separation of the two natural frequencies.   Beyond this, consider the effect of increasing the system to three coupled oscillators.   There will now be three natural frequencies corresponding to three modes of oscillation: In one case the masses will again oscillate in unison at the natural frequency of

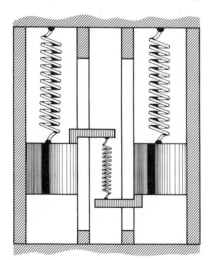

Fig. 1-1 A pair of coupled mechanical oscillators.

an unperturbed oscillator. A higher frequency will be exhibited in the mode wherein the center mass is stationary and the outer two move in opposition. A still higher frequency will be observed in the case where the two outer masses move in unison and in opposition to the center mass.

Each new oscillator added to the coupled system will contribute an additional natural frequency. In an analogous way, a total of N interacting atoms will exhibit a grouping of N electronic energy levels in place of a single level of the isolated atom. This grouping or set of closely spaced levels is referred to as an energy *band*. The spacing of the constituent energy states is so small that for many purposes the band is treated as a continuum of allowed states. To develop a feeling for this situation consider, for example, that there are 50 billion atoms in a cubic micron of single-crystal silicon. Since the energy bands of interest to us have an overall width on the order of an electron volt, it is clear that the constituent levels have a spacing which is indeed small, even in such a microscopic specimen.

Band Structure of Some Column IV Elements. For a somewhat more detailed consideration of band structure in a solid, it is instructive to visualize a crystal having a number of atoms equal to N, in which atomic spacing can be varied at will within wide limits. Let us then plot electronic energy levels vertically and assumed atomic spacing horizontally, as shown in Fig. 1-2. The theoretical information presented here applies in general to the diamond structure, and thus applies in particular to crystalline silicon. For large spacings, of course, we see the system of discrete energy levels associated with an isolated atom. As atomic spacing is diminished from very large values, splitting will occur, with the higher levels being the first to split. (For example, compare n-shell levels and $(n - 1)$-shell levels.) With a somewhat smaller atomic spacing the energy bands will merge. This signals a new electronic behavior in the crystal, and from this point toward still

$l \equiv$ ORBITAL ANGULAR MOMENTUM STATE

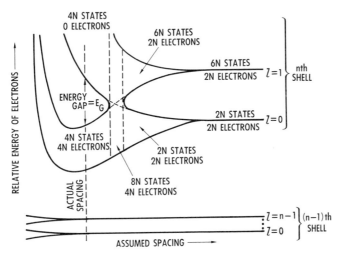

Fig. 1-2 Theoretical energy level scheme versus atomic spacing for the diamond structure. (*After Adler and Longini.* [1])

smaller spacings a simple identification of states in the crystal with the original state in the isolated atom is no longer possible. As Fig. 1-2 shows, at the spacing realized in an actual crystal there is once more an *energy gap* between the two bands of interest. Furthermore, the lower band has a number of electrons ($4N$) precisely equal to the number of available states, and is thus completely filled, while the upper band is empty, provided the electrons reside in the lowest states available to them. It may seem strange that the actual atomic spacing for the crystal is larger than that required to give the electronic system minimum energy. This condition is brought about by the mutual repulsion of the atomic nuclei. At the actual spacing the overall atomic system is at an energy minimum.

Let us focus on three elements from column IV of the periodic table: carbon, silicon, and germanium. Each of these can form crystals having the diamond structure for which the energy diagram of Fig. 1-2 is applicable. Though these crystals have qualitative similarities such as hardness, they have important quantitative differences in other properties. Among these properties energy gap E_G is preeminent. Table 1-1 gives the room-temperature values of E_G for the three materials. At room temperature in pure germanium a significant number of electrons in the crystal acquire enough energy to make a transition from the lower band to the upper band. (As temperature increases, increasing numbers of electrons acquire enough energy to make this transition.) In pure silicon a far smaller number of electrons can achieve this feat because the gap in silicon is more than 50 per cent larger than in germanium, but nonetheless, the number is still significant. The presence of electrons in the almost empty upper band imparts enough conductivity to pure silicon and germanium to cause them to be *semiconductors*. In carbon (diamond) on the other hand, conductivity is so low that we class it as an *insulator*. Its upper band is almost completely empty at room temperature because of diamond's tremendous energy gap. The important point to be made here is that semiconductors and insulators differ only in degree; both incorporate bands which are either completely full or completely empty at absolute zero.

Table 1-1   Energy Gap Values at Room Temperature

In electron volts

Carbon	6–7
Silicon	1.11
Germanium	0.72

Conductors, however, differ in kind from semiconductors and insulators. Conductors are characterized by a band which is partially filled even at absolute zero. An understanding of this situation can be secured by considering the region of band overlap in Fig. 1-2 to be larger, extending to the left, well beyond the line representing actual atomic spacing. In a metal, indeed, bands stemming from several of the discrete levels of the isolated atom become enmeshed at the actual atomic spacing, and the result is a broad band of states only fractionally filled with electrons, no matter what the temperature.

1-2   The Fermi Distribution Function and Fermi Level

The preceding section described how the energy states available to electrons in solids exist in groups or energy bands; the states in a band are so numerous and so closely spaced that it is valid to treat a band as a continuum of states. Now we wish to inquire how the electrons in a solid will distribute themselves in energy.

An analogy given by Shive[2] aids visualization of the electronic distribution in energy. Figure 1-3a represents a container of water which is subjected to agitation so that the water's surface has been disturbed. The stylized waves are to represent the disturbance. Let us now ask what is the probability of finding water in the container at a given height h, measured above an arbitrary reference level such as the bottom of the container. Figure 1-3b is a plot of height against probability P. Such a function can reasonably be used to describe the distribution of water in the container.

Turn now to Fig. 1-3c which represents through its shading the distribution of

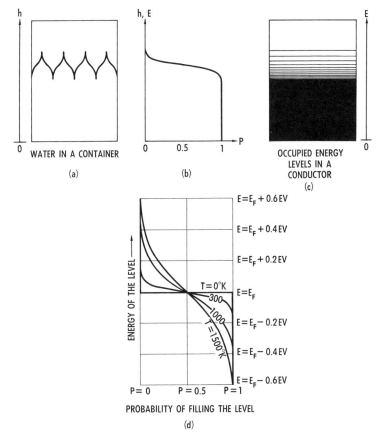

Fig. 1-3 (a) Water in a container that is being agitated; (b) probability of finding water (electrons) at various heights (energies); (c) occupied energy levels in a conductor; (d) Fermi distribution function for four temperatures. (*After Shive.[2]*)

energy levels occupied by electrons in the energy band of a conductor. As we saw in the previous section, such a band is only partially filled with electrons and thus can be likened to a partly filled container of water. To complete the analogy, electronic energy E is likened to height (and hence potential energy) of the water. Agitation of the water is the analogue of temperature in the electronic example. In the absence of agitation, the water's calm surface would lead to a perfectly rectangular probability function. The same function applies for the electronic distribution at absolute zero. As temperature is raised, the function becomes stretched vertically, but maintains its symmetry about the point at which probability equals one-half.

This is illustrated in Fig. 1-3*d* which plots the electronic distribution function for four different temperatures. This important function is known as the *Fermi distribution function.* It is based upon Fermi-Dirac statistics.

The level of energy passing through the center of symmetry of the function enters in an important way into any quantitative treatment of electrons in solids. It is known as the *Fermi level,* or sometimes as the Fermi *brim.* The latter terminology has particular significance with respect to the water analogy just given. Specifically, the Fermi level is the level of energy at which the probability of occupancy by an electron is one-half. It is not necessary to have an electronic state available at that energy; but if one does exist there, it has a 50 per cent probability of being filled.

The significance of the last statement becomes clear when we consider the electronic distribution problem for a material having an energy gap—a semiconductor or an insulator. At this point the water-container analogy must be set aside. Figure 1-4 shows the Fermi distribution function corresponding to room temperature, plotted beside a band structure diagram for pure silicon. The zero of energy is arbitrarily taken at the lower band edge. It is clear that occupancy of the lower band will be almost complete. Occupancy of the upper band, even at its lower edge, will have an exceedingly low but finite probability. As suggested earlier, occupancy of the upper band is necessary for electronic conductivity. As a consequence the resistivity of pure silicon at room temperature is in the range from 10^5 to 10^6 ohm cm. As one goes to materials with greater energy gaps, the number of electrons with enough energy to reach the upper band and become available for conduction diminishes drastically; in an insulator the gap is so large that the number of electrons available for conduction is negligible.

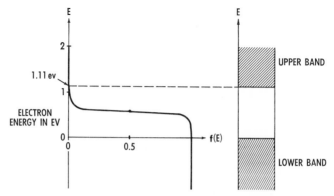

Fig. 1-4   The Fermi distribution function for room temperature plotted beside a band structure diagram for pure silicon.

In a silicon crystal which is not perfect in structure or purity, energy states do exist in the energy gap region. This is, of course, the usual condition in realizable crystals. The probability of filling these intra-gap states will depend upon their positions relative to the Fermi level, and upon the temperature-dependent shape of the distribution function. At this point a complication enters: Because intra-gap states in general affect electron supply and demand within the crystal, they alter Fermi level position with respect to the band edges, though they have no effect whatsoever on the shape of the distribution function. It is often of interest to know the position of the Fermi level, but determining this requires a graphical or a trial-and-error calculation.

The Fermi distribution function $f(E)$ can be written as

$$f(E) = \frac{1}{1 + e^{(E-E_F)/kT}} \tag{1-1}$$

where E is energy in electron volts measured from an arbitrary reference level, E_F is the height of the Fermi level above the same arbitrary reference level, T is absolute temperature in degrees Kelvin, and k is Boltzmann's constant, which has the value 8.63×10^{-5} ev/deg K. For energy levels above the Fermi level, when $(E - E_F)$ is several times kT, the exponential term in the denominator dominates, and hence the entire function can be well approximated by a simple declining exponential function. For example, when $E - E_F = 4kT$, or about 0.1 ev at room temperature, then the exponential term equals approximately 55. Hence, Eq. (1-1) can be replaced with less than a 2 per cent error by

$$f(E) = e^{-(E-E_F)/kT} \tag{1-2}$$

For still higher energies the error diminishes rapidly. Thus, Eq. (1-2) is frequently used to approximate the Fermi distribution function in the upper band for situations where the Fermi level is sufficiently below the band edge. Equation (1-2) is simply the *Boltzmann distribution function,* which is based upon Maxwell-Boltzmann statistics.

For energies below the Fermi level (i.e., where $E - E_F < 0$), Eq. (1-1) is approximated by

$$f(E) = 1 - e^{-(E_F-E)/kT} \tag{1-3}$$

This is the Boltzmann approximation applicable to energies below the Fermi level, valid under conditions parallel to those given above. Figure 1-5 shows these two

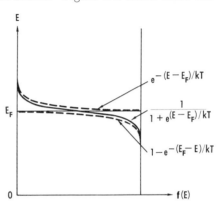

Fig. 1-5 The Fermi distribution function at room temperature and the Boltzmann approximations appropriate to its two branches.

Boltzmann approximations in their relation to the Fermi distribution function at room temperature.

1-3 Electrons and Holes in Semiconductor Crystals

For the preceding sections the starting point was the ladder of electronic energy levels in an atom. The consequence of forming a solid crystal from many identical atoms was then sketched, and a distinction was made between a conductor and a semiconductor. All this was done in terms of electronic distributions in energy. In this section the starting point will be a geometrical view of a particular crystal. We will confine our attention here to silicon—a semiconductor and the only important semiconductor in present-day integrated circuits.

Silicon is in column IV of the periodic table and has four electrons in its outer shell. As noted earlier, silicon crystallizes in the very stable diamond structure. The bonds in this crystal are of the shared electron or *covalent* type. Thus one can consider that each of these outer-shell electrons pairs with one other electron from another atom. The two electrons involved in a particular covalent bond have their spins oppositely directed. The stability of this arrangement is suggested by the

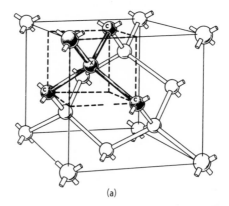

(a)

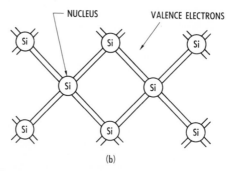

(b)

Fig. 1-6 (*a*) A portion of a crystal having the diamond structure (*After Shockley*[4]); (*b*) two-dimensional representation of the silicon lattice.

extreme stability of a pair of bar magnets arranged side by side with opposite poles adjacent.

Figure 1-6a depicts a portion of a silicon lattice, showing in particular one silicon atom X surrounded by the four additional silicon atoms with which it shares electrons. That is, here we have represented the covalent bonds as straight rods directly connecting the atoms so bonded. These four rods emanate from the atom X in a manner symmetrical in space. That is, the four neighboring atoms lie at the corners of a tetrahedron. The same spatial relationship of bond directions exists for every atom in the crystal. Figure 1-6a also shows that a larger unit of the crystal is cubic. In fact, the diamond structure can be regarded as a pair of interpenetrating face-centered cubic lattices; the three atoms marked C are located at the centers of the faces toward the viewer. The atom X is then the corner of another face-centered cube identical to the large one shown.

As Fig. 1-6b shows, the silicon crystal lends itself very readily to a two-dimensional representation. The covalently bonded pairs of electrons can be regarded as structural elements connecting the atoms. This situation is very different from that in a metal where the outer-shell electrons form a sort of cloud or "gas" which permeates the solid.

At room temperature there is a small amount of thermal energy in the crystal in the form of vibrations of the atoms in the lattice. Moving through the crystal are packets of vibrational energy called *phonons*, in analogy to the packet of electromagnetic energy, the photon. A small but finite probability exists that enough energy can converge on one bond to break it, ejecting an electron. In pure silicon at room temperature one bond in 7×10^{13} bonds is broken at any given time. In a similar way a light quantum or photon is capable of breaking a bond and releasing an electron. The electron so ejected now is free to move about the crystal, much as does a conduction electron in a metal. The situation is shown schematically in Fig. 1-7.

A second consequence of bond breaking, and one of paramount importance, is that there is left behind a *hole* in the valence structure. Its special importance arises from the fact that a valence electron from an adjacent bond can move over to fill the original hole, but in the process leaves a hole in the adjacent bond. This can occur repeatedly, so that the hole can be said to move about within the crystal. In fact, the hole appears to move in response to an applied electric field,

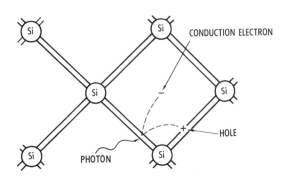

Fig. 1-7   A hole-electron pair produced by the breaking of a valence bond.

as though it were a particle exhibiting both a positive charge and a positive mass. It is amenable to treatment as a particle of positive charge and mass in a manner analogous to that accorded to an electron. Thus, a single event, the breaking of a covalent bond by light or heat, has given rise to both electron and hole conduction.

One is entitled to ask why the artificial hole concept has been introduced when it is actually the motion of valence electrons that gives rise to the second kind of conduction. An answer is well provided by considering the analogy of a bubble in a liquid. The bubble is really an absence of liquid. One could describe its motion by detailing the surrounding liquid motion, but it is more convenient to treat the bubble as a real entity and develop the rules which govern its motion.

The phenomenon of bond breaking by light or heat is called carrier *generation*. In this event a pair of carriers has been created: a hole and a conduction electron. The reverse process is also possible and is called *recombination*. In this case a passing electron in a conduction state drops into the hole in the valence structure, and in the process both carriers disappear. In a crystal at equilibrium a dynamic balance exists between carrier generation and recombination.

Relating Physical Crystal Concepts and Band Concepts. At this point it is appropriate to relate the picture of electrons and holes just sketched to the band picture of the preceding sections. The lower band in Fig. 1-4, of course, represents the states occupied by the electrons residing in the valence structure suggested in Fig. 1-7. The conduction electron shown in Fig. 1-7 occupies a state in the upper band. The difference in energy between these two states is the minimum energy required from a source of light or heat to break the bond. As we shall see below, there is a strong probability that both the valence state vacated and the conduction state occupied as a consequence of generation will lie close to a band edge. Thus the energy employed in generation to change an electron from valence to conduction status is very nearly E_G.

The Fermi distribution function $f(E)$ gives the probability of occupancy of a particular conduction state by an electron. It was indicated above that the Boltzmann approximation, Eq. (1-2), is often valid for the conduction states. Now that the absence of a valence electron is to be described as a hole, it is reasonable to speak in terms of the *occupancy* of valence states by holes. Clearly the probability in this case is given, from Eq. (1-3), by

$$1 - f(E) = e^{-(E_F - E)/kT} \qquad (1\text{-}4)$$

Thus up to this point we have perfect symmetry between electrons and holes.

In summary, it has been pointed out that for a pure semiconductor crystal at room temperature, a number of electrons will be elevated or "excited" into the conduction band from the valence band. Conduction electrons will be referred to hereafter simply as *electrons*. Both holes and electrons contribute to conduction as positive and negative charges, respectively. It now remains to calculate their concentrations or densities as functions of temperature and band gap.

1-4   Carrier Concentrations in Intrinsic Semiconductors

Let us focus attention on the conduction band in a pure or *intrinsic* silicon specimen. Given the distribution of states in energy, and the distribution function giving the occupancy probability for each, it is necessary to integrate the product of these functions over the conduction band to determine the conduction electron density n. That is, the number of electrons per unit volume is given by

$$n = \int_{E_{\text{bottom of conduction band}}}^{E_{\text{top of conduction band}}} N(E) f(E) \, dE \tag{1-5}$$

where $N(E)$ is defined as the number of states per unit energy interval and unit volume for the conduction band. Figure 1-8a depicts the approximately parabolic lower portion of the density-of-states function $N(E)$ for the conduction band. The Boltzmann "tail" of the Fermi distribution function is shown in Fig. 1-8b as it extends into the conduction band of the intrinsic specimen. The behavior of this function near the conduction band edge is shown with the $f(E)$ scale greatly magnified in the circle. The product of these functions is depicted in Fig. 1-8c. Thus n is represented by the area of the product curve. The important point here is that the exponential decline of the distribution function is so steep that it strongly dominates the parabolic density-of-states function. Hence, most of the electrons in the conduction band at ordinary temperatures are confined to states very near the band edge.

When the integration is actually carried out for a simple model of the band structure, that is, a simple form of $N(E)$, the result is

$$n = 2 \left(\frac{2\pi m_n kT}{h^2} \right)^{3/2} e^{-(E_C - E_F)/kT} \tag{1-6}$$

Here $(E_C - E_F)$ is the energy difference between the conduction band edge and the Fermi level. Note that location of the energy zero for reference is immaterial since

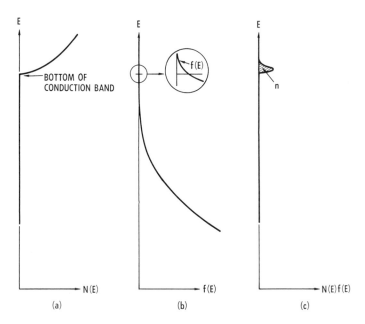

Fig. 1-8 Graphical representation of factors determining electron concentration: (a) the density of states function for the conduction band; (b) the Fermi distribution function; (c) the function resulting when a and b are multiplied.

we are only interested in an energy difference. Also, m_n is the effective mass of an electron in the conduction band of silicon, which has been reported to be about 10 per cent larger at $4°K$ than the mass of a free electron,[3] and h is Planck's constant which has the value 6.63×10^{-27} erg sec. Reference 4 presents the integration yielding this expression. From the mathematical form of Eq. (1-6) it is apparent that we can think in terms of an equivalent density of states N_C, all located right at the band edge. This density (in conduction states per unit volume) is, of course, given by this defining equation:

$$N_C \equiv 2 \left(\frac{2\pi m_n kT}{h^2} \right)^{3/2} \tag{1-7}$$

(Accordingly the quantity m_n is sometimes called the *density-of-states effective mass* of a conduction electron.) Thus the problem of determining n reduces simply to a matter of multiplying N_C by the value of $f(E)$ at the band edge.

A completely analogous procedure is valid for determining p, the density of holes in the valence band. From Eq. (1-4) the appropriate form of the distribution function is $\exp[-(E_F - E_V)/kT]$. Multiplying this by the density-of-states function for the valence band and integrating gives

$$p = 2 \left(\frac{2\pi m_p kT}{h^2} \right)^{3/2} e^{-(E_F - E_V)/kT} \tag{1-8}$$

where $(E_F - E_V)$ is the energy difference between the Fermi level and the valence band edge, and where the coefficient represents an equivalent density of states all residing at the valence band edge. Thus we have a second defining equation for an equivalent density of states:

$$N_V \equiv 2 \left(\frac{2\pi m_p kT}{h^2} \right)^{3/2} \tag{1-9}$$

Here m_p is the density-of-states effective mass of holes in the valence band and has the value $0.59m$ at $4°K$ for silicon, where m is the mass of the free electron.[3] The difference in effective mass between electrons and holes is the first asymmetry we have encountered with respect to these two types of carriers.

A result of the utmost importance is obtained by forming the product of n and p as given in Eqs. (1-6) and (1-8), and utilizing the definitions of N_V and N_C given in Eqs. (1-7) and (1-9):

$$np = N_C N_V e^{-(E_C - E_V)/kT} = N_C N_V e^{-E_G/kT} \tag{1-10}$$

In the intrinsic specimen under consideration the Fermi level was located at the middle of the energy gap. However, the Fermi energy E_F dropped out when Eq. (1-10) was formed. Hence the np product is a quantity which is independent of Fermi level position and which depends only on gap E_G and temperature. Basically this is a consequence of the nature of the Fermi distribution function; in particular, it results from the symmetry of the Fermi distribution function and from the exponential nature of its two branches away from the center of symmetry.

In following sections we will introduce factors which cause the Fermi level to assume various positions relative to the band edges, but still the np product will be constant for a given material and temperature. The usefulness of this fact in everyday engineering calculations is very great indeed. An empirical expression for silicon based on best available experimental data is[3]

$$np = 1.5 \times 10^{33} T^3 e^{-1.21/kT} \qquad (1\text{-}11)$$

where T is in $°K$, and k is in ev/deg K. Factored into the expression is the variation of E_G with temperature, which has been determined empirically. This variation is slow and linear except near absolute zero. The linearly extrapolated value at $0°K$ for silicon is 1.21 ev, as compared to a value of 1.11 ev at $300°K$.

A quantity n_i, the number of electrons or holes per unit volume in intrinsic (absolutely pure) material, is

$$n_i = \sqrt{np} = \sqrt{N_C N_V}\, e^{-E_G/2kT} \qquad (1\text{-}12)$$

That is, in intrinsic material $n = p = n_i$. The quantity n_i is plotted versus temperature in Fig. 1-9 for silicon, the experimental data being those of Morin and Maita.[5]

1-5 Donor and Acceptor Impurities in Semiconductors

As the first departure from crystalline perfection in silicon, let us substitute impurity atoms for a small fraction of the silicon atoms, and let these impurity atoms

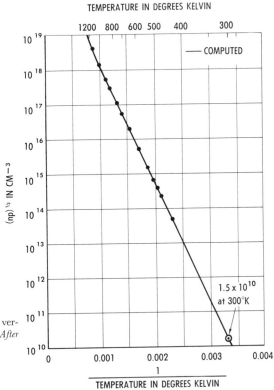

Fig. 1-9 Intrinsic carrier concentration n_i versus reciprocal temperature for silicon. (*After Morin and Maita.*[5])

occupy sites which are randomly distributed throughout the specimen. Such a crystal is said to be impurity *doped.* A typical concentration for these impurities is one part per ten million. Hence each impurity atom can realistically be regarded as isolated in the crystal and unaffected by neighboring impurity atoms, because the mean spacing is relatively large.

First consider that the impurity is a *donor* species such as phosphorus. Donors have five outer-shell electrons and occur in column V of the periodic table. Table 1-2 shows the donor elements commonly used in silicon in their relation to the column IV elements we have considered before, together with some acceptor elements in column III which will be discussed later.

Table 1-2   A Portion of the Periodic Table

III	IV	V
B	C	
Al	Si	P
Ga	Ge	As
		Sb

When a phosphorus atom is substituted for a silicon atom, four of its outer-shell electrons are consumed in covalent bonds. The fifth electron is very weakly bound to the phosphorus atom. Another way of stating this is to say that the orbit of the fifth electron (or better, its wave function) is quite extensive, spreading out through a region that includes many silicon atoms. This is suggested in Fig. 1-10. The electron is bound to the phosphorus atom almost purely by the mutual attraction of its single negative charge and the net single positive charge on the phosphorus atom. Thus the donor atom in silicon can be likened to a hydrogen atom. Indeed the similarity is so great that a calculation based on the *hydrogen model* of a donor gives a useful approximation of the energy binding the fifth electron to the atom.

In the hydrogen atom the electron's binding energy is 13.6 ev. Or this can be termed the *ionization energy* since it is the amount of energy which must be supplied to the electron to free it or to drive it away from the atom. In the present case, however, the two charges are immersed in a dielectric medium, silicon, and this has the effect of cutting the force between them by a factor equal to the dielectric constant κ. In consequence, the binding energy is cut by the factor κ^2. For silicon $\kappa = 12$; hence the ionization energy E_i becomes

$$E_i \approx \frac{13.6 \text{ ev}}{(12)^2} = 0.09 \text{ ev} \tag{1-13}$$

The observed values for phosphorus, arsenic, and antimony in silicon are about half this amount.[3] A factor not considered in this approximate calculation is the effective mass of an electron bound to a donor in silicon. It may differ enough from the mass of a free electron to remove the discrepancy.

This binding or ionization energy is so small that room-temperature thermal energy in the silicon crystal is sufficient to dislodge most of the fifth electrons from donor atoms. In fact, the assumption of complete ionization is a common basis for engineering calculations. The electrons so liberated become conduction electrons.

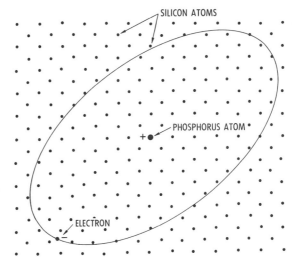

Fig. 1-10 An electron bound to a donor atom or "filling a donor state."

A conduction electron is the solid-state analogue of the free electron mentioned in the discussion above of the hydrogen atom. This leaves behind a donor ion with a charge of $+1$, which is permanently lodged in the silicon lattice and is not free to move as is a carrier. It must be emphasized, however, that the crystal retains over-all neutrality. For every positively charged donor ion there is a *donated* electron somewhere in the crystal with the compensating negative charge.

In donor-doped silicon, holes are still present because the bond-breaking mechanisms named earlier are still present. But, as the supply of electrons is built up by means of donors, the number of holes diminishes. This should be regarded again in terms of the dynamic equilibrium that exists. A larger supply of electrons makes it more probable that some will drop into the holes in the valence structure, annihilating them in the process. This is, of course, consistent with the main point of the last section, namely, that $np = $ constant for a particular material and temperature. The number of electrons has been enhanced over that of pure silicon by the addition of donors to the crystal; hence the supply of holes has diminished. Donor-doped silicon is termed "n-type" silicon because the dominant carriers are negative electrons; the electrons are termed *majority* carriers in this case, and the holes *minority* carriers.

All the factors just outlined are conveniently summed up by means of a diagram which presents jointly the Fermi distribution function (with the associated Fermi level concept) and a band structure diagram. Figure 1-11 depicts a silicon crystal doped with 10^{16} phosphorus atoms/cm³. The symbol N_D stands for this donor concentration. The states introduced by the phosphorus atoms are localized in space since the atoms are immobilized in the lattice. Hence the donor states are represented on the band structure diagram (Fig. 1-11) as short lines, localized with respect to x, the distance variable in our one-dimensional crystal model. These lie about 0.044 ev below the conduction band edge. At room temperature the Fermi level in such a specimen resides about 0.2 ev below the conduction band edge. (Principles underlying calculation of the Fermi level position will be discussed below.) Hence, as the distribution function sketched in Fig. 1-11 shows, the prob-

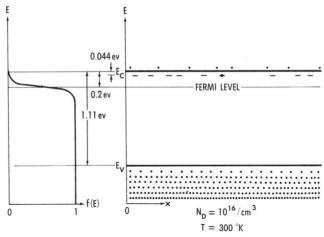

Fig. 1-11   Energy band diagram for donor-doped silicon.

ability of occupancy for donor states is very low. In fact, only about one donor atom in 450 will have an electron in orbit about it, or in other words, only one donor state in 450 will be *filled*. But occupancy of the equivalent conduction states which we assume to be concentrated at the band edge is even less probable, by a factor of 5 at 300°K. Why then are conduction electrons so much more numerous than electrons bound to donors? The answer, of course, is that the equivalent density of states N_C is very much larger than N_D. N_C is in the neighborhood of $10^{19}/\text{cm}^3$, while N_D was taken here as $10^{16}/\text{cm}^3$. In other words, the number of available states in the conduction band is vastly larger than the number of electrons supplied by donors. In Fig. 1-11 electrons are represented as dots. The diagram is too coarse for precision, but the qualitative message it conveys is that the valence band (depicted as a band and not as equivalent states at the band edge) has almost no holes in it; the donor states are almost all ionized, or have lost their weakly bound electrons; and the conduction electrons are approximately equal in number to the donor states. This last approximation is a convenient one and is valid over a wide range of donor concentrations. We write for the electron concentration in a donor-doped specimen

$$n \approx N_D \tag{1-14}$$

Coupling this statement with Eq. (1-12) enables us to determine also the hole concentration in a donor-doped specimen:

$$p \approx \frac{n_i{}^2}{N_D} \tag{1-15}$$

Acceptor Doping. Next let us consider a semiconductor crystal doped with *acceptor* impurities. These are column III elements having three electrons in the outer shell. Table 1-2 shows boron, aluminum, and gallium, the acceptor elements commonly used for doping silicon, in their relation to the other elements considered above. Suppose we concentrate specifically on boron-doped silicon. The boron

atom has one too few outer electrons to complete the covalent bond structure link-
ing it to the surrounding silicon atoms. So strong, however, is the affinity of two
electrons paired with opposite spins (recall the bar magnet analogy) that it is possible for the boron to "accept" an electron in order to complete its bond structure.
Thus, the acceptor atom becomes a negative ion with the extra electron bound
almost as tightly as an ordinary valence electron is bound to a silicon atom in the
crystal. Hence the resulting energy state for this electron resides only a short distance above the top of the valence band in the energy band diagram.

It is most probable that the extra electron accepted by the boron atom is excited
out of the valence band, or in other words, stolen from a nearby valence bond. This
event has the important consequence of introducing a hole in the valence band.
Thus every acceptor atom so ionized creates a hole. Paralleling the equations
above for electrons in n-type silicon, we can write for the hole concentration (or
majority-carrier concentration) in a "p-type" or acceptor-doped specimen

$$p \approx N_A \tag{1-16}$$

where N_A is the acceptor concentration in atoms/cm^3. Hence the electron concentration (or minority-carrier concentration) in acceptor-doped material is

$$n \approx \frac{n_i{}^2}{N_A} \tag{1-17}$$

Figure 1-12 shows a band structure diagram for silicon doped with 10^{16}
atoms/cm^3 of boron. Once again the Fermi level lies about 0.2 ev from the
valence band edge, while the impurity states are 0.045 ev from the valence band
edge. Consequently there is a very large probability that the acceptor states will
be filled by electrons which have come from the valence band, creating holes. At
this point, however, it is advisable to make the discussion consistent and symmetrical by speaking in terms of holes where the lower branch of the distribution function is concerned: Holes tend to fall *up* in this diagram (since electrons with their

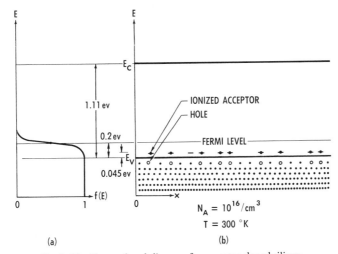

Fig. 1-12 Energy band diagram for acceptor-doped silicon.

opposite charge tend to fall down).   Only one acceptor state in Fig. 1-12 has a hole bound to it, or is non-ionized; the remaining holes have been excited to the valence band, where their concentration is given approximately by Eq. (1-16).

Impurity Compensation.   Next consider a crystal of silicon containing both donors and acceptors, but more of the former.   Suppose that it contains 1.1×10^{16} phosphorus atoms/cm^3 and 1×10^{15} boron atoms/cm^3.   Clearly this crystal will exhibit n-type conductivity because donors predominate.   It follows that the Fermi level will lie above the middle of the energy gap, and hence the acceptor states will be almost totally filled by electrons.   It is valid to think of these electrons as having fallen down from some of the donor states.   Thus a donor state which has so contributed no longer has an electron to contribute to conduction.   That donor state has been canceled by an acceptor state insofar as its ability to contribute to conduction is concerned.   This cancellation process is termed *compensation*.   Consequently, the important quantity for assessing the conductivity of a compensated specimen is $(N_D - N_A)$, which for the case at hand is 1.0×10^{16} atoms/cm^3.   [When acceptors predominate, we are concerned with $(N_A - N_D)$].   Semiconductor materials with a significant net doping of either donors or acceptors are often termed *extrinsic*, in contrast to materials of small net doping which are termed *intrinsic*.

Once again all these factors and mechanisms can be summed up in an energy band diagram (Fig. 1-13).   The important point here is that this specimen strongly resembles that of Fig. 1-11 in terms of Fermi level position and conductivity.   All practical semiconductor crystals are, of course, compensated to some degree.   But it is often true that the minority dopant concentration is several orders of magnitude lower than that of the majority dopant (rather than a single order of magnitude lower as in our example), and hence has a negligible effect.

When the two impurity concentrations approach each other, the effect is low conductivity and the material is often described as *compensated intrinsic*.   There is a limit to how far one can go in this direction, however, without sacrificing certain

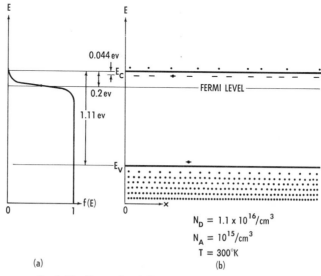

$$N_D = 1.1 \times 10^{16}/cm^3$$
$$N_A = 10^{15}/cm^3$$
$$T = 300°K$$

(a)   (b)

Fig. 1-13   Energy band diagram for compensated silicon.

properties. As we will see below and in Chap. 3, carrier lifetime and mobility can be diminished. Furthermore, the assumed picture of isolated or widely scattered impurity atoms begins to break down, and new conduction mechanisms enter as a result.

Donors and acceptors of the type we have been discussing are frequently termed *conventional* doping impurities. They are similar in that the states they introduce are near the band edge. In fact, the near equivalence of the ionization energies associated with these differing elements lends credence to the simple hydrogen model that has been sketched to describe their effects in silicon. (One can construct a hydrogen model for an acceptor atom and a hole as well as for a donor atom and an electron.) But other elements introduce other states, several per element in some cases, which are apparently not hydrogen-like. They range through the full width of the energy gap, from band to band. Those near the center of the gap are sometimes described as *deep* states. Table 1-3, compiled by Conwell,[3] lists the states introduced by a number of elements. It can be seen that most of those above the gap

Table 1-3   Impurity Energy Levels in Silicon Measured from Nearest Band Edge*

Element	Energy interval, ev	Donor	Acceptor
Conduction Band Edge			
Li	0.033	X	
Sb	0.039	X	
P	0.044	X	
As	0.049	X	
Bi	0.067	X	
Mn	0.53	X	
Au	0.54	..	X
Zn	0.55	..	X
Fe	0.55	X	
Energy Gap Center			
Cu	0.49	..	X
Fe	0.40	X	
Au	0.35	X	
Zn	0.31	..	X
Tl	0.26	..	X
Cu	0.24	X	
In	0.16	..	X
Zn	0.126	..	X
B	0.092	..	X
Zn	0.083	..	X
Ga	0.083	..	X
Zn	0.078	..	X
Al	0.078	..	X
Ga	0.065	..	X
Al	0.057	..	X
B	0.045	..	X
Valence Band Edge			

* After Conwell[3]

centers are donors, and most of those below are acceptors. Some of these unconventional dopants, gold in particular, play an important role in integrated circuit technology, as we shall see in Chaps. 2, 3, 7, and 12.

The Neutrality Equation. The overall neutrality of a semiconductor crystal is an important basis for calculations. A simple equation expresses the neutrality condition. First consider the positive charges in the specimen; there are two entities contributing positive charge—holes and ionized donors. There are p holes and $(N_D - n_D)$ ionized donors, where n_D is the concentration of electrons in donor states. Similarly the negative charge is contributed by conduction electrons and ionized acceptors. There are n electrons and $(N_A - p_A)$ ionized acceptors, where p_A is the concentration of holes bound to acceptor atoms (a mathematically convenient way of describing a non-ionized acceptor). Equating the positive and negative charge and transposing yields

$$p + N_D + p_A = n + N_A + n_D \qquad (1\text{-}18)$$

The position of the Fermi level can be evaluated by a graphical solution of this equation.[4] The terms on each side are plotted as a function of Fermi level for some particular temperature, a sum curve is drawn for each side, and the intersection of the two gives the position of the Fermi level.

Fermi Level versus Temperature. Certain qualitative aspects of Fermi level behavior as a function of temperature are intuitively apparent. Over a considerable range of low temperatures, the Fermi level will reside near the position of the dominant impurity states. This can be seen by referring back to the brim concept. At absolute zero in the case of an n-type specimen, for example, there will be some electrons in the donor states and none in the conduction band. At a considerably higher temperature the donor states will be half ionized, and the Fermi level by definition will be at the donor level. This occurs somewhere in the 50 to 200°K range for ordinary impurity concentrations in silicon. At room temperature, as we have seen in foregoing examples, the Fermi level is somewhat below the donor state level, and the donors are virtually all ionized. With further increase in temperature, the Fermi level continues its movement toward the center of the gap because additional electrons are thermally excited from the valence band into the conduction band. That is, as temperature increases, the Fermi level progresses downward for n-type specimens and upward for p-type specimens.

As the Fermi level approaches the center of the gap, the specimen "goes intrinsic," with the impurity concentration no longer having a serious effect on its conductivity properties. This can be understood by visualizing how the two branches of the Fermi distribution function penetrate deeply into the two bands at high temperature. In the lower band there is a rich source of electrons (on valence states), and in the upper band a rich supply of available states, so that the modest numbers of electrons and states supplied by doping impurities are "washed out." Silicon doped with 5×10^{14} impurity atoms/cm³, which is about the purest silicon in ordinary integrated circuit use, becomes intrinsic at about 500°K. This transition temperature increases steadily as doping is increased because the impurity-contributed carriers and states are able to dominate the situation up to higher temperature.

Hole–Electron-spin Asymmetry. An interesting departure from symmetry in the hole-electron comparison (in addition to differing effective mass) is worth mentioning. The spin of an electron which occupies a donor state is not determined a priori. On the other hand, to enter an acceptor state, an electron must pair with another electron whose spin is already determined. The practical effect of this is that donor states enjoy a higher probability of occupancy than acceptor states for a given distance of the Fermi level from the state in question, but the small factor of difference does not seriously disturb preceding arguments. The Fermi distribution function varies so strongly with energy that a slight shift of Fermi level can compensate this asymmetry. In other words, the small degree of asymmetry introduced by the probability factor is usually unimportant.

1-6 Resistivity and Conductivity

To introduce this subject it is appropriate to review the macroscopic concept of *resistivity*. Basically it is the tendency of bulk materials to resist the flow of an electric current. Consider a bar of material with contacts attached to both ends, as shown in Fig. 1-14. If we were to connect the two leads on the bar to an ohmmeter, we would read a resistance R between them. Intuitively, we realize this resistance would be proportional to the length l of the bar and inversely proportional to its cross-sectional area A. Thus, we can write that

$$R = \rho \frac{l}{A} \tag{1-19}$$

where ρ, the resistivity, is the constant of proportionality which relates the length and cross-sectional area of the bar to its resistance. Examining the units in Eq. (1-19), we find that ρ must have the units of resistance times length. If R is in ohms, l is in cm, and A is in cm^2, ρ will then have the units of ohm cm; resistivity is most commonly expressed in these units.

Resistivity can be defined as the ratio of electric field $\mathcal{E}$, in volts/cm, at some point

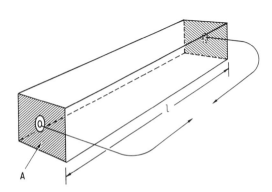

Fig. 1-14 Physical arrangement for visualizing and defining resistivity.

in the specimen to the value at that point of the current density J, in amp/cm², or

$$\rho = \frac{\mathcal{E}}{J} \qquad (1\text{-}20)$$

That Eq. (1-20) is a form of Ohm's law can be shown as follows: Consider a cube of material with uniform properties and having an edge length of l. Suppose that a current I is passing through the cube in a uniformly distributed manner, entering one face and leaving only through the face opposite. If the cube has a resistance R, the voltage across it will be V, consistent with Ohm's law:

$$\frac{V}{I} = R \qquad (1\text{-}21)$$

However, the voltage can also be expressed as the electric field $\mathcal{E}$ times the distance across the cube l, or $V = \mathcal{E}l$. Likewise, the current I can be expressed as the current density J times the cross-sectional area of the cube l^2, or $I = Jl^2$. Putting this into Eq. (1-21), Ohm's law, we have,

$$\frac{\mathcal{E}l}{Jl^2} = R \qquad (1\text{-}22)$$

or

$$\frac{\mathcal{E}}{J} = Rl = \rho \qquad (1\text{-}23)$$

It is important to realize that the imaginary cube can be made as small as desired. Neither $\mathcal{E}$ nor J would be altered by shrinking the cube. (Note that for a cube, as l decreases, R increases.) In the limit of vanishing cube size we have defined the resistivity at a point, as was done above. The integrated circuit engineer frequently must deal with material in which the resistivity varies from point to point in the volume of interest.

The range of resistivities exhibited by materials in engineering use is extremely wide, from the low neighborhood of 10^{-6} ohm cm for conductors up to values as high as 10^{22} ohm cm for insulators. Semiconductors are identified as those materials lying in a vaguely defined central portion of that range, from about 10^{-3} to about 10^{9} ohm cm.

After this review, let us return to microscopic concepts and descriptions of the conduction process. It is instructive for this purpose to employ both particle and wave ideas.

Carrier Mobility. An electron possesses wave properties as well as particle properties, according to the well-known principle of De Broglie. The same is true of a hole. Therefore, the motion of carriers in a semiconductor can be described in terms of waves being propagated in a periodic structure, the crystal lattice. This is mentioned to remind the reader not to give too much literal credence to the particle models which we so frequently employ because of their simplicity and intuitive appeal. If the crystal is pure and perfect, and if the thermal vibrations of the constituent atoms are quieted by reducing temperature, then waves of certain allowed frequencies will move for relatively long distances through the periodic *transmission line,* with ultimate limits being set by the surface of the sample. But any variations in the perfect periodicity of the structure will disturb the electron wave. In a real crystal these variations, of course, exist. They take the form of lattice vibrations described earlier as phonons, and impurities or other crystal defects, either of which can interact with an electron or a hole, causing it to be deflected. As temperature is raised so that thermal energy in the crystal in the form of lattice vibrations increases, phonon-electron interactions become more frequent; at room temperature, even in an intrinsic crystal the carriers move about in erratic, random fashion.

Now consider an impurity-doped or extrinsic crystal. The interaction of a carrier in silicon with an acceptor or donor ion has been analyzed successfully on a particle basis.[6] That treatment calculated the deflection or *scattering* experienced by carriers passing near an ionic charge as a consequence of the electrostatic attraction or repulsion between carrier and ion; it was based, of course, on the classic calculation and experiment by Rutherford on alpha-particle scattering by atomic nuclei. At low temperatures, impurity scattering is the dominant mechanism. It becomes more severe as temperature is reduced because the carriers move more slowly; hence, they are influenced for a longer time by a given ion and are deflected to a greater extent.

Next, let us consider the effect of an externally applied electric field. For convenience (with respect to algebraic sign) let us employ a p-type silicon example with its predominating positive carriers. All the principles are, of course, equally valid for electrons. The combination of lattice and impurity scattering causes carrier motion, which can be represented from the convenient particle viewpoint in the manner of Fig. 1-15. The solid line represents the erratic path of a hole with no electric field applied. It moves about with a high *thermal velocity,* and is repeatedly deflected by interactions with phonons and impurities. The average length of the straight segments of path between collisions is called *mean free path,* and the average time to travel one of these is called *mean free time.* Had an electric field of magnitude $\mathcal{E}$ been present, as indicated by the arrow, the hole would have followed the path suggested by the dashed line. (This description is purely hypothetical since such an experiment could not be performed.) The main point here is that after each interaction or collision, velocity is essentially random again so that acceleration of the charged particle by the field starts afresh, and thus the carrier never goes very far out of *thermal equilibrium* with the lattice.

Because the motion of the hole in response to the applied electric field is being randomly interrupted, the result can be described in terms of an average *drift velocity* v_D, which is proportional to electric field. Applying this concept to an aggregation of holes extends the averaging process and further stabilizes the resulting average velocity. The validity of the drift-velocity concept can be verified easily through the long-established em-

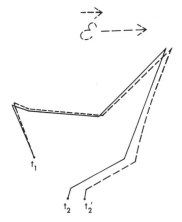

Fig. 1-15 Random path of a hole and modification of the same path by an electric field.

pirical authority of Ohm's law.   Bulk semiconductor specimens obey Ohm's law (within limits discussed later), as do conductors.   Ohm's law [Eq. (1-20)] asserts the proportionality of electric field and current density.

If a group of holes with concentration p drifts with a uniform velocity v_D, then elementary considerations enable us to write for the current density

$$J = qpv_D \tag{1-24}$$

where q is the magnitude of the electronic charge, or is the charge on each hole. Then from Eq. (1-20),

$$v_D = \frac{1}{qp\rho}\mathcal{E} \tag{1-25}$$

and v_D is indeed proportional to $\mathcal{E}$.   For convenience we define a *hole mobility*

$$\mu_p = \frac{1}{qp\rho} \tag{1-26}$$

as the proportionality constant between drift velocity and electric field.

The data of Ryder[7] show that mobility in silicon is constant at room temperature up to fields of a few thousand volts/cm.   In higher fields the carriers achieve such high velocities in a mean free time that their mode of interaction with crystal changes.   The net result is a declining mobility.   In fact, carrier velocity appears to approach a constant value for very high fields.   This value is in the range 10^6 to 10^7 cm/sec at room temperature.   Carriers experiencing high electric fields are sometimes called "hot" carriers because their field-produced velocity component is very significant in comparison to the velocity of their normal thermal migration depicted in Fig. 1-15.

In precise work a distinction is made between drift mobility and conductivity mobility.   In the former a pulse of minority carriers is injected, and its motion in

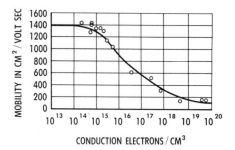

CONDUCTION ELECTRONS / CM^3

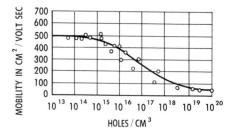

HOLES / CM^3

Fig. 1-16   Carrier mobilities in silicon.   (*Data of Ludwig, Watters, Prince, Horn, Carlson, Backenstoss, and Smits, compiled and adjusted by Conwell.*[3])   Solid curve is sketched through data points.

the presence of an electric field is observed. Conductivity mobility is determined from an expression similar to Eq. (1-26), where carrier density is determined from impurity concentrations, and these may in turn be inferred from radioactive impurity experiments, for example. Thus conductivity mobility relates chiefly to majority carriers. In Fig. 1-16 we present data on room-temperature mobility versus impurity concentration, and here we have ignored the relatively small quantitative distinction between the drift and conductivity mobilities. These curves are based on a compilation of experimental and theoretically adjusted data assembled by Conwell.[3] As is evident in these curves, adding doping impurities causes the mobilities to decline steadily because impurity scattering becomes progressively more important.

The dependence of carrier mobility in silicon on temperature is also of interest. Mobility usually exhibits a maximum at a temperature somewhat below room temperature. At very low temperatures impurity scattering is the dominant mechanism, and it becomes more pronounced with decreasing temperature, as pointed out earlier. At higher temperatures mobility declines with increasing temperature because phonon scattering becomes more important. The combination of these effects produces the observed maximum in mobility.

Conductivity. From Eq. (1-26) we can write for a p-type specimen

$$\frac{1}{\rho} = \sigma = q\mu_p p \tag{1-27}$$

where σ stands for conductivity, the reciprocal of resistivity. Similarly, for an n-type specimen

$$\sigma = q\mu_n n \tag{1-28}$$

where μ_n is defined as electron mobility, and n is electron concentration. Equations (1-27) and (1-28) are valid for silicon in numerous practical situations where carriers of one type or the other predominate. Still there are other situations where both carrier types contribute significantly to conductivity at the same time. Then we must use the following equation of general validity:

$$\sigma = q\mu_p p + q\mu_n n \tag{1-29}$$

This expression must be used for intrinsic silicon, for example. In this case it simplifies to

$$\sigma_i = qn_i(\mu_p + \mu_n) \tag{1-30}$$

Evaluating this with the aid of Figs. 1-9 and 1-16 yields at room temperature

$$\sigma_i = 5 \times 10^{-6} \text{ ohm}^{-1} \text{ cm}^{-1} \tag{1-31}$$

corresponding to a room-temperature resistivity of 2×10^5 ohm cm. Pure silicon exhibits n-type behavior, however, in the sense that the electron contribution to conductivity is about three times the hole contribution because of the difference in mobilities.

The variation of conductivity with temperature is a matter of extreme importance. To analyze this variation let us arbitrarily select an n-type silicon specimen. Thus

Eq. (1-28) applies and clearly indicates that n and μ_n are the factors determining conductivity. In Eq. (1-6) we saw that n was given by an equivalent density of states N_C, with a gentle temperature dependence ($T^{3/2}$), multiplied by the Fermi distribution function with its strong exponential temperature dependence. Thus n varies essentially in an exponential manner through a considerable temperature range. The exponential nature of n also dominates μ_n which exhibits a comparatively weak (also $T^{3/2}$) dependence on temperature through a certain low range of temperatures. As a result of these factors, σ exhibits an approximately exponential variation below about 60°K. This can be seen for n-type silicon in Fig. 1-17a in the data of Morin and Maita.[5]

Further increases in temperature exhaust the supply of electrons available from donors. As pointed out above, at room temperature it is often a good approximation to assume that the donors are totally ionized. Thus n departs from its drastic exponential variation and levels off at

$$n \approx N_D - N_A \tag{1-32}$$

As noted above, μ_n diminishes with increasing temperature at room temperature and above because of phonon scattering. This factor, in combination with an approximately constant n, causes σ to exhibit the maxima clearly visible in Fig. 1-17a. With still further increases in temperature, electrons are finally elevated from the valence band to the conduction band as the specimen goes intrinsic. In this range doping effects are left behind, and hence all of the curves in Fig. 1-17a converge on the intrinsic line, shown dashed in the diagram.

Thus we have accounted qualitatively for the major features of the temperature *profile* of n-type silicon conductivity. Figure 1-17b presents analogous data for p-type specimens, and once again the similarity is apparent. The curve at the top

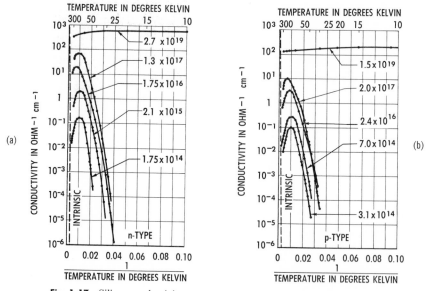

Fig. 1-17   Silicon conductivity versus temperature. (*After Morin and Maita.*[5])

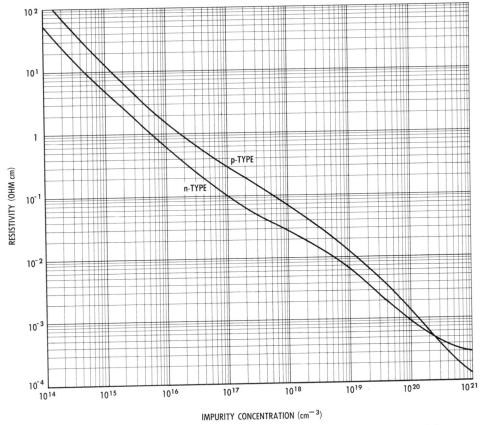

Fig. 1-18   Silicon resistivity at 300° K as a function of impurity concentration.   (*After Irvin.*[8])

in each case applies to specimens so heavily doped that they are *degenerate* or essentially metallic, so that the approximations we have made in describing semi-conductor behavior do not apply.

Of paramount practical importance is resistivity (or conductivity) versus net impurity concentration in silicon at room temperature.   The following chapters take up the relation of this fundamental property to junction properties such as breakdown voltage, capacitance, and injection efficiency.   The data generated and collated by Irvin[8] on resistivity versus impurity concentration are presented in Fig. 1-18.

REFERENCES

1. Adler, R. B., and R. L. Longini: "Introduction to Semiconductor Physics," John Wiley & Sons, Inc., New York, 1963.
2. Shive, J. N.: "The Properties, Physics and Design of Semiconductor Devices," D. Van Nostrand Co., Inc., Princeton, N.J., 1959.
3. Conwell, E. M.: Properties of Silicon and Germanium: II, *Proc. IRE,* vol. 46, pp. 1281–1300, June, 1958.

4. Shockley, W.: "Electrons and Holes in Semiconductors," D. Van Nostrand Co., Inc., Princeton, N.J., 1950.

5. Morin, F. J., and J. P. Maita: Electrical Properties of Silicon Containing Arsenic and Boron, *Phys. Rev.,* vol. 96, pp. 28–35, Oct. 1, 1954.

6. Conwell, E. M., and V. F. Weisskopf: Theory of Impurity Scattering in Semiconductors, *Phys. Rev.,* vol. 77, pp. 388–395, Feb. 1, 1950.

7. Ryder, E. J.: Mobility of Holes and Electrons in High Electric Fields, *Phys. Rev.,* vol. 90, pp. 766–769, June 1, 1953.

8. Irvin, J. C.: Resistivity of Bulk Silicon and of Diffused Layers in Silicon, *Bell System Tech. J.,* vol. 41, pp. 387–410, March, 1962.   Figure 1-18 reprinted by permission of the copyright owner, American Telephone & Telegraph Company, and the author.

2

JUNCTION THEORY AND PROPERTIES

In the preceding chapter, basic properties of bulk semiconductors were treated for conditions which always included thermal equilibrium, either tacitly or explicitly. While it is true that the existence of a net current in a specimen requires a departure from equilibrium in the strict sense, it is also true that we were able to generate accurate expressions for conductivity by reasoning on the basis of equilibrium properties. Carrier concentrations were not altered by the existence of a net current, and for moderate electric fields, even carrier velocity distributions were negligibly affected. But when net current crosses a p-n junction, important departures from equilibrium occur. For a treatment of such circumstances we must add the concepts of carrier diffusion and of lifetime to the ideas already discussed. These two subjects are discussed in the first two sections of this chapter.

A p-n junction may, of course, be defined as the interface between a p region and an n region coexisting in a single crystal. Before discussing its important nonequilibrium properties, we will consider its equilibrium properties at some length in the third section of this chapter. We will see that the diffusion mechanism plays an important role even in the equilibrium junction situation. Diffusion current, to be described in the first section, is precisely balanced by drift current, discussed in Chap. 1, so that net current is zero in the junction at equilibrium.

The fourth section then takes up the junction under nonequilibrium conditions and develops the important rectifier equation. The fifth and sixth sections treat junction capacitance and avalanche breakdown, respectively.

2-1 Carrier Diffusion

Let us consider a piece of silicon having a nonuniform carrier distribution, without being concerned for the moment about how the distribution has been brought about. To be specific, let us discuss electrons. We will now confine our attention to a small region in the interior, where the distribution has one-dimensional variation only.   That is, electron concentration n is a function of x, but not of y and z. The small region of interest is depicted in Fig. 2-1a.   During a diffusion process the electrons, represented as small circles, will execute random jumps in the crystal. Because concentration does not vary in the y direction, it is clear that on the average the number of electrons diffusing into one of the little sub-boxes across a face normal to the y axis will be balanced by an equal number of electrons moving in the opposite direction.   Similar claims can be made for the z faces.   Therefore, we need to consider only jumps in the x direction—more precisely, only the x component of each jump displacement.

In Fig. 2-1a are represented the electrons in each box which in a certain time interval Δt are going to diffuse out of the box.   It is reasonable that for a given geometry and Δt, that number should be proportional to the average concentration in the box.   We have further assumed equipartition in this process; that is, equal numbers move in the $+x$ and in the $-x$ directions.   Although that is obviously not valid for the small numbers given here, these numbers could be enlarged by altering geometry until it was valid to any desired degree of accuracy.   Small numbers are used in the example to simplify the arithmetic.   The numbers and arrows above the boxes represent the equally divided flows from the boxes within the time interval Δt.   Those below the boxes show the net flux across each of the separating boundaries.   Evidently there is a uniform flow to the right, *down* the concentration gradient, which is depicted graphically in Fig. 2-1b.   The important point to be made here is that this net flow has not resulted from any forces in the usual sense, but merely from the kinetics of the model we have constructed.

This model can be pursued further with profit.   Let the concentration gradient be doubled, thus doubling the number of atoms shown in each box.   Repeating the net flow calculation, we see that the uniform flux to the right has also doubled.   This observation makes reasonable a basic principle of diffusion known as *Fick's first law*. It states that the rate of flow or flux f is proportional to the negative of the concentration gradient:

$$f = -D_n \frac{\partial n}{\partial x} \tag{2-1}$$

The minus sign enters because a concentration increasing to the left leads to diffusion to the right.   The constant of proportionality D_n is the diffusion constant for

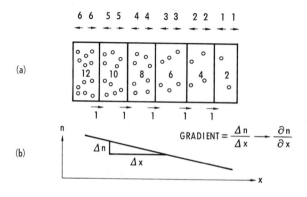

(a)

(b)

Fig. 2-1   An illustration of carrier diffusion: (a) Physical representation of a concentration gradient showing resulting diffusion; (b) graphical representation of a concentration gradient.

electrons and has the dimensions cm²/sec. The flux is in particles/cm² sec. The partial derivative is necessary when n is time-varying.

By multiplying the particle flux by the charge on each particle, we obtain current density. For electrons, since the charge on each particle is $-q$, we obtain for electron diffusion current density under steady-state conditions

$$J_n = qD_n \frac{\partial n}{\partial x} \tag{2-2}$$

A precisely analogous diffusion model could of course be constructed for holes. Because the charge in this case is $+q$ on each particle, the minus sign in Eq. (2-1) will be preserved, and hence the current density of holes arising from diffusion is given by

$$J_p = -qD_p \frac{\partial p}{\partial x} \tag{2-3}$$

The diffusion constant for a carrier is, of course, a measure of the readiness with which it moves about the crystal. So too is its mobility. Hence it is not surprising to find that these two quantities are related. In fact, for a given temperature they are proportional through an important equation known as the *Einstein relation*. For electrons and holes, respectively, this equation is represented as follows:

$$D_n = \frac{kT}{q} \mu_n \tag{2-4}$$

$$D_p = \frac{kT}{q} \mu_p \tag{2-5}$$

The quantity kT/q at room temperature is approximately 0.026 volt. Thus for lightly doped silicon where the electron and hole mobilities, respectively, are approximately 1,400 and 500 cm²/volt sec, as read from Fig. 1-16, the diffusion constants are $D_n = 36$ cm²/sec and $D_p = 13$ cm²/sec.

2-2   Carrier Lifetime

The introduction of the carrier lifetime concept always implies a situation in which electron and hole concentrations have been caused to change from their equilibrium values by some disturbing influence. The characteristic time required for recovery to equilibrium concentrations, once the disturbing influence has been removed, is defined as the *carrier lifetime*.

As an example, consider a thin crystal of n-type silicon which is subjected to radiation (light) capable of generating hole-electron pairs. Through appropriate choice of wavelength and sample thickness it is possible to have these pairs generated uniformly throughout the specimen. That is, as suggested in Fig. 2-2a, only a small fraction of the incident radiation will be absorbed within the silicon. Therefore the carrier concentrations are increased throughout the specimen in a uniform manner. Clearly the hole and electron concentrations will increase by the same absolute amount, since the carriers are always produced in pairs and disappear in pairs. If

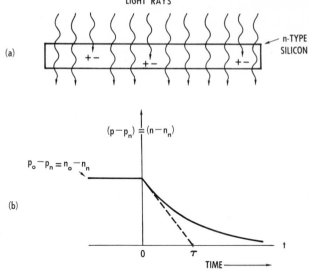

Fig. 2-2 (*a*) Schematic representation of a specimen subjected to penetrating radiation; (*b*) exponential decline of the excess carrier population; penetrating radiation is turned off at $t = 0$.

p_n and n_n are the equilibrium concentrations of holes and electrons, respectively, in the n-type specimen, then we can write for the increment in their concentrations

$$p_0 - p_n = n_0 - n_n \qquad (2\text{-}6)$$

where p_0 and n_0 represent the respective carrier concentrations during steady irradiation of the specimen.

If the source of radiation is turned off abruptly, the carrier concentrations return to their equilibrium values, declining exponentially with a characteristic time τ, known as carrier lifetime. That is, τ is the time required for the extra carrier concentrations to fall to $1/e$ of their initial values. The functions describing decay which have been confirmed through experiment can be written as follows:

$$p - p_n = (p_0 - p_n)e^{-t/\tau} \qquad (2\text{-}7)$$
$$n - n_n = (n_0 - n_n)e^{-t/\tau} \qquad (2\text{-}8)$$

This behavior is illustrated in Fig. 2-2*b*, for a case in which the radiation was switched off at time zero. (In practice this abrupt switching is often achieved by mechanically "chopping" a light beam.) Two points deserve emphasis. First, the same functional relation describes the behavior of the extra holes *and* the extra electrons. This is true in spite of the fact that p_n and n_n may (and usually do) differ by many orders of magnitude. Thus τ is the lifetime characterizing both minority and majority carriers in a specific region of a *given specimen*. Second, through an elementary and important property of a declining exponential function, τ is the intercept on the t axis of the tangent to the function at $t = 0$.

Now let us examine situations where the external disturbance initially alters the concentration of only one type of carrier. These situations are somewhat more complex than the one just described, but an understanding of them is of basic importance to the integrated circuit engineer or the semiconductor device engineer.

Neutralization of Carrier Space Charge. Consider first a "thought experiment" involving the n-type silicon specimen depicted in Fig. 2-3a. Suppose that when $t = 0$, the concentration of electrons only is suddenly increased at the right end of the bar, in the manner suggested in Fig. 2-3b. We assume here that this sudden increase in electron concentration (brought about by some unspecified means) produces at the right end of the bar a negative space-charge concentration given by $(n_o - n_n)$, which is the concentration of electrons above the equilibrium value.

The following sequence of events would then occur: This space charge would give rise to an electric field which would be propagated with approximately the speed of light through the rest of the bar. Conduction electrons throughout the bar would undergo a slight net displacement to the left, and a number of electrons equal to the number instantaneously injected would be pushed out of the bar at the left. The space charge of the electrons initially introduced decays with a characteristic time known as the *dielectric relaxation time* which is given by $\kappa\epsilon_o\rho$. Thus the magnitude of the space charge as a function of time is given by

$$(n - n_n) = (n_o - n_n)e^{-t/\kappa\epsilon_o\rho} \tag{2-9}$$

as suggested in Fig. 2-3c.

For silicon with a resistivity of 1 ohm cm, this characteristic time is about 1 picosecond (10^{-12} sec), since $\kappa\epsilon_o$ for silicon is approximately 1 pf/cm. As impurity doping is increased, causing ρ to decrease, the dielectric relaxation time becomes even shorter. The main point to be made here is that carrier space charges in semiconductors of ordinary doping are neutralized in times so short that they are practically unmeasurable, and therefore this neutralization process may be treated as instantaneous.

It is quite true, however, that for insulators the dielectric relaxation time can be minutes, hours, or even days. To make this seem plausible, recall that the range

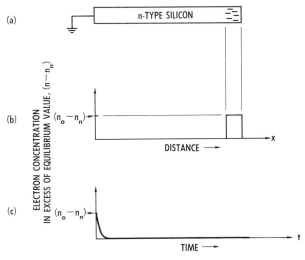

Fig. 2-3 The decay of electron space charge in n-type silicon through the "dielectric relaxation" process. This is very rapid for ordinary semiconductors (e.g., 10^{-12} sec): (a) Schematic representation of an n-type silicon specimen with a momentary space charge of electrons at one end; (b) distribution of the assumed momentary space charge of electrons; (c) rapid decay of the space charge.

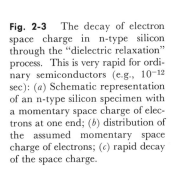

of resistivities in ordinary engineering materials extends over some 24 orders of magnitude!   Experimental confirmation of the long characteristic times for the dissipation of charge on or in an insulator can be found in the familiar elementary experiments in electrostatics involving cat's fur, sticks of sealing wax, and the like.

The situation just outlined for electron introduction into n-type silicon, that is, involving the introduction of *majority* carriers, is qualitatively the same as would exist if a space charge of electrons were somehow created in a metal; neutrality returns to the specimen almost instantaneously, and carrier concentrations are left unperturbed.   But for the semiconductor situation wherein *minority* carriers are introduced (or holes into the same n-type crystal), a new effect enters.   Neutrality is restored as quickly as before, but the carrier concentrations are left in a perturbed state. This distinctive difference between cases involving majority-carrier and minority-carrier introduction is of fundamental importance to one trying to understand the properties and behavior of semiconductor devices.

Let us consider the sequence of events when holes are instantaneously injected into the same bar of n-type silicon, in the manner suggested in Fig. 2-4a and b. Once again electrons throughout the bar would undergo a slight net displacement, but this time it would be to the right.   A number of electrons equal to the number of injected holes would be pulled into the bar from "ground."   Once more space charge would be neutralized with a characteristic time equal to the dielectric relaxation time, as suggested by the rapidly rising electron concentration in Fig. 2-4c. Hence, at this point the concentrations of the two types of carriers in excess of equilibrium values would once more be equal.   These concentrations would then begin

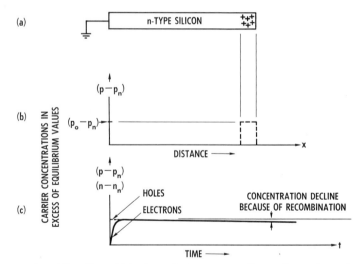

Fig. 2-4   The effect of injecting holes into n-type silicon.   Space charge is neutralized very rapidly by the action of electrons, while the equal increments in the hole and electron populations decay much more slowly through recombination.   (a) Schematic representation of an n-type silicon specimen with a momentary space charge of holes at one end; (b) distribution of the assumed momentary space charge of holes; (c) rapid decay of the space charge (where the curves merge), and the much slower recombination decay of the enhanced carrier populations.

to decay with the far longer characteristic time for recombination τ, the carrier lifetime, as also suggested in Fig. 2-4c.   Dielectric relaxation time, as noted earlier, is in the picosecond neighborhood, while carrier lifetimes in integrated circuits range from nanoseconds (10^{-9} sec) to microseconds.

Because the dielectric relaxation process is so rapid in semiconductors, quantitative treatment of it is usually neglected in elementary treatments of their properties. Although it is true that treating relaxation of space charge as instantaneous is an excellent approximation in practically all the areas covered in this book, the resulting neutrality condition must be clearly understood, and the above discussion is aimed at driving home this point.   Now we will turn to a further discussion of carrier lifetime.   Quantitative aspects of this subject have substantial significance, both practically and theoretically.

Recombination and Generation.   Given the exponential relations [Eqs. (2-7) and (2-8)] governing the disappearance of extra carriers, the expressions for the rate of concentration change assume a simple form.   For holes, for example, from Eq. (2-7),

$$\frac{dp}{dt} = -\frac{p - p_n}{\tau} \tag{2-10}$$

This expression yields the change in the number of holes per unit time and unit volume.   The minus sign ensures that the change is a decrease when extra carriers are present (recombination), and an increase when the concentration is recovering from a temporary depletion (generation).   Similarly, for electrons in the n-type sample being considered here,

$$\frac{dn}{dt} = -\frac{n - n_n}{\tau} \tag{2-11}$$

It is apparent that the rate of change of the concentration of extra carriers is proportional to their number, a feature which is of course inseparably connected with the governing exponential law.   A further important related fact is that τ is actually the average life of a carrier, as can be seen by integrating the time-varying concentration [e.g., Eq. (2-7)] from zero to infinity and dividing by the concentration at zero time.

Although there are several mechanisms through which holes and electrons can recombine, the one which dominates practically is a mechanism involving recombination "centers," which contribute electronic states in the energy gap.   These states are associated with imperfections of some kind in the crystal or at its surface.   We saw in Table 1-3 that metallic impurities are capable of introducing energy states in the forbidden gap at various locations with respect to the band edges.   Some of these elements function as the centers which enhance the process of carrier recombination, and the reciprocal process, carrier generation.   The Shockley-Read-Hall theory of hole-electron recombination is based on a model which takes account of such imperfections.[1,2]

Gold is technologically a very important recombination agent.   It is introduced into silicon under controlled conditions actually enabling the integrated circuit engineer to "tailor" carrier lifetime according to his needs.[3,4]   Important aspects of the diffusion process used for introducing gold into silicon are treated in Chaps. 3

and 12, while the consequences of "gold doping" on integrated transistor and diode electrical properties are discussed at length in Chap. 7.

Surface Recombination Velocity.   A concept which is closely related to that of carrier bulk lifetime (or that which applies in the interior of a specimen) is *surface recombination velocity*.   It can be defined as the rate at which excess carriers recombine at a surface (with units of reciprocal area and reciprocal time) divided by the magnitude of the excess carrier concentration at the surface (with units of reciprocal volume).   It is clear that the quantity s so defined has velocity dimensions.   The situation here can be visualized in terms of a uniform cloud of carriers (having a concentration equal to the extra carrier concentration at the surface in question), moving toward the surface with a velocity s and disappearing as they reach the surface.   The minority-carrier current density in an n-type specimen, for example, associated with the process is given by

$$J_p = qs(p - p_n) \qquad (2\text{-}12)$$

where p and p_n are the perturbed and equilibrium values, respectively, of hole concentration.

Surface recombination velocity is a sensitive function of surface treatment.   In most device situations we want it to be as low as possible.   If it is high, injected carriers will be lost to the surface, or leakage current will be generated at the surface, depending upon whether operation of the device exposes the surface to conditions of minority carrier "flooding" or depletion.   Much of the art which has been developed with such difficulty in transistor and integrated circuit work has had to do with the achievement of favorable and stable surface conditions with respect to surface recombination velocity.

2-3   The Junction at Equilibrium

Having discussed the phenomenon of carrier diffusion and the concept of carrier lifetime, we may now consider the theory for an ideal junction.   A p-n junction is, of course, the boundary between a p region and an n region in a single crystal.   A basic question which must be answered at the outset is this: How do the electrons in the p region distribute themselves in energy with respect to some arbitrary reference energy, and how do the electrons in the n region distribute themselves with respect to the same reference energy?   The answer is that the Fermi level is constant throughout the specimen when it is at equilibrium, and of course the same Fermi distribution function gives the probabilty of occupancy of states at any point in the crystal, because equilibrium implies uniform temperature throughout.

The constancy of Fermi level throughout the specimen could be illustrated readily by means of the water-container analogy (Chap. 1) if we were dealing with an assemblage of conductors.   Indeed, the familiar elementary physics diagram of a series of interconnected water containers of various shapes and sizes, all exhibiting the same water level, would serve nicely.   But for interconnected semiconductor regions, the water-container analogy is less appealing because the Fermi level (or brim) usually lies in the energy gap where few or no states are available.   An important principle on "detailed balancing" supplies the necessary assurance for the semiconductor case. This principle asserts that under equilibrium conditions a given process and its reverse occur with equal frequency. Hence the flux of electrons in one direction across any real or imaginary surface in the semiconductor crystal is equal to the flux in the reverse direction under equilibrium conditions. (A similar statement can be made for holes.) If the Fermi levels for adjacent regions were *not* equal, a transfer of electrons would take place, filling states of lower energy in one region by emptying higher-lying filled states in the other region, and the principle of detailed balancing would be violated.

Chemists find it illuminating to note that the Fermi level is identically the electrochemical potential for carrier particles (electrons and holes), or the partial derivative of the Gibbs free energy with respect to the number of particles. Leaning further toward chemical terminology, the Fermi level can be described as the partial molar free energy per particle.[5]

Accepting the constancy of the Fermi level throughout the specimen has an interesting consequence: We have seen in Chap. 1 that the band edge positions relative to the Fermi level are a function of the type and degree of impurity doping. Therefore band edge positions in energy must vary from point to point in a crystal of nonuniform doping. The deviations in band edge position (consider, for example, the conduction band edge) from point to point within the crystal will, by definition, describe accurately the variations in potential energy that an electron will undergo as it moves between the same two points, remaining at the band edge. Hence it is clear that the band edge diagram or "map" of a specimen is accurately a description of the potential energy of a carrier at the band edge. Because the level of reference for potential energy is arbitrary, the valence band edge constitutes just as good a potential energy map as does the conduction band edge. For the sake of symmetry and the resulting simplifying effects, it is customary to choose neither for representing potential energy, but rather to choose the mid-gap or *intrinsic level* line. Figure 2-5a shows the band diagram for a specimen of nonuniform doping and emphasizes the constancy of the Fermi level E_F at equilibrium and the varying potential energy $E_i(x)$ under the same conditions. The particular specimen represented here is n type throughout, since the Fermi level lies above the middle of the gap in all regions.

It is customary and convenient in junction theory to change the vertical scale from energy in electron volts to potential in volts. Now electrostatic potential may be defined in terms of the change in potential energy of a *test charge* moved from one point to another divided by the magnitude of the charge. Hence the band structure diagram can be modified in the desired way simply by dividing the energies of interest by the electronic charge $-q$. Thus, Fermi level φ is now given by

$$\varphi = -\frac{E_F}{q} \tag{2-13}$$

Also, potential $\psi(x)$ is given by

$$\psi(x) = -\frac{E_i(x)}{q} \tag{2-14}$$

The choice of φ and ψ for Fermi level and potential, respectively, is made because of the phonic aid to memory, following Shockley.[6]

A band diagram in terms of potential is given in Fig. 2-5*b*, corresponding to the diagram in Fig. 2-5*a*, which is in terms of electron energy. The minus signs in Eqs. (2-13) and (2-14) require the downward direction in Fig. 2-5*b* to be the direction of increasing potential. This small but annoying inconsistency arises of course because a positive test charge is used in the definition of potential, whereas the electron's charge is negative. We will resolve the matter by maintaining the convention of Fig. 2-5*b* (rather than flipping the diagram over as is sometimes done), in order to preserve consistency in the band diagrams throughout the book.

A Thought Experiment on Junction Formation. Suppose that a piece of n-type silicon and a piece of p-type silicon of equivalent net doping could be brought together at room temperature and joined perfectly, even on an atomic scale, to form an ideal junction. It is clear that this experiment can be performed only in the realm of thought. Such a junction would be perfectly abrupt and in the general class of step junctions. How would the carriers respond to this single-crystal synthesis? First, at the moment of joining there would be an extremely steep drop in electron concentration in going from the n side to the p side, and there would be a correspondingly steep drop in hole concentration in proceeding from the p side to the n side. These large gradients would give rise to diffusion, as we saw earlier in this chapter. As a consequence, some electrons would be lost from the n side to the p side, and vice versa. But the resulting diffusion of carriers would "uncover" some

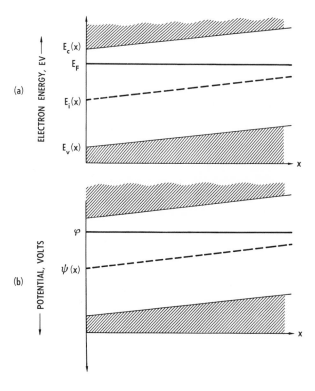

Fig. 2-5   (*a*) Band structure diagram in terms of electron energy for an n-type silicon specimen of nonuniform doping; (*b*) band structure diagram of the same specimen in terms of potential.

impurity ions locked in the crystal on either side of the junction. That is, carriers which normally maintain charge neutrality in the crystal by counterbalancing ionic charge would depart from ions near the newly formed junction. The unbalanced ionic charge would in turn give rise to an electric field (plus to minus, or donor ion to acceptor ion, or n side to p side). This field then offers the means to counteract the carrier diffusion just described; carriers will diffuse in one direction and will drift (in the field) in the opposite direction.

In accordance with the principle of detailed balancing, the drift and diffusion components of hole current must be precisely equal in magnitude but opposite in direction everywhere. Independently, the very same statement of dynamic equilibrium must apply to electrons. Thus, by equating currents it is easy to formulate equations governing carrier distributions in the depletion layer, but it is not possible to obtain simultaneous solutions of them in closed form. Appendix A presents a formulation of the junction problem from a somewhat different point of view and outlines approximations customarily made in order to obtain analytical solutions.

The situation in a symmetrical junction at equilibrium is summarized in Fig. 2-6. The carrier gradients giving rise to diffusion are clearly visible in Fig. 2-6a. Elec-

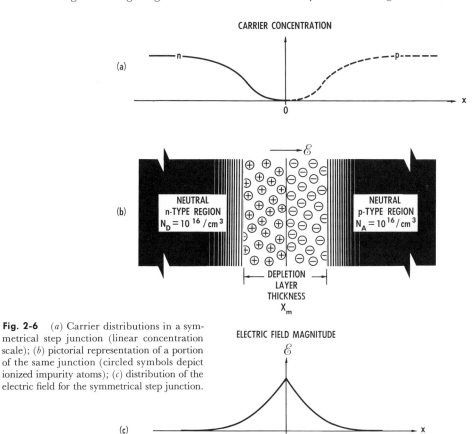

Fig. 2-6 (*a*) Carrier distributions in a symmetrical step junction (linear concentration scale); (*b*) pictorial representation of a portion of the same junction (circled symbols depict ionized impurity atoms); (*c*) distribution of the electric field for the symmetrical step junction.

trons diffuse to the right and holes to the left. Carrier concentrations are greatly diminished near the junction, and hence this region is frequently termed the *depletion layer*. Because carrier depletion exposes ionic charge, there is a *space-charge layer* which is always associated with a p-n junction. Simple analysis, we shall see below, usually assumes that a sharp boundary exists between the region of carrier depletion and the adjoining neutral region. Under these conditions the depletion and space-charge regions coincide. But there are (in some real junctions) situations where the carrier concentration decline extends over an appreciable *x* distance. The space-charge region may be considered to start where there is modest depletion with respect to net impurity concentration, whereas the depletion region may be considered to start only where carrier concentration is negligible with respect to net ion concentration. Hence, under these conditions a distinction between the two terms must be carefully maintained.

A portion of the junction is depicted in Fig. 2-6b, with circled symbols representing the ionic charge. Thus the space-charge layer is a thin two-region sandwich of charge, a charge configuration which is known in physics as a double layer or dipole layer. The plane along which the n and p crystals were joined in our thought experiment is known as the metallurgical junction. In general, it is simply the surface where net doping changes from n type to p type. In the present symmetrical example the metallurgical junction bisects the space-charge region.

Field Distribution in the Junction. Because charges of equal magnitude reside on the two sides of the junction, the field is entirely internal except for some fringing at the edges. Since Fig. 2-6b represents a region lying deep inside the junction specimen, we can visualize lines of force extending straight through the junction from positive ions on the left to negative ions on the right. The density of these lines of force as a function of x, or $\mathcal{E}(x)$, thus assumes the form shown in Fig. 2-6c.

For the idealized step junction formed in our thought experiment and treated in Fig. 2-6, the sharp peak shown in Fig. 2-6c is correct. This is because we considered the change from n doping to p doping to be abrupt on an atomic scale. But for any real junction, the field distribution will exhibit a rounded peak at $x = 0$. This is because all practical junction-forming procedures are carried out at elevated temperatures, and hence there is always some interchange of doping impurities across the metallurgical junction through the mechanism of solid-phase diffusion. (Note carefully that here we refer to the diffusion of impurity *atoms* and not to carriers.) This mechanism has great importance in integrated circuit work, both as a means of actually forming junctions and as an inescapable concomitant of other junction-forming procedures. Consequently, the entire following chapter is devoted to the subject of solid-phase diffusion.

The grading or softening of the field distribution at the boundaries of the depletion layer is valid for the idealized step junction and for a real junction as well. It is a consequence, of course, of the fact that the carriers are mobile. In figurative language we may say that a measure of how far away the effect of an immobile charge (such as an ion) can be "felt" when it is immersed in an environment of mobile charges is a characteristic length called the Debye length. For extrinsic or doped semiconductors an *extrinsic Debye length* (as opposed to the *intrinsic Debye length* of Appendix A) has been defined and is given by

$$L_D = \left(\frac{\kappa\epsilon_0 kT}{q^2 N}\right)^{1/2} \tag{2-15}$$

where N is the net impurity concentration. As the term extrinsic implies, $N \gg n_i$. Gray et al. have studied this problem as it relates to the depletion layer boundary, and estimate by semiempirical means that the transition from nearly complete depletion to nearly complete neutrality occurs within a distance X of about 6 extrinsic Debye lengths.[7] For $N = 10^{16}/\text{cm}^3$ we find, then, that X is approximately 0.07 micron. The total depletion layer thickness X_m in a symmetrical step junction at equilibrium with $N = 10^{16}/\text{cm}^3$ on each side is about 0.4 micron. Thus the region of depletion is five to six times greater than the region of transition from neutrality to depletion for such a junction. The ratio of these quantities, X_m/X, is roughly independent of N for symmetrical extrinsic step junctions because X_m also varies approximately inversely with the square root of N for the symmetrical step junction at equilibrium.

Approximate Analysis of the Symmetrical Junction at Equilibrium. From Fig. 2-6a it is apparent that the charge distribution in the symmetrical step junction is as shown in Fig. 2-7a. As pointed out in Appendix A, it is customary to substitute for this distribution the simple rectangular distribution shown in Fig. 2-7b to permit an approximate analysis. Since Figs. 2-6 and 2-7 have been prepared roughly to scale for the junction at equilibrium, it is apparent that the rectangular approximation for charge distribution is only moderately accurate. However, the approximation improves considerably with reverse bias on the junction and is entirely adequate for engineering calculations on depletion layer properties, as we will point out later in this chapter. Let us proceed with the analysis from Fig. 2-7b.

The fundamental equation describing this problem is Poisson's equation. As explained in Appendix A, to obtain an approximate solution it can be written as follows in MKS units:

$$\nabla^2\psi = \frac{q(N_A - N_D)}{\kappa\epsilon_0} \tag{2-16}$$

The one-dimensional form of Poisson's equation is appropriate to the problem addressed here. Thus the Laplacian reduces to $d^2\psi/dx^2 = -d\mathscr{E}/dx$, where $\mathscr{E}$ is electric field strength; for $x < 0$, Eq. (2-16) becomes

$$d\mathscr{E}/dx = qN_D/\kappa\epsilon_0 \tag{2-17}$$

Hence the electric field distribution can be found by integrating:

$$\int_{-X_m/2}^{x} d\mathscr{E} = \frac{qN_D}{\kappa\epsilon_0}\int_{-X_m/2}^{x} dx \tag{2-18}$$

$$\mathscr{E}(x) = \frac{qN_D}{\kappa\epsilon_0}x + \mathscr{E}_m \tag{2-19}$$

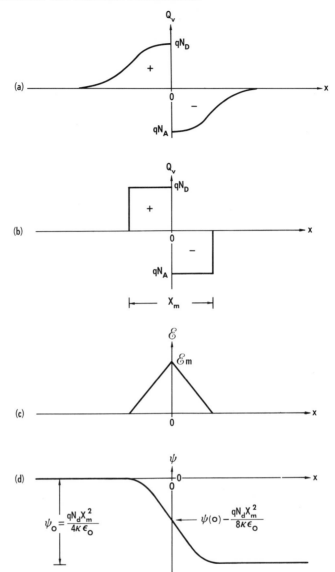

Fig. 2-7   (*a*) Space-charge distribution in a symmetrical step junction; (*b*) assumed space-charge distribution for the approximate treatment of the same junction; (*c*) electric field distribution in the approximate case; (*d*) potential distribution in the approximate case.

where $\mathcal{E}_m$ stands for maximum or peak field and is given by

$$\mathcal{E}_m = \frac{qN_DX_m}{2\kappa\epsilon_o} \tag{2-20}$$

We have taken $\mathcal{E}(-X_m/2) = 0$, which accounts for the vanishing of the term contributed by the lower limit in Eq. (2-18) to the left side of Eq. (2-19).   The latter equation is plotted in Fig. 2-7c, giving the left half of the field distribution. The right half is plotted by symmetry.

In other words, the plane at $x = -X_m/2$ is taken as a sharp boundary between the completely neutral and field-free region to its left and the depletion or space-charge region to its right. We are, in effect, assuming that the region to the left of $x = -X_m/2$ exhibits the same strong tendency toward neutrality, and achieves the same degree of neutrality as the models containing no junctions discussed in the earlier sections of the present chapter. Still we must bear in mind the nature of the approximation and the fact that some space charge and hence some field will be present in this region because a junction constitutes a major perturbation of the simpler junction-free models.

The potential distribution is determined from Eq. (2-19) as follows:

$$\int_{-X_m/2}^{x} d\psi = -\int_{-X_m/2}^{x} \left(\frac{qN_D}{\kappa\epsilon_o} x + \mathcal{E}_m \right) dx \tag{2-21}$$

Integrating on the left and substituting $qN_D X_m/2\kappa\epsilon_o$ for $\mathcal{E}_m$ on the right:

$$\psi(x) = -\frac{qN_D}{\kappa\epsilon_o} \int_{-X_m/2}^{x} \left(x + \frac{X_m}{2} \right) dx \tag{2-22}$$

Hence

$$\psi(x) = -\frac{qN_D}{\kappa\epsilon_o} \left(\frac{x^2}{2} + \frac{X_m}{2} x + \frac{X_m^2}{8} \right) \tag{2-23}$$

We have arbitrarily taken the zero of potential at $\psi(-X_m/2)$. Equation (2-23) is plotted in Fig. 2-7d, giving the parabola which constitutes the left branch of the potential distribution. Once again the right branch is drawn by symmetry. Thus an analytical expression can be written relating the height of the potential "barrier" ψ_o of a symmetrical junction at equilibrium at room temperature to the thickness of the depletion layer X_m for the "equivalent" rectangular charge distribution model. Substituting $x = 0$ in Eq. (2-23) gives, through symmetry, half the desired value, and hence the magnitude of the total *built-in voltage* or potential barrier ψ_o is

$$\psi_o = \frac{qN X_m^2}{4\kappa\epsilon_o} \tag{2-24}$$

where N is the impurity concentration on either side. The inverse of this, which is more commonly written and used, is of course

$$X_m = \left(\frac{4\kappa\epsilon_o \psi_o}{qN} \right)^{1/2} \tag{2-25}$$

For the simple rectangular charge distribution model, the barrier region, or the region through which potential is changing significantly with distance, coincides with the depletion region. In a real junction it is not necessarily true, as we will see later.

Band Diagram for the Symmetrical Junction at Equilibrium. Given the parabolic potential distribution just derived for the simple junction model, we can apply the principles developed at the beginning of Sec. 2-3 and can draw a qualitative band diagram for the junction (Fig. 2-8). As indicated there, the Fermi level φ is constant throughout the specimen at equilibrium. The potential hill in the conduction band edge can be regarded as the means which keeps electrons on the n side. It is, of course, a representation in different terms of the field which moves electrons leftward. The counterbalancing diffusion mechanism which keeps net electron current zero is not displayed in this kind of diagram. In Chap. 1 the point was made that holes fall *up* on a diagram of this kind. Hence the potential hill in the valence band edge similarly keeps the holes on the p side.

The height of the potential hill could be inferred from the Fermi level position for the two net doping concentrations involved (one for each side), as determined by the rather tedious methods mentioned in Chap. 1. However, a much simpler method for computing ψ_o is developed in the next section. With this knowledge it is then possible to go back to Eq. (2-25) and to calculate X_m on the basis of the simple junction model, thus completing a quantitative analysis for the equilibrium case.

Logarithmic Carrier Concentration Diagram for the Symmetrical Junction.
Figure 2-6*a* presented carrier concentration on a linear scale. Additional worthwhile information is conveyed by a diagram showing carrier concentration on a logarithmic scale, versus distance. In particular, it is possible to show the minority-carrier concentrations and their relationship to the majority-carrier concentrations, even though there are many decades of difference. Figure 2-9 is such a diagram for a step junction having $10^{16}/cm^3$ net donors on the left and an equal number of net acceptors on the right. Note that we are plotting true distributions here and not the rectangular approximation.

Several points should be made in connection with Fig. 2-9. First, the carrier concentration curves are symmetrical about $x = 0$. This is true, of course, because the junction is a symmetrical one. Second, the curves are also symmetrical about the line labeled n_i. This is true for *any* junction at equilibrium. Basically it is a consequence of Eq. (1-12), which states that $n_i = \sqrt{np}$. On Fig. 2-9 it is easy to

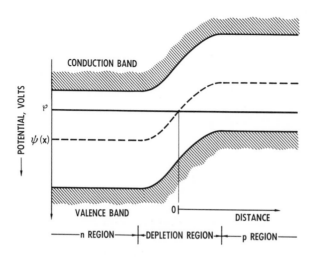

Fig. 2-8 Band diagram for the symmetrical n-p junction at equilibrium.

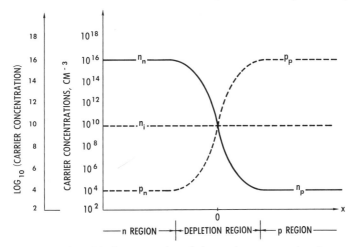

Fig. 2-9 Logarithmic presentation of the carrier concentrations in a symmetrical n-p junction at equilibrium.

verify that half the sum of the logarithms of n and p equals the logarithm of n_i at all values of x. It is important to realize that this relationship holds just as surely in the depletion region as it does in the neutral end regions.

A third point to note in Fig. 2-9 is that the depletion region does not look very "depleted." This is of course a consequence of the logarithmic distortion of the distribution curves. A second look verifies, for example, that n_n, the electron concentration on the n side, has dropped one decade at about the same value of x for which the n curve in Fig. 2-6a has done so. In summary, we can say that the linear diagram and the logarithmic diagram complement each other and reinforce each other in the description of a junction.

Moderately Unsymmetrical Step Junction at Equilibrium. Most of the real junctions encountered in integrated circuits and semiconductor device technology are unsymmetrical. A good example of an unsymmetrical step junction is afforded by the junction between an integrated circuit substrate (10-ohm-cm p-type silicon) and the *epitaxially grown* film (0.5-ohm-cm n-type silicon). The doping ratio in this case between the n- and the p-type sides is about 10:1. Such junctions are amenable to the same kind of approximate analysis carried out for the symmetrical case in the preceding sections. The starting point is an assumed rectangular charge distribution; requiring as before that equal quantities of charge reside on the two sides makes it clear, according to the simple model, that the ratio of depletion layer penetrations into the two sides is equal to the inverse of the doping ratio. That is, if X_1 and X_2 are the penetrations on the n and p sides, respectively, then

$$\frac{X_1}{X_2} = \frac{N_A}{N_D} \tag{2-26}$$

Repeated integrations of Poisson's equation again give a linear field distribution and parabolic potential distribution. Constants are evaluated by imposing field continuity at $x = 0$ (which is physically equivalent to matching the charges on the two sides), by imposing potential continuity at $x = 0$, and by once more letting electric field vanish at the depletion layer boundaries.

Details of this approximate analysis can be found in the literature.[8]   The results are

$$X_1 = \left(\frac{2\kappa\epsilon_o}{q} \frac{N_A}{N_D} \frac{\psi_o}{N_D + N_A}\right)^{1/2} \tag{2-27}$$

and

$$X_2 = \left(\frac{2\kappa\epsilon_o}{q} \frac{N_D}{N_A} \frac{\psi_o}{N_D + N_A}\right)^{1/2} \tag{2-28}$$

for the penetrations into the two sides.   Thus the total depletion layer thickness is given by

$$X_m = \left(\frac{2\kappa\epsilon_o\psi_o}{q(N_D + N_A)}\right)^{1/2} \left[\left(\frac{N_A}{N_D}\right)^{1/2} + \left(\frac{N_D}{N_A}\right)^{1/2}\right] \tag{2-29}$$

The potential at the junction is given by

$$\psi(o) = -\frac{N_A}{N_D + N_A}\psi_o \tag{2-30}$$

where the n side is placed at zero potential.

One-sided Step Junction at Equilibrium.   A step junction in which net doping on one side is many times larger than net doping on the other is sometimes called a *one-sided* step junction because the depletion layer lies entirely on the lightly doped side.   Alternatively it may be called a "p⁺-n" junction or an "n⁺-p" junction, as the case may be, where the plus sign denotes very heavy doping.   It is quite possible in such a case for the metallurgical junction to lie entirely outside the depletion layer.[7]   The reason for this is that far less than complete carrier depletion on the heavily doped side is able to provide a generous amount of ionic charge.   On the lightly doped side of the junction, the equilibrium concentration of carriers diffusing from the heavily doped side constitutes an appreciable fraction of the opposite-type space charge.   True carrier depletion occurs somewhere beyond this carrier-enhanced region, and hence lies away from the metallurgical junction.

The term *step junction* in daily parlance usually implies a p⁺-n or an n⁺-p junction because one-sided junctions or *effective* one-sided junctions are so common in practical semiconductor work.   Figure 2-10a shows an n⁺-p junction.   Figure 2-10b, c, and d shows the charge distribution, field distribution, and potential distribution for such a step junction on the basis of the simple model.   This model gives useful answers in spite of the complications mentioned above.   The result of approximate analysis of this junction is the following relationship between depletion layer thickness X_m and voltage barrier ψ_o:

$$X_m = \left(\frac{2\kappa\epsilon_o\psi_o}{qN_A}\right)^{1/2} \tag{2-31}$$

Once again we should point out that the validity of this kind of simple treatment improves with reverse bias; general statements on the degree of validity of these

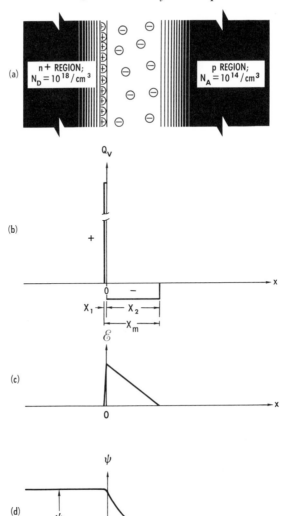

Fig. 2-10 (*a*) Pictorial representation of a portion of an n^+-p junction; (*b*) assumed space-charge distribution for approximate analysis of the same junction; (*c*) electric field distribution in the approximate case; (*d*) potential distribution in the approximate case.

simple analyses for symmetrical, moderately unsymmetrical, and one-sided step junctions at equilibrium have not yet been outlined.

Figure 2-11*a* depicts estimated true carrier concentrations on a logarithmic scale for the same one-sided junction as in Fig. 2-10. Figure 2-11*b* and *c* describes the same junction with linear scales. Note that a carrier concentration scale change is necessary in going from Fig. 2-11*b* to *c*. Hole concentrations are everywhere too small to show on Fig. 2-11*b*, but a portion of the electron concentration shows on Fig. 2-11*c*.

Applying Fermi Statistics to the Step Junction at Equilibrium. Once again the Boltzmann approximation will serve adequately in lieu of the exact Fermi distribution function. Through this analysis it is possible to express the built-in voltage

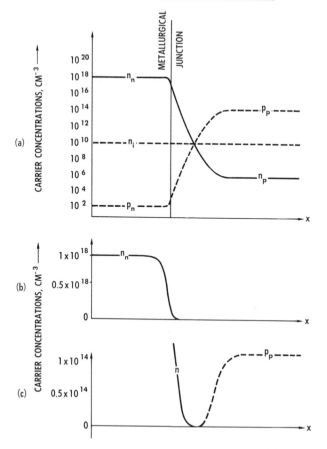

Fig. 2-11 (*a*) Logarithmic presentation of carrier concentrations in an n$^+$-p junction at equilibrium; (*b*) linear presentation of electron distribution for the same junction; (*c*) linear presentation of hole distribution for the same junction.

barrier height in terms of fundamental properties of the n and p regions. Further, we will lay the groundwork for treating the problem of the junction with an external voltage bias applied.

In Fig. 2-12 is a band representation of the grossly asymmetrical or one-sided step junction of Fig. 2-11. We must generate expressions for the carrier concentrations in the two neutral end regions of this sample. Equations (1-6) and (1-7) together yield an expression for n:

$$n = N_C e^{-(E_C - E_F)/kT} \tag{2-32}$$

Thus the problem is one of writing an equivalent expression in the potential representation used in Fig. 2-12. Specifically, consider the n side where we want to write the majority-carrier concentration n_n. The voltage interval to be expressed in the exponent of the Boltzmann factor is that between the conduction band edge and φ. This can be written as the difference between $V_G/2$ (where V_G is the magnitude of the gap expressed in volts) and the quantity $(\psi_n - \varphi)$. Note that $(\psi_n - \varphi)$ is positive because the downward direction is positive for potential. ψ, it will be remembered, is electrostatic potential which for symmetry was set equal to φ at that point in the specimen where $n = p$. In other words, ψ always resides at the center of the gap. Hence in voltage terms, in view of Eqs. (2-13) and (2-14) we have

$$n_n = N_C e^{-q[(V_G/2)-(\psi_n-\varphi)]/kT} \tag{2-33}$$

On the p side where electrons are minority carriers, the large voltage interval from the conduction band edge to the Fermi level is the interval of interest. The expression for n_p has a form precisely parallel to that of Eq. (2-33); the quantity $(\psi_p - \varphi)$ is negative here:

$$n_p = N_V e^{-q[(V_G/2)-(\psi_p-\varphi)]/kT} \tag{2-34}$$

Forming the ratio of the two foregoing equations and making the approximation that the two equivalent densities of states are approximately equal ($N_C \approx N_V$) yields

$$\frac{n_n}{n_p} = e^{q\psi_o/kT} \tag{2-35}$$

where

$$\psi_o = \psi_n - \psi_p \tag{2-36}$$

Thus the contact potential at the junction, or the built-in voltage ψ_o, can be written in a simple way in terms of fundamental properties of the end regions:

$$\psi_o = \frac{kT}{q} \ln \frac{n_n}{n_p} \tag{2-37}$$

With the help of Eqs. 1-14 and 1-17 this can be rewritten conveniently as

$$\psi_o \approx \frac{kT}{q} \ln \frac{N_D N_A}{n_i^2} \tag{2-38}$$

where N_D and N_A are the impurity concentrations on the n and p sides, respectively.

Carrier concentrations can be written simply in terms of n_i and an exponential factor depending on Fermi level position, and this is frequently a convenient thing

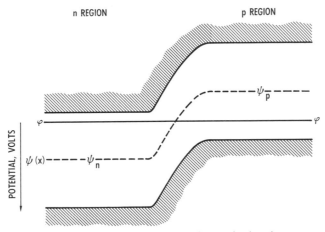

Fig. 2-12 Band structure diagram for an n^+-p junction.

to do.   In view of Eq. (1-12), it is evident that Eqs. (2-33) and (2-34) can be rewritten thus:

$$n_n = n_i e^{q(\psi_n - \varphi)/kT} \tag{2-39}$$

$$n_p = n_i e^{q(\psi_p - \varphi)/kT} \tag{2-40}$$

The expressions for hole concentration on the p and n sides, respectively, are developed by arguments similar to those above, and take the form

$$p_p = n_i e^{q(\varphi - \psi_p)/kT} \tag{2-41}$$

and

$$p_n = n_i e^{q(\varphi - \psi_n)/kT} \tag{2-42}$$

Once again the ratio of these carrier concentrations is simply related to built-in voltage:

$$\frac{p_p}{p_n} = e^{q\psi_o/kT} = \frac{n_n}{n_p} \tag{2-43}$$

This is an analytical statement of the symmetry about the line n_i which is apparent in Fig. 2-11a.

2-4   The Junction Not at Equilibrium

To approach the subject of the junction under nonequilibrium conditions it will be helpful to review a simpler case of nonequilibrium.   In particular, let us return to the case treated in Sec. 2-2 and depicted in Fig. 2-2a.   Here was a uniform n-type silicon specimen with thermal equilibrium disturbed by steady-state radiation. The result was an increment $(p_o - p_n)$ in the hole population, and an equal increment $(n_o - n_n)$ in the electron population.   A convenient way of handling this situation analytically can be developed as follows:

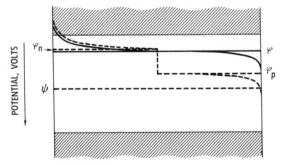

Fig. 2-13   The Fermi distribution function (solid curve) shown in relation to band edge positions in an n-type silicon specimen.   When the conductivity is modulated (i.e., when equal quantities of extra electrons and holes are present), the hole concentration can be described by a displaced distribution function (lower dashed curve) referred to a "quasi-Fermi level for holes," φ_p, and the electron concentration can be related in a similar way to a "quasi-Fermi level for electrons," φ_n.   Note that in the n-type specimen $(\varphi_p - \varphi)$ is large, while $(\varphi - \varphi_n)$ is small.

Figure 2-13 shows a diagram of the Fermi distribution function at room temperature, with the band structure for silicon superimposed on it for reference. The position of the Fermi level shows that this is an n-type specimen. We recall that the carrier concentrations were found by taking the value of this function at each band edge times an effective density of states at that band edge. One way of describing the new populations resulting from the irradiation is to define new reference levels, or *quasi-Fermi levels*. By splitting the Fermi function at its center of symmetry and translating the right branch down, we can find a level φ_p such that the value of the displaced Fermi function at the valence band edge times the effective density of valence states gives the perturbed or enhanced value for hole concentration. Similarly, translating the left branch up will enable us to obtain the enhanced electron concentration, using a new reference level, φ_n. It is important to note, however, that in this nonequilibrium situation we are adding to both populations the same *absolute* number of carriers, $n_o - n_n = p_o - p_n$. (We are not producing equivalent *ratios* of increase.) Hence, from purely geometrical considerations it is clear that φ_p is displaced from φ a far greater amount than is φ_n. In fact, for ordinary departures from equilibrium, we neglect the displacement of the quasi-Fermi level for majority carriers (φ_n here) from the equilibrium level φ.

We should stress that in the strict sense, the Fermi level is defined only for equilibrium situations. The quasi-Fermi levels have been introduced as a mathematical convenience. A quasi-Fermi level is often termed an *imref* (Fermi spelled backwards). There is an imref for holes, φ_p, and an imref for electrons, φ_n. Once again the Boltzmann approximation is used in lieu of the Fermi function. On this basis, the defining equations for the imrefs or quasi-Fermi levels are

$$n = n_i e^{q(\psi - \varphi_n)/kT} \tag{2-44}$$

$$p = n_i e^{q(\varphi_p - \psi)/kT} \tag{2-45}$$

The Junction under Forward Bias. With this introduction, let us turn to the case of a silicon specimen containing a junction. With a voltage source we will apply a forward bias V to the junction. Let it be, for example, 0.18 volt. Making the p region positive with respect to the n region constitutes forward bias. Let the end regions of this junction-containing specimen be very extensive in the x direction, so that their extremities are far from the perturbing influence of the junction. The Fermi level in the n region will be 0.18 volt higher than the Fermi level in the p region (higher, that is, on our conventional diagram where potential increases downward). In the remote end regions, *ohmic* current is flowing, but we use the Fermi level representations anyway because departures from equilibrium there can be small. In pointing out that the Fermi levels in the end regions will be separated by 0.18 volt, we are making the point that Fermi level difference, $\varphi_p - \varphi_n = V$, is what is measured by a voltmeter.

The primary effect of the applied voltage on the junction is to reduce the height of the potential barrier and also to reduce its thickness. This is shown in Fig. 2-14. For purposes of this diagram, the n side has been taken as reference, and the band edge positions on the p side have been translated down. The same junction at equilibrium was shown in Fig. 2-12.

Because the potential hill is diminished, electrons are able to cross the barrier to the right, and holes cross it moving to the left. Their motion through and beyond the barrier is by the mechanism of diffusion, treated in Sec. 2-1. The distances that carriers diffuse before recombining are normally large compared to the barrier thickness. For this reason we customarily make the convenient assumption that φ_n is constant on the left side, remains constant through the barrier, and then gradually settles back to rejoin φ_p on the right (forming a common φ), as the extra electrons diffuse away from the junction and recombine. Similarly, φ_p is constant on the right, and through the barrier. On the left it gradually rejoins φ_n. Hence, within the barrier region we deal with two constant imrefs in this approximate treatment. Obviously this would be a poor approximation with carrier diffusion distances so small that effective equilibrium would be regained very close to the junction.

As a consequence of the situation assumed, we can write an especially simple expression for the *pn* product in the barrier region. At any value of *x* in that region the electron concentration is given by

$$n = n_i e^{q[\psi(x)-\varphi_n]/kT} \tag{2-46}$$

as can be seen by applying the same principles used to generate Eq. (2-39) and from the definition of φ_n. Similarly in the barrier region

$$p = n_i e^{q[\varphi_p - \psi(x)]/kT} \tag{2-47}$$

Thus
$$pn = n_i^2 e^{q(\varphi_p - \varphi_n)/kT} \tag{2-48}$$

But $(\varphi_p - \varphi_n)$ is simply the externally applied voltage V, as pointed out above. Hence, in the barrier region for forward bias, the *pn* product at any value of *x* is inflated by an amount which depends exponentially on the applied voltage:

$$pn = n_i^2 e^{qV/kT} \tag{2-49}$$

Let us now focus on the boundaries of the barrier or depletion region. From

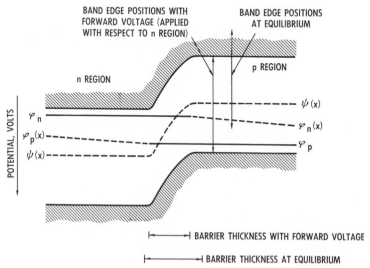

Fig. 2-14 Band structure diagram for a forward-biased n⁺-p junction.

Eq. (2-49) the minority-hole concentration at the left boundary in Fig. 2-14 can be written as

$$p = \frac{n_i^2}{n} e^{qV/kT} \tag{2-50}$$

and in view of Eq. (1-12) it can be rewritten as

$$p = p_n e^{qV/kT} \tag{2-51}$$

where p_n is, of course, the equilibrium-hole concentration on the n side. This specifically assumes that n at the left boundary under forward bias differs negligibly from n_n, the equilibrium value in the n region. This is a good approximation, as pointed out in connection with Fig. 2-13. By a similar argument, the minority-electron concentration at the right boundary of the barrier is given approximately by

$$n = n_p e^{qV/kT} \tag{2-52}$$

Equations (2-51) and (2-52) collectively constitute a very important statement known as the *law of the junction*. They constitute the starting points for numerous items of analysis in this book on integrated circuits.

The Rectifier Equation. Figure 2-15a shows the effect of forward voltage on the n^+-p junction of Figs. 2-10 through 2-14. Let us assume as before that the forward bias is 0.18 volt. Once again a logarithmic carrier concentration scale is used to permit both types of carriers to be displayed on the same diagram. The light solid and dashed lines show the equilibrium-electron and hole distributions, respectively. The heavy solid and dashed lines show the perturbed distributions existing under forward bias. This representation, following Moll,[9] is convenient for showing that the concentrations of minority carriers at both barrier boundaries are increased above the equilibrium values in the neutral regions by the same factor. The factor is, of course, $\exp{(qV/kT)}$ where V is the applied voltage, consistent with Eqs. (2-51) and (2-52). The equal factors of increase on the two sides are represented by equal *increments* on the logarithmic plot (Fig. 2-15a). With a forward bias of 0.18 volt, the factor of increase is about 1,000. This diagram also shows the diminution of barrier thickness which accompanies a reduction in voltage barrier height.

Electrons move through the barrier region and into the nearly neutral p region by the process of diffusion. Figure 2-15b shows the concentration profile responsible for this diffusion, on a linear scale. Note that the hole concentration at the left boundary of the barrier is, for practical purposes, negligible. Thus, accepting the monotonic decline of hole gradient toward the left, it follows that the hole gradient in the nearly neutral n region is virtually zero. A question may arise as to why the appreciable gradient of holes (the heavy dashed line) in the barrier region does not give rise to a hole diffusion current comparable to the electron diffusion current just cited. The answer is that it does, but in the left-hand portion of the barrier region, electric field is a maximum—much larger than at the right. Recall the asymmetric field distribution for this (approximated) junction (Fig. 2-10c). Thus, a counterbalancing drift current of holes, which we do not attempt to show in Fig. 2-15, almost cancels out the hole diffusion current.

The result of the combined effects is that current through the n^+-p junction under forward bias is almost entirely electron diffusion current.   Therefore, let us focus on the behavior of electrons in the lightly doped p region.   Figure 2-15c shows just the portion of interest with the linear concentration scale appropriately magnified, and with $x = 0$ being set at the right-hand boundary of the barrier region. The electron distribution in this region can be determined by the following continuity argument:

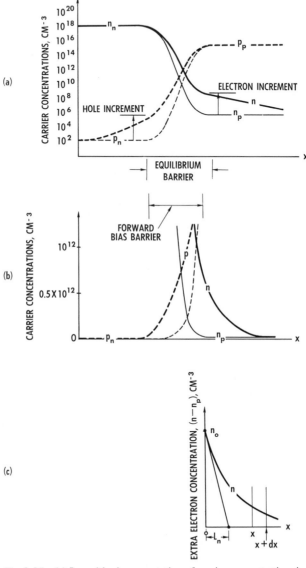

Fig. 2-15   (*a*) Logarithmic presentation of carrier concentrations in a forward-biased n^+-p junction with equilibrium distributions (light curves) shown for reference; (*b*) linear presentation of carrier distributions for the same junction; (*c*) linear presentation of the injected extra electron concentration on the p side of a forward-biased n^+-p junction.

The flux f of electrons across the plane at x is given by Eq. (2-1), which we repeat here for convenience:

$$f = -D_n \frac{\partial n}{\partial x} \tag{2-1}$$

The flux crossing the plane at $(x + dx)$, and hence leaving the region between the planes, is

$$f + \frac{\partial f}{\partial x} dx \tag{2-53}$$

Thus the net flux into the region between the planes is

$$f - \left(f + \frac{\partial f}{\partial x} dx \right) = -\frac{\partial f}{\partial x} dx \tag{2-54}$$

Evaluating this net flux with the aid of Eq. (2-1) gives

$$-\frac{\partial f}{\partial x} dx = -\frac{\partial}{\partial x} \left(-D_n \frac{\partial n}{\partial x} \right) dx = D_n \frac{\partial^2 n}{\partial x^2} dx \tag{2-55}$$

Thus the diffusion mechanism can contribute a net rate of concentration change. Another mechanism that must be taken into consideration is the recombination-generation mechanism inherent in all semiconductors and aided by recombination centers in many practical cases, as outlined in Sec. 2-2. We know in advance that recombination will dominate regeneration because the electron concentration is above the equilibrium value. The rate of concentration change from this cause is given by the expression $-(n - n_p)/\tau$, which parallels Eq. (2-10). Thus the rate of concentration change between the planes at x and $(x + dx)$ is

$$-\frac{n - n_p}{\tau} dx \tag{2-56}$$

Another factor which could potentially contribute to concentration change would be generation caused by some other agency, such as irradiation of the specimen. This we will rule out for purposes of the present discussion. Finally, drift current must be considered. However, we treat the n region as charge-free and field-free in this analysis; hence only Eqs. (2-55) and (2-56) enter into consideration. (The *continuity equation* for electrons is the name of the four-term expression based on the four considerations just named, set equal to the time rate of change of electron concentration.) Postulating steady-state current in the forward-biased junction and steady-state conditions in the n region, the overall net rate of concentration change must be zero. Therefore,

$$D_n \frac{d^2 n}{dx^2} - \frac{n - n_p}{\tau} = 0 \tag{2-57}$$

We wish to solve this equation for the region shown in Fig. 2-15c. The applicable boundary conditions are $n = n_o$ at $x = 0$, and $n = n_p$ at $x = \infty$. The solution of this equation for these boundary conditions is

$$n - n_p = (n_o - n_p)e^{-x/\sqrt{D_n \tau}} \tag{2-58}$$

The electron concentration declines exponentially with a characteristic length which is known as the *diffusion length* for electrons:

$$L_n \equiv \sqrt{D_n \tau} \tag{2-59}$$

The analogous definition for holes is, of course,

$$L_p \equiv \sqrt{D_p \tau} \tag{2-60}$$

From Eq. (2-58), the slope of $n(x)$ at $x = 0$ is

$$\left. \frac{dn}{dx} \right|_{x=0} = - \frac{n_o - n_p}{L_n} \tag{2-61}$$

Hence L_n is the intercept on the x axis of the tangent to $n(x)$ at $x = 0$, as shown in Fig. 2-15c. The electron diffusion current density flow into the p region, assumed to be the only net current present, can thus be written through reference to Eq. (2-2) as

$$J_n = J = qD_n \left. \frac{dn}{dx} \right|_{x=0} = qD_n \frac{n_o - n_p}{L_n} \tag{2-62}$$

But n_o is given by

$$n_o = n_p e^{qV/kT} \tag{2-63}$$

in view of Eq. (2-52).

Hence we have an equation relating the density of current passing through a junction and the voltage applied to it on the basis of a simple model:

$$J = \frac{qD_n n_p}{L_n} (e^{qV/kT} - 1) \tag{2-64}$$

This important relation is known as the *rectifier equation*. The coefficient

$$J_s = \frac{qD_n n_p}{L_n} \tag{2-65}$$

is often termed the *saturation current* density, for reasons that will be explained in the discussion of the reverse-biased junction.

The rectifier equation constitutes a triumph of simple theory, describing with remarkable accuracy the current-voltage characteristics of some junctions; it describes junctions in germanium particularly well, as was shown early in the transistor era.[10] (For a bibliography on still earlier rectification theory, see Ref. 9.) In silicon, experimental results do not agree as well with the simple theory, but it still represents a useful point of departure for approximate analyses. At low forward voltages on silicon junctions, the *injected* minority-carrier currents are often less than the simple theory predicts. It has been pointed out by Sah, Noyce, and Shockley[11] that recombination centers (of the sort mentioned in Sec. 2-2) located in the barrier region can account for this. Carriers diffusing into the barrier under the influence of the forward bias recombine so rapidly that negligible diffusion into the neutral region occurs. In the bias range where the recombination currents are dominating, total current through the junction is greater than Eq. (2-64) predicts (even though injected current is less than it predicts). At somewhat higher bias levels then, these centers become surfeited and injection can proceed. Here the rectifier equation is then obeyed through a restricted voltage range. At still higher voltages, the experimental current deviates again from the predicted value because of effects connected with the high density of injected carriers. At higher voltages still, ohmic voltage drops in the quasi-neutral end regions cause even greater departures from the rectifier equation. Both the latter departures are in the direction of less current than the rectifier equation predicts.

A subtlety which was justifiably ignored in developing the rectifier equation deserves brief attention before we leave the forward-biased junction, because it contributes to an understanding of an important facet of transistor operation. After reading Sec. 2-2, the reader can appreciate that the electrons depicted in Fig. 2-15c must somehow be accompanied by neutralizing charge. Indeed, a distribution of extra holes very similar to the distribution of injected electrons forms instantaneously. But it appears that the holes must then also diffuse to the right as do the electrons, and this is precisely what happens. There then arises a small electric field (as a result of a trifling departure from neutrality) which is just adequate to provide a flow counter to the hole diffusion current. The sea of majority holes is so copious even in this lightly doped specimen that a very small value of electric field is sufficient to do the job. The important point here is this: Diffusion currents depend only on concentration *gradients* and not on concentration *magnitudes*. Hence the hole and electron diffusion currents are roughly equal in the region under discussion, even though their concentration magnitudes differ by several decades. But drift currents depend on concentration *magnitudes*. Hence the electric field sufficient to produce matching hole counterflow produces a negligible electron drift current; in the region of interest in the foregoing example, the electron drift current varied from about one-hundred-thousandth of the electron diffusion current at the left extreme to about one-hundred-millionth at the right extreme. For this reason we were justified in treating electron diffusion current as the only important current in the very nearly neutral p region.

One might expect to see the hole concentration enhancement on Fig. 2-15a in the vicinity of the right-hand barrier boundary. For the example taken, it would be far too small to show on this logarithmic plot. But on a diagram representing heavy forward bias, the enhancement there would indeed be visible. When this enhancement becomes appreciable, the *high-level injection* range has been entered; the perturbation of concentrations for both types of carriers on the same side of the junction causes departures from the predictions of simple theory, as noted earlier.

The Junction under Reverse Bias. Now let a reverse bias be applied to the same n^+-p step junction discussed above and represented in Fig. 2-12. Making the p side negative with respect to the n side will raise the band edges at the right side of this diagram. Clearly this will raise the potential barrier which majority carriers on both sides must surmount if they are to cross the junction. Because majority-carrier population in energy diminishes exponentially in accordance with the Boltzmann factor (neglecting the relatively slow density-of-states variation) fewer majority carriers now have the energy to cross the barrier by diffusion. Thus the diffusion component of current through the barrier rapidly approaches zero with increasing reverse bias.

Figure 2-16 shows the field and potential distribution for this same junction for a reverse applied voltage equal in magnitude to the built-in voltage ψ_o, all for the simple rectangular-charge-distribution model. That these two voltage components are additive is shown plainly in Fig. 2-16b. Also apparent is that the barrier region and depletion region have expanded, by a factor of $\sqrt{2}$ for the simple model, since the base of the triangle in Fig. 2-16a increases by this factor when the area of the triangle (or voltage) is doubled.

Now let us focus our attention on minority carriers. Since the electric field is directed from left to right in this example, minority holes on the left and minority electrons on the right are swept by the field through the barrier. The depletion layer boundaries of course act as sinks for minority carriers. Since electron population on the right n_p greatly exceeds hole population on the left p_n (see Fig. 2-11a) the electron current will dominate strongly in this example, as it did under forward bias. Figure 2-17 depicts the minority-electron distribution on the right side in the neighborhood of the barrier boundary. The region considered is roughly that in Fig. 2-15c for forward bias, but the concentration scale has been expanded for clarity, and total rather than excess carrier concentration is plotted. Once again it is a linear scale. Also, the origin of the x coordinate has been placed once more at the barrier boundary. (The boundary itself has shifted with respect to an absolute reference, such as the metallurgical junction, because of the applied voltage.)

Referring back to Eq. (2-64), we can see that as V becomes more negative, the diode current density approaches the magnitude J_s, which is given by Eq. (2-65). For example, at room temperature and with a reverse voltage $V = 0.1$ volt, the diode current density is approximately $0.98J_s$. Close scrutiny of the reverse-biased junction situation raises a question at this point, however. The rectifier equation was developed through consideration of the forward-biased junction, and for these circumstances the imref concept was employed. The imref concept may be questioned in the case of the reverse-biased junction because its use would imply a

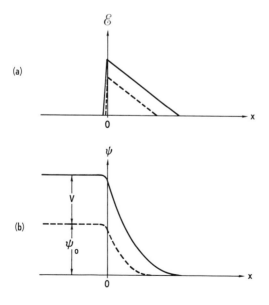

Fig. 2-16 (*a*) Electric field distribution, and (*b*) potential distribution in an n⁺-p junction with an applied reverse bias V equal to the contact potential difference ψ_o. These curves are based on the rectangular space-charge distribution approximation.

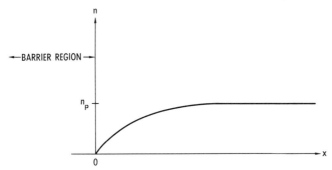

Fig. 2-17   Electron distribution on the p side of a reverse-biased n$^+$-p junction.

double-valued distribution function in the vicinity of the Fermi level. However, a simple argument shows that reverse current will approach J_s, consistent with the rectifier equation, as reverse voltage is increased.

For this situation the applicable differential equation once more is Eq. (2-57). This time the boundary conditions are $n = n_p$ at $x = \infty$, and $n \ll n_p$ at $x = 0$. Hence the solution is approximately

$$n = n_p \left(1 - e^{-x/L_n}\right) \tag{2-66}$$

Again the solution involves the characteristic length L_n, the electron diffusion length. Thus the gradient of electrons for x very slightly greater than zero is

$$\left.\frac{dn}{dx}\right|_{x \approx 0} = \frac{n_p}{L_n} \tag{2-67}$$

Applying Eq. (2-2) once more, the electron diffusion current density can be written

$$J_n = qD_n \frac{n_p}{L_n} \tag{2-68}$$

The hole diffusion current is negligible for the unsymmetrical junction we have chosen to analyze because hole concentration is vanishingly small on the n$^+$ side. (It is interesting to note that hole current was also negligible under forward bias.) Hence Eq. (2-68) gives essentially the total reverse current, and it further is consistent with Eq. (2-65), as we set out to show.

In germanium junctions the *saturation* effect is very marked in the reverse branch of the *I-V* characteristic. Both theory and experiment yield saturation current values in the microampere neighborhood for junctions in small germanium devices.

In silicon, however, minority-carrier concentration at a given doping is far smaller than in germanium because of silicon's larger energy gap and smaller pn product. Theoretical saturation currents in silicon are over a million times smaller than for comparable germanium junctions. As a result, these current components in reverse-biased silicon junctions are swamped by other effects. Notable among these is carrier generation in the barrier region, caused by the traps cited earlier.[11] Those workers have shown that current density resulting from this phenomenon can be calculated from

$$J = qgX_m \tag{2-69}$$

where g is generation rate in $cm^{-3} sec^{-1}$. The generation rate g has the form $n_i/2\tau$, where n_i is the intrinsic carrier concentration and τ is, of course, lifetime. It must be emphasized that lifetime can vary from specimen to specimen and from point to point within a given specimen. Comparing this to Eq. (2-11) shows its similarity to the expression for rate of generation (or recombination) in a region of reasonably uniform doping (a description which is, of course, not satisfied by a junction region). The theoretical magnitude of this component is in the nanoampere neighborhood for junctions in small silicon devices, and this agrees well with experiment. Furthermore, this contribution to reverse current increases with reverse voltage because X_m, the depletion layer thickness, increases with reverse voltage in accordance with principles that will be developed next.

Depletion Layer Calculations for Reverse-biased Junctions. As the height of the potential barrier is increased, the x distance required for transition from near-neutrality to near-depletion probably does not change very much.[7] That is, the thickness of the fuzzy or smeared-out boundary of the depletion region is fairly independent of reverse-bias voltage. This is because approximately the same potential is still required to produce the transition from the constant majority-carrier concentration level to a concentration level near zero. A transition region thickness in the neighborhood of 6 extrinsic Debye lengths is still reasonable [see Eq. (2-15)]. Therefore with increasing reverse voltage and increasing depletion layer thickness, the fuzzy region thickness becomes progressively less important percentagewise. It is for this reason that the rectangular-charge-distribution calculations assume greater validity with increasing reverse bias.

From the discussion of the reverse-biased junction it is clear that the voltage value to use in a depletion layer thickness calculation is the total barrier height, or the total electrostatic potential difference between the neutral regions—built-in voltage plus the magnitude of the applied reverse voltage. At large reverse biases the built-in voltage, which is usually in the 0.6- to 0.7-volt range for silicon, can, of course, be ignored. But with the low voltages frequently employed in integrated circuits this is less valid.

The method employed for calculating depletion layer thickness is precisely that used in connection with the equilibrium examples, substituting V_t, total voltage, for ψ_o, built-in voltage. For convenience, the equations developed there are presented here, properly modified, and one is added.

For the n^+-p or p^+-n step junction the depletion layer thickness is given by

$$X_m = \left(\frac{2\kappa\epsilon_o V_t}{qN}\right)^{1/2} \qquad (2\text{-}70)$$

where N is the net impurity concentration on the lightly doped side. As is evident from this equation, the relationship between X_m and voltage can be compressed into a single curve by using V_t/N as the independent variable. This has been done in Fig. 2-18, which follows a diagram given previously by Phillips.[12]

For the moderately unsymmetrical step junction the depletion layer thickness is

$$X_m = \left(\frac{2\kappa\epsilon_o V_t}{q(N_1 + N_2)}\right)^{1/2}\left[\left(\frac{N_1}{N_2}\right)^{1/2} + \left(\frac{N_2}{N_1}\right)^{1/2}\right] \qquad (2\text{-}71)$$

where N_1 and N_2 are the net impurity concentrations on the two sides. The respective components of depletion layer spread into the two sides are

$$X_1 = \left(\frac{2\kappa\epsilon_o}{q} \frac{N_2}{N_1} \frac{V_t}{N_1 + N_2}\right)^{1/2} \qquad (2\text{-}72)$$

and

$$X_2 = \left(\frac{2\kappa\epsilon_o}{q} \frac{N_1}{N_2} \frac{V_t}{N_1 + N_2}\right)^{1/2} \qquad (2\text{-}73)$$

It is apparent that this is the general step-junction case; letting N_1 (or alternately N_2) become very large causes Eq. (2-71) to approach (2-70). Similarly, letting $N_1 = N_2$ gives the symmetrical step-junction case:

$$X_m = \left(\frac{4\kappa\epsilon_o V_t}{qN}\right)^{1/2} \qquad (2\text{-}74)$$

where N is the common net doping value. Thus for step junctions in general, the total depletion layer thickness varies directly with the square root of total voltage.

Another important simple junction type is the linearly graded junction. This received attention along with the step junction in Shockley's early paper on junction theory.[6] For this case

$$X_m = \left(\frac{12\kappa\epsilon_o V_t}{qa}\right)^{1/3} \qquad (2\text{-}75)$$

where a is the concentration gradient, sometimes called the *grade constant,* or constant rate of change of concentration, dN/dx, in cm^{-4}. In this important case, depletion layer thickness varies directly with the cube root of total voltage.

Practical junctions frequently lie between the step junction and linearly graded junction extremes. Chapter 3 takes up two important junction profiles produced by solid-phase diffusion and frequently encountered in integrated circuit work.

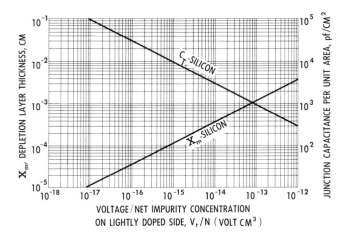

Fig. 2-18 Depletion layer thickness X_m and transition capacitance C_T for an n^+-p or p^+-n junction in silicon. The independent variable V_t/N is the total voltage across the junction divided by net impurity concentration on the lightly doped side of the junction. (*After Phillips.*[12])

2-5   Junction Capacitance

When an increment of reverse voltage is applied to a junction, the depletion layer expands, and ionic charge is "stored" on both sides of the junction in the region of transition from neutrality to depletion.   Removing the voltage increment will "recover" the charge; i.e., carriers will flow and will neutralize that increment of ionic charge.   From the external circuit viewpoint, electrons have been recovered. Hence the junction possesses capacitance.   A definition for capacitance C is

$$C = \frac{dQ}{dV} \tag{2-76}$$

For an ordinary capacitor which is linear in charge versus voltage, $dQ/dV = Q/V$, of course, and the derivative definition is unnecessary.   But with a junction we *never* remove all the charge, and we are interested in the capacitance exhibited by the junction when a signal voltage, usually small in relation to bias, is impressed upon it.

Let us take the one-sided step-junction example for simplicity.   Proceeding formally, the *total* charge per unit area of junction on one side of the junction (we always deal with the charge on one plate of a capacitor) can be written with the aid of Eq. (2-70):

$$Q = qN \left(\frac{2\kappa\epsilon_o V_t}{qN}\right)^{1/2} \tag{2-77}$$

where V_t is total voltage on the junction.   Hence the *transition capacitance* per unit area, C_T (so-called because charge is stored in the transition region), for the n$^+$-p or p$^+$-n step junction is

$$C_T = \frac{dQ}{dV_t} = \left(\frac{q\kappa\epsilon_o N}{2V_t}\right)^{1/2} \tag{2-78}$$

where N is the net doping on the lightly doped side.   Now it is apparent that this is the same capacitance one would calculate for a conventional capacitor having a silicon dielectric (or equivalent) and a plate spacing of X_m, given by Eq. (2-70). Upon reflection we see that this is to be expected, because we are concerned only with charge stored and recovered at the depletion layer boundaries.   The relationship between C_T and V_t/N is plotted in Fig. 2-18.

The capacitance per unit area for the unsymmetrical step junction is

$$C_T = \left[\frac{q\kappa\epsilon_o(N_1 + N_2)}{2V_t}\right]^{1/2}\left[\left(\frac{N_1}{N_2}\right)^{1/2} + \left(\frac{N_2}{N_1}\right)^{1/2}\right]^{-1} \tag{2-79}$$

For the symmetrical step junction,

$$C_T = \left(\frac{q\kappa\epsilon_o N}{4V_t}\right)^{1/2} \tag{2-80}$$

Finally, for the linearly graded junction, capacitance per unit area is

$$C_T = (\kappa\epsilon_o)^{2/3}\left(\frac{qa}{12V_t}\right)^{1/3} \tag{2-81}$$

For the step junction and the linearly graded junction the capacitance varies inversely as the square root and cube root, respectively, of the total voltage V_t.

Depletion layer capacitance measurements agree very well with calculations based on the rectangular-charge-distribution model. Reasons for this can be seen by referring to Fig. 2-7. If the actual shape of the boundary shown in Fig. 2-7*a* does not change much with bias, then the *mean thickness* of the true depletion layer is clearly going to be close to the thickness of the idealized layer in Fig. 2-7*b*, especially at appreciable voltages. From a slightly different point of view, we could state that the *center of gravity* of a charge increment stored by an increment in reverse voltage will match rather closely with respect to *x* position in Fig. 2-7*a* and *b*. The agreement of simple theory and experiment is good enough so that capacitance measurements can be exploited under some circumstances for determining net doping.

2-6   Reverse Breakdown

In Secs. 2-3 and 2-4 we dwelt at some length on the electric field associated with a p-n junction. From Fig. 2-7*b* and *c* it is apparent that the maximum field for a given total voltage on the junction increases as doping on either or both sides is increased. Total voltage across the junction V_t is the area under the curve in Fig. 2-7*c*:

$$V_t = \int \mathcal{E}\, dx$$
through the barrier region

(2-82)

Simple expressions for peak field can be generated on the basis of the rectangular-charge-distribution model, using the methods of Sec. 2-3.

For junctions very heavily doped on both sides, the peak field can be quite high indeed, even at modest applied voltages. For this reason, early consideration was given to the possibility that the field in such junctions could excite electrons directly from the valence band to the conduction band,[13] thus accounting for the reverse 'breakdown" effect shown in Fig. 2-19*a*, with current increasing sharply at a criti-

(a)

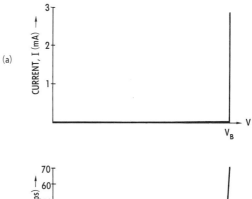

(b)

Fig. 2-19 (*a*) The *I-V* characteristic of a typical silicon p-n junction biased in the reverse direction; (*b*) the same curve with current scale expanded to show avalanche multiplication.

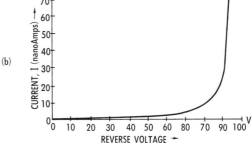

cal voltage V_B. The basic mechanism involved was discussed earlier by Zener (1934) without specific reference to p-n junctions. It is now felt that this mechanism can dominate only in junctions with very thin depletion layers, that is, in junctions so heavily doped that they break down at a few volts.

Today there is an important family of commercial junction diodes exploiting the breakdown phenomenon shown in Fig. 2-19 for its voltage-regulating properties. For historical reasons they are known as *Zener diodes,* even though another breakdown mechanism dominates through most of the range of available voltages— roughly 3 to 200 volts. (The *I-V* characteristic shown in Fig. 2-19a is that of a typical Zener diode.) In this other mechanism, carriers are accelerated in the field to such a degree that they are capable of carrier pair generation upon impact with a silicon atom. The carriers so created are in turn accelerated, producing additional pairs, and so on. The result is an "avalanche" effect. McKay[14] has pointed out that the fact that both holes and electrons can ionize introduces an element of positive feedback into the process, with a result that is analogous to the Townsend avalanche in gases.

Multiplication of carriers injected externally (as by a light pulse) occurs in the avalanche process at voltages below the breakdown voltage V_B. This multiplication affords an experimental criterion for discerning the dominant mechanism, since in the Zener effect, a critical field and an abrupt change in current with voltage is expected, with no multiplication. The multiplication associated with the avalanche process is shown in Fig. 2-19b. This is simply the curve in Fig. 2-19a, redrawn with an expanded current scale. Miller[15] studied the multiplication factor as a function of voltage, $M(V)$, and generated the following empirical expression to fit his observations:

$$M(V) = \frac{1}{1 - (V/V_B)^n} \tag{2-83}$$

The value of the exponent n depends on whether electrons or holes are dominant in the ionization process. Electrons have a higher ionization rate (leading to a smaller value for n) than holes. Which carriers dominate is elected experimentally by choosing either an n^+-p junction or a p^+-n junction. In the former case it is minority electrons which determine the result, and in the second it is minority holes. Miller found values for the exponent n of approximately 2 and 4, respectively, for electrons and holes in silicon. That is to say, the appropriate values of the exponent n are 2 and 4 for an n^+-p and a p^+-n junction, respectively.

The concept of a *critical field* at breakdown makes sense for the Zener mechanism, but not for the avalanche mechanism. In the latter case it is field magnitude and distance over which it obtains that matters. In a very heavily doped junction the peak field at breakdown is substantially larger than that in a lightly doped junction (even though the former has a lower breakdown voltage).

There is a positive temperature coefficient associated with breakdown voltage in a silicon junction. At a breakdown value of 100 volts, the temperature coefficient

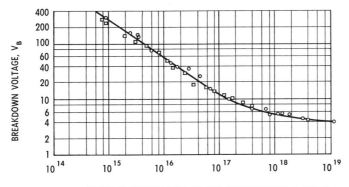

IMPURITY CONCENTRATION ON HIGH-RESISTIVITY SIDE, N (CM⁻³)

Fig. 2-20 The breakdown voltage of silicon step junctions (n^+-p or p^+-n) as a function of net impurity concentration on the lightly doped side of the junction. (*The squares are the data of Wilson and Pearson as reported by McKay,*[14] *and the circles are the data of Miller.*[16])

is about 0.1 volt per C°. At about 5 volts the coefficient is zero, and the coefficient exhibits a nearly linear variation between these voltages.

Figure 2-20 gives an experimental curve of breakdown voltage versus impurity concentration on the lightly doped side of either an n^+-p or p^+-n junction. It is based on data of Wilson and Pearson as reported by McKay,[14] and of Miller.[16]

REFERENCES

1. Shockley, W., and W. T. Read, Jr.: Statistics of the Recombinations of Holes and Electrons, *Phys. Rev.,* vol. 87, pp. 835–842, Sept. 1, 1952.
2. Hall, R. N.: Electron-Hole Recombination in Germanium, *Phys. Rev.,* vol. 87, p. 387, July 15, 1952.
3. Collins, C. B., R. O. Carlson, and C. J. Gallagher: Properties of Gold-doped Silicon, *Phys. Rev.,* vol. 105, pp. 1168–1173, Feb. 15, 1957.
4. Bemski, G.: Recombination Properties of Gold in Silicon, *Phys. Rev.,* vol. 111, pp. 1515–1518, Sept. 15, 1958.
5. Hannay, N. B. (ed.): "Semiconductors," Reinhold Publishing Corp., New York, 1959.
6. Shockley, W.: The Theory of p-n Junctions in Semiconductors and p-n Junction Transistors, *Bell System Tech. J.,* vol. 28, pp. 435–489, July, 1949.
7. Gray, P. E., D. Dewitt, A. R. Boothroyd, and J. F. Gibbons: "Physical Electronics and Circuit Models of Transistors," John Wiley & Sons, Inc., New York, 1963.
8. Stone, H. A. Jr., and R. M. Warner, Jr.: The Field-effect Tetrode, *Proc. IRE,* vol. 49, pp. 1170–1183, July, 1961. (In eq. (79) of this reference, the factor N/P should be inverted.)
9. Moll, J. L.: The Evolution of the Theory for the Voltage-Current Characteristic of P-N Junctions, *Proc. IRE,* vol. 46, pp. 1076–1082, June, 1958.
10. Shockley, W.: "Electrons and Holes in Semiconductors," D. Van Nostrand Co., Inc., Princeton, N.J., 1950.
11. Sah, C. T., R. N. Noyce, and W. Shockley: Carrier Generation and Recombination in

P-N Junctions and P-N Junction Characteristics, *Proc. IRE,* vol. 45, pp. 1228–1243, September, 1957.

12. Phillips, A. B.: "Transistor Engineering," Mc-Graw Hill Book Company, New York, 1962.

13. McAfee, K. B., E. J. Ryder, W. Shockley, and M. Sparks: Observations of Zener Current in Germanium p-n Junctions, *Phys. Rev.,* vol. 83, pp. 650–651, Aug. 1, 1951.

14. McKay, K. G.: Avalanche Breakdown in Silicon, *Phys. Rev.,* vol. 94, pp. 877–884, May 15, 1954.

15. Miller, S. L.: Avalanche Breakdown in Germanium, *Phys. Rev.,* vol. 99, pp. 1234–1241, Aug. 15, 1955.

16. Miller, S. L.: Ionization Rates for Holes and Electrons in Silicon, *Phys. Rev.,* vol. 105, pp. 1246–1249, Feb. 15, 1957.

3

IMPURITY DIFFUSION AND
DIFFUSED JUNCTION PROPERTIES

Present-day commercial methods for fabricating integrated circuits rely heavily on the process of solid-state diffusion[1] for forming p-n junctions. Furthermore, other operations commonly employed in making integrated circuits can be characterized and controlled only by giving careful consideration to the diffusion phenomena inevitably accompanying them. Examples of these other operations are epitaxial growth (treated in Chap. 11) and silicon oxide growth (Chap. 12).

The first section below will take up basic diffusion theory and the solution of the diffusion equation for two important sets of boundary conditions. The next section considers the effects on the diffused distribution of variations in certain process factors. Next the problem of evaluating a diffused layer is treated. A tying together of diffusion theory and some of the junction theory developed in Chap. 2 is presented in the fourth section. And finally, the fifth section takes up the important matter of gold diffusion.

The diffusion process is usually carried out on a silicon *wafer*. This is a term of the trade for a slice cut from the customary roughly cylindrical single crystal of silicon. A crystal is typically about an inch in diameter and ten inches in length. A wafer has approximately the size and shape of a 50-cent piece or a quarter, and in the as-cut condition is not very different from these in monetary value. At the start of the diffusion process, a high concentration of impurity atoms is presented to the surface of the wafer. During diffusion, then, these impurity atoms are dissolved in the still-solid silicon crystal according to well-established laws. We will consider important special diffusion situations. For the reader interested in more general discussions of diffusion or a wider range of special cases, there are excellent treatises available.[2-4]

3-1   Diffusion Theory

Fick's first law of diffusion was developed in Chap. 2 for the case of mobile carriers. It is equally valid for impurity atoms, which also become mobile in a silicon crystal when it is heated to high temperatures (e.g., 1000 to 1300°C). According to Fick's first law, there will be a flow (a diffusion) from the region of high concentration at the surface to the regions of low concentration in the interior. Figure 3-1*a* presents pictorially the qualitative distribution of diffused impurity atoms in a wafer of somewhat exaggerated thickness. Figure 3-1*b* shows graphically the impurity distribution resulting from a diffusion procedure, again in qualitative terms.

Diffusion flow will continue until the impurity concentration becomes uniform throughout the sample. In practical situations where p-n junctions are being formed by diffusion, the process is arrested (by reducing temperature) long before a uniform distribution has been obtained. But in special cases such as gold diffusion, it is sometimes desirable to approach uniformity of impurity doping throughout an entire sample by means of the diffusion process.

(a)

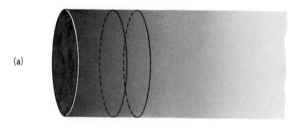

(b)

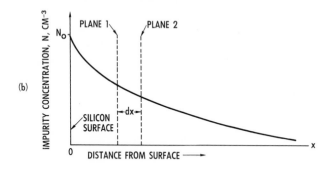

Fig. 3-1 Impurity diffusion into a silicon wafer from one face: (*a*) A silicon wafer with thickness greatly exaggerated, having an impurity concentration which diminishes from the left face toward the interior; (*b*) graphical representation of the same impurity distribution.

Fick's first law, repeated here for convenience with appropriately modified notation, states that particle flux is proportional to the concentration gradient:

$$f = -D\frac{\partial N}{\partial x} \tag{3-1}$$

Here f is the particle flux (or rate of flow of impurity atoms in this case) through a plane parallel to the surface, such as plane 1 in Fig. 3-1, for example. The dimensions of particle flux are number per unit area and unit time. D is a proportionality constant called the *diffusion coefficient*, having dimensions of area per unit time.

N is the impurity concentration in number per unit volume, and x is distance from the surface. We consider that concentration does not vary with y or z in this situation (i.e., the problem is *one-dimensional*). The minus sign enters because a concentration rising to the left leads to diffusion to the right.

Fick's second law, derived from the first by a continuity argument, is more useful than the first for diffusion calculations. On a per-unit-area basis, the number of particles lying between planes 1 and 2 which are separated by a distance dx will be $N\,dx$. Now, permitting N to be a function of time as well as of x, we can write the rate of accumulation of particles in that region as

$$\frac{\partial N}{\partial t}\,dx \tag{3-2}$$

But it can also be written as the difference between flow across the two planes. The departing flux at plane 2 is

$$f + \frac{\partial f}{\partial x}\,dx \tag{3-3}$$

and the entering flux at plane 1 is simply f. Hence the net flow into the region is

$$-\frac{\partial f}{\partial x}\,dx \tag{3-4}$$

Applying Fick's first law,

$$-\frac{\partial f}{\partial x}\,dx = -\frac{\partial}{\partial x}\left(-D\frac{\partial N}{\partial x}\right)dx \tag{3-5}$$

Since expressions (3-2) and (3-4) are equal,

$$\frac{\partial N}{\partial t}\,dx = D\frac{\partial^2 N}{\partial x^2}\,dx \tag{3-6}$$

which gives us Fick's second law:

$$\frac{\partial N}{\partial t} = D\frac{\partial^2 N}{\partial x^2} \tag{3-7}$$

When this equation is solved and appropriate boundary conditions are applied, the result is an expression for impurity concentration N as a function of distance x from the surface. Two different boundary situations are common in integrated circuit diffusion work. For one of these the solution of Fick's second law is the complementary error function, and for the other it is the gaussian function.

The Complementary Error Function Distribution. Suppose we raise the temperature of an undoped silicon wafer to 1200°C with one of the large-area faces exposed to a volume of gas having a uniform concentration N_g of an n-type impurity, such as phosphorus. The volume of gas is considered to be large so that the impurity concentration N_g will remain constant. The phosphorus atoms will then diffuse from the gas phase into the silicon, forming a distribution in which the phosphorus concentration decreases with distance from the exposed surface. This diffused distribution is illustrated in Fig. 3-2. If the diffusion were allowed to proceed for a sufficient length of time, the silicon would become uniformly doped with phosphorus to a concentration N_o, determined by the value of a quantity known as the equilibrium distribution coefficient K. This coefficient is defined as the ratio of the concentration of the impurity in silicon to the concentration of the impurity in the gas phase, or

$$K = \frac{N_o}{N_g} \qquad (3\text{-}8)$$

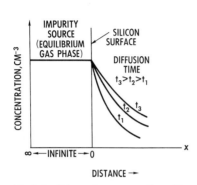

If K is assumed to be 1, as is the case shown in Fig. 3-2, then $N_g = N_o$. It should be emphasized that N_o is the concentration in atoms per unit volume existing in an infinitesimally thin layer of silicon at the surface, and that it is not stated in terms of atoms per unit area.

At zero time the surface concentration of phosphorus is zero. However, as diffusion proceeds, the surface concentration increases rapidly to the value N_o, and remains constant thereafter. This simple and convenient picture is valid, provided that the rate of transport of phosphorus from the gas phase to the silicon surface is much faster than the rate at which phosphorus diffuses from the surface into the bulk of the sample.

Fig. 3-2 Schematic representation of the constant-surface-concentration boundary condition which leads to a complementary error function impurity distribution. The depth of penetration increases as diffusion time is increased.

The boundary conditions for the situation just described may be stated mathematically as follows:

1. Assume that N_g is constant for diffusion times from $t = 0$ to $t = \infty$.
2. Assume that $N = 0$ at $t = 0$, where $N =$ the phosphorus concentration in the silicon.
3. Assume that the surface concentration N_o is independent of diffusion time; that is, consider only cases where diffusion time is long compared to the time required to establish the equilibrium surface concentration N_o.

When Fick's second law is solved with these boundary conditions, the following function is obtained for the phosphorus concentration at any depth x from the surface:

$$N(x) = N_o\left(1 - \frac{2}{\sqrt{\pi}} \int_0^{x/2\sqrt{Dt}} e^{-\lambda^2}\, d\lambda\right) \qquad (3\text{-}9)$$

where λ is an integration variable. Since the integral in Eq. (3-9) is commonly referred to as the *error function,* this equation is frequently written as

$$N(x) = N_o\left(1 - \operatorname{erf}\frac{x}{2\sqrt{Dt}}\right) \qquad (3\text{-}10)$$

or
$$N(x) = N_o \operatorname{erfc}\frac{x}{2\sqrt{Dt}} \qquad (3\text{-}11)$$

where *erfc* is the abbreviation for error function complement.

Inspection of Eq. (3-11) shows that three quantities define a specific diffused concentration distribution: the surface concentration of the diffusant N_0, the diffusion coefficient D of the impurity, and the time of diffusion t.

A typical example of the conditions which result in a complementary error function distribution are those employed in the emitter diffusion for transistors. Here, the wafers at a high temperature are exposed to an atmosphere containing, for example, if the devices are to be n-p-n transistors, phosphorus. The wafers are maintained in this atmosphere, which is kept at as uniform conditions as possible, throughout the entire diffusion cycle. At the end of the cycle, the wafers are removed from the hot zone and allowed to cool somewhat before being removed from the phosphorus atmosphere.

A special example of circumstances leading to a complementary error function distribution is provided by *epitaxial* technology. Although this is a new process, the example it supplies fits a classical textbook diffusion situation.[2] This process, described at length in Chap. 11, involves the growth of silicon from the vapor phase upon a single-crystal silicon *substrate*. The final result is a wafer which is an integral single crystal with a thin layer on one side, which has been grown there at an elevated temperature by the epitaxial process.

It is possible, for example, to grow a lightly doped epitaxial layer on a heavily doped substrate wafer. Under these conditions the growth process is accompanied by an out-diffusion of impurities from the substrate into the growing epitaxial layer. Although an idealized boundary condition for an epitaxial layer is shown in Fig. 3-3, this abrupt change in impurity concentration is never achieved in practice because of the resulting out-diffusion. For a negligible initial concentration of the substrate dopant in the film, solution of Fick's law gives the following equation for the concentration $N(x)$ of substrate impurity at a distance x from the epitaxial-substrate interface:

$$N(x) = \frac{N_0}{2} \operatorname{erfc} \frac{x}{2\sqrt{Dt}} \qquad (3\text{-}12)$$

where N_0 is the original concentration of the impurity in the substrate. Note the close similarity between this equation and the complementary error function for an in-diffusion from an infinite impurity source [Eq. (3-11)]. Inspection of Eq. (3-12) shows that the concentration at the substrate-epitaxial interface drops to one-half the initial value after a finite diffusion time, for a reason made qualitatively obvious in Fig. 3-3.

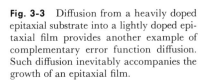

Fig. 3-3 Diffusion from a heavily doped epitaxial substrate into a lightly doped epitaxial film provides another example of complementary error function diffusion. Such diffusion inevitably accompanies the growth of an epitaxial film.

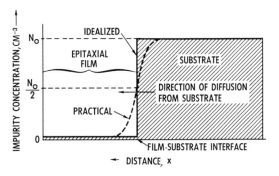

The Gaussian Distribution. Consider another diffusion experiment on an undoped silicon wafer. Instead of exposing the sample to an essentially infinite source containing a constant concentration of phosphorus, let us deposit a specific number of phosphorus atoms per unit area, Q, on one face of the wafer, and then heat the material in an atmosphere which prevents evaporation of the phosphorus from the surface. In this experiment, as in the first one, the phosphorus atoms will diffuse into the silicon. The essential difference between the two experiments is that the diffusant source in the second one consists of a finite amount of phosphorus rather than the infinite source of phosphorus available in the first experiment. When the boundary conditions for the present case are applied to Fick's second law, the following function is obtained for the concentration of phosphorus at any depth x below the surface:

$$N(x) = \frac{Q}{\sqrt{\pi Dt}} e^{-x^2/4Dt} \tag{3-13}$$

where as before D and t are the diffusion coefficient and time, respectively.

Figure 3-4 shows a series of gaussian distributions for various diffusion times. In comparing these curves with those shown in Fig. 3-2, note that for the complementary error function (erfc) distribution the concentration near the surface is independent of diffusion time, while the gaussian distribution is characterized by a steadily *decreasing* surface concentration.

Junction Formation by Diffusion. An undoped silicon wafer was the starting material for each of the situations shown in Figs. 3-2 and 3-4. However, all the facts outlined there would hold equally well in a case where the n-type impurity is diffused into a silicon wafer which initially has a uniform p-type doping. In such a case, at the depth below the surface where the n-type impurity concentration equals the p-type impurity concentration ($N_A = N_D$), by definition a p-n junction is present. Figure 3-5 illustrates this important concept. N_{BC} stands for background concentration (p-type impurity in this case). The diagram is not drawn to scale inasmuch as N_o is typically several orders of magnitude larger than N_{BC}. Because of this, it is very common to diagram impurity distributions with a logarithmic concentration scale. An example of such a diagram can be seen in Fig. 7-3 for the case

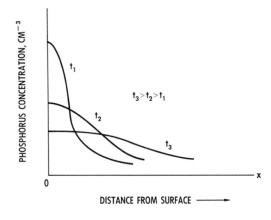

Fig. 3-4 The gaussian distribution. Surface concentration diminishes with time, while the total quantity of diffusant (area under the curve) remains constant.

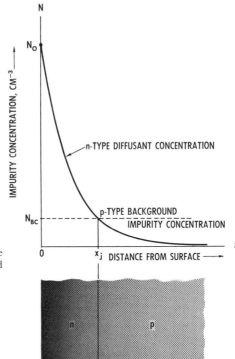

Fig. 3-5 An n-p junction is produced at x_j, where the diffusant concentration equals the background impurity concentration.

of an integrated circuit transistor. In this case a p-type diffusion into an n-type background has been followed by an n-type diffusion which has, in turn, formed an additional junction. Thus a double-diffused n-p-n structure has been achieved.

3-2 Effect of Process Variables on the Diffused Distribution

The integrated circuit process engineer is usually concerned with establishing diffusion profiles which conform to one of the two boundary conditions discussed earlier. The shape of the diffused distribution in practice is determined by a number of variables such as diffusion time, temperature, impurity solid solubility, and surface condition and crystalline perfection of the underlying silicon. We will now consider the effects of these individual variables.

Solid Solubility of Diffusant. Suppose that for design reasons we wish to produce a specific complementary error function distribution of an n-type impurity in silicon. Potentially we have three elements from which to choose: phosphorus, arsenic, and antimony. When dissolved in silicon, all three are fully ionized at room temperature and occupy substitutional positions in the semiconductor lattice. One of the first criteria for judging the feasibility of using a specific element is the determination that the maximum concentration required by the diffusion curve is less than the diffusant's solid solubility. The term *solid solubility* denotes the maximum concentration N_0 of the element which can be dissolved in the solid silicon at any specified temperature. If we attempt to dissolve more than this amount by, for

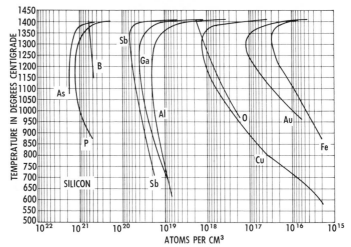

Fig. 3-6   Solid solubilities of some impurity elements in silicon. (*After Trumbore.*[5])

example, exposing the solid to a phase containing a higher concentration of the element, reactions will occur which result in the conversion of a portion of the solid silicon to the liquid phase. Figure 3-6 shows curves of the solid solubility of a number of common diffusants as a function of temperature.[5] If the specified diffusion curve requires a surface concentration higher than the maximum solid solubility of a given impurity, we cannot utilize that particular element to obtain the desired distribution. Thus, the maximum solid solubility sets the upper limit on the diffusant surface concentration.

Before leaving the subject of solid solubility, consider the ordinate in Fig. 3-6. Note that some elements, for example, phosphorus, have a maximum solid solubility of approximately 10^{21} atoms/cm³. Since pure silicon contains 5×10^{22} atoms/cm³, the maximum concentration of phosphorus in solid silicon is 2 per cent. On the other hand, for an element such as aluminum, the maximum concentration in the solid silicon is 0.002 per cent. The wide range of solid solubilities for the group III and group V elements provide a liberal choice of potential diffusant surface concentrations for both complementary error function and gaussian diffusion conditions.

Diffusion Temperature.   In a qualitative way we can understand that an increase in the diffusion temperature would increase the rate of diffusion; higher temperatures impart greater energy to the diffusant atoms and thus increase the speed with which they move through the lattice. For typical integrated circuit diffused structures, the necessary profiles are such that an essentially infinite time would be required if the diffusions were carried out at room temperature. In practice, such processes are conducted in the range of 1000 to 1300°C so as to produce the desired profile in a time between a few minutes and several hours.

The strong effect of temperature on the diffusion process arises from the very sensitive temperature dependence of the diffusion coefficient D. The quantitative relationship between the diffusion coefficient and temperature is as follows:

$$D = D_o e^{-\Delta H/RT} \tag{3-14}$$

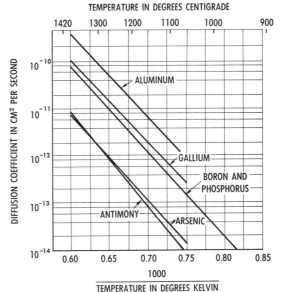

Fig. 3-7 Diffusion coefficients as a function of temperature for some impurity elements in silicon. (*After Fuller and Ditzenberger.*[1])

in which D_o and R are constants, T is the temperature in degrees Kelvin, and ΔH is the *activation energy* for the diffusion of an impurity into a material. For a specific diffusant and medium, the activation energy may be regarded as a constant. Therefore, it can be seen that if the logarithm of the diffusion coefficient is plotted against the reciprocal of the diffusion temperature, a straight line results. Figure 3-7 shows log D plotted versus $1/T$ values for several of these elements.[1] There is actually little difference between the slope of these lines for the common diffusants, thus indicating similar values for the activation energies. However, because of variations in the constant D_o, considerable differences exist in the diffusion coefficient for the various elements at a given temperature. For example, at 1200°C the diffusion coefficient for aluminum is almost ten times that of boron. On the other hand, boron and phosphorus, two of the more common diffusants in integrated circuits technology, have nearly equal diffusion coefficients.

Expansion of the temperature scale in Fig. 3-7 would show that a few degrees increase in temperature could double the diffusion coefficient. The effect of this increase in D can be seen graphically in Fig. 3-8. The junction depth is significantly increased. If the diffusion profile in Fig. 3-8 represents a transistor base diffusion, an uncontrolled increase in the diffusion temperature of only a few degrees can significantly increase the impurity penetration, and thus, the base thickness.

In Fig. 3-8 we assumed the surface concentration to be independent of the diffusion temperature. Actually, in any diffusion system, an increase in temperature may increase the surface concentration slightly, thereby also increasing base thickness. This is illustrated in Fig. 3-9 which shows the case where N_o, the surface concentration, is raised as a result of an increase in the temperature.

This critical influence of temperature on the diffusion profile has forced the semiconductor industry to acquire extremely sophisticated furnaces and controls, capable of holding temperatures in the range of 1000 to 1300°C to a tolerance of

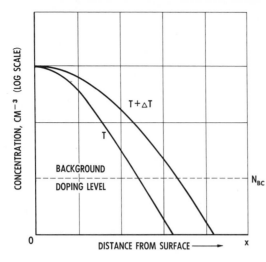

Fig. 3-8 Effect of a temperature increase on diffused distributions produced in equal times. Temperature and impurity element are chosen so that surface concentration does not change (see Fig. 3-6).

$\pm 0.5°$C, in order that modern transistor and integrated circuit structures can be made reproducibly.

Diffusion Time. In both the complementary error function and gaussian distributions, the diffusion time t appears only in the product Dt. Thus, increases in either diffusion time or diffusion coefficient have similar effects on junction depth and diffusant density. For a silicon sample of uniform but opposite conductivity type, the junction depth associated with a complementary error function distribution of a given diffusant can be shown to be a linear function of the square root of the diffusion time. While this linear relationship is approximated for gaussian distributions, for long diffusion times the junction depth tends to be lower than the linear value. For a gaussian distribution the net concentration will *decrease* because of impurity compensation, and can approach zero with increasing diffusion times. For complementary error function distribution, the net diffusant concentration on the diffused side of the p-n junction shows a steady *increase* with time.

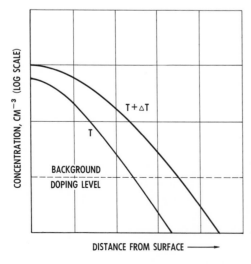

Fig. 3-9 Effect of a temperature increase on diffused distributions produced in equal time in a case where surface concentration increases.

In practice, time is a relatively easy variable to control. However, should the diffusion time be less than a few minutes, consideration must be given both to the time required for the silicon to reach the desired temperature and to the post-diffusion cooling period. To minimize temperature variations for short diffusions, the process engineer usually standardizes on a constant thermal mass in his diffusion system and a fixed rate of entry into and removal from the furnace for the silicon samples.

Surface Cleanliness and Silicon Imperfections. Two process variables which subtly influence the diffusion profile are the cleanliness of the silicon surface and the crystalline perfection of the silicon. Both affect localized regions within the diffused areas, in contrast to such variables as time and temperature which influence the entire diffusion profile.

Small foreign particles on the surface during diffusion can interfere seriously with the uniformity of the diffusion profile. The result of this interference can be a p-n junction of varying depth which, for double-diffused transistor structures, results in a nonuniform base thickness. Thus, it is imperative that the integrated circuit silicon wafer enter the diffusion furnace with a surface as free as possible of any foreign particles. Maximum cleanliness is often obtained by gas-phase etching of the silicon surface in the furnace, immediately prior to formation of the diffusion profile.

Crystalline imperfections in the body of the silicon, such as dislocations or stacking faults, can serve as sites for the localized concentration of a diffusant. In turn, these phenomena can degrade the electrical properties of the p-n junction. For this reason, silicon of high crystalline perfection is necessary to produce diffused junctions of maximum uniformity.

3-3   Evaluation of Diffused Layers

A technique which is fundamental in diffused layer evaluation is chemical staining.[1] By this means it is possible to delineate p-n junctions for visual observation, since p and n regions take on differing colors or shades through this treatment. The staining reagent is usually applied to a specimen which has been beveled at a very low angle, in a process outlined in Chap. 12 on the subject of wafer processing. The purpose of the beveling operation is to magnify depth dimensions by purely geometrical means for easier and more accurate observation and measurement. Depth measurements are usually made in terms of wavelengths of monochromatic visible light, with the aid of an interferometer.[6] In this way, junction depths can be measured to ± 0.05 micron. Knowledge of junction depth is of course basic to fundamental calculations.

Diffused Distribution Determinations. Refer back to Fig. 3-5 which shows a complementary error function diffused distribution of an n-type impurity in a uniformly doped p-type silicon sample. As mentioned before, a p-n junction is located at the depth x_j below the surface, where the concentrations of the two impurities are equal. If this junction depth is measured, and if the concentration of the p-type impurity is known (N_{BC} in Fig. 3-5), then we have one point on the diffusion profile; that is, the concentration of the n-type impurity at the distance x_j is also N_{BC}. If the diffusion coefficient D is known, then we have enough data to calculate the surface concentration N_o by means of Eq. (3-11).

When working with materials where D is not known, a slightly different approach may be used. Two wafers of different, but known, background concentrations, N_{BC1} and N_{BC2}, are given identical diffusion treatments. N_o is assumed to be the same for both. The junction depths, x_{j1} and x_{j2}, are measured by chemical staining methods. We may then write:

$$N_{BC1} = N_o \operatorname{erfc} \frac{x_{j1}}{2\sqrt{Dt}} \tag{3-15}$$

$$N_{BC2} = N_o \operatorname{erfc} \frac{x_{j2}}{2\sqrt{Dt}} \tag{3-16}$$

Simultaneous trial-and-error solution of Eqs. (3-15) and (3-16) yields the value for D. Analogous procedures could also be used for gaussian distribution situations.

Four-point Probe Measurements on a Semi-infinite Specimen.   Principles which have been in use for several decades for earth resistivity measurement were applied by Valdes[7] to the problem of semiconductor resistivity measurements. Basically the apparatus employs four sharply pointed and equally spaced points, as shown in Fig. 3-10a. A regulated current is passed through the outer pair of points, and the resulting potential difference between the inner pair is measured by means of a null instrument, such as a potentiometer.

Analysis of this situation takes recourse in the fact that the differential equations of electrostatics are identical in form to those of ohmic flow. Thus the two outer probes which are respectively a source and a sink for current are taken as a positive and a negative charge. In this role these points are a source and a sink for lines of

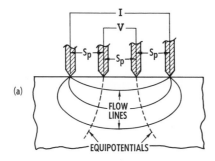

(a)

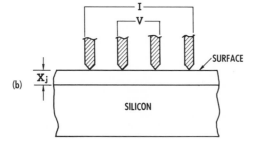

(b)

Fig. 3-10   (*a*) Four-point probe on a "semi-infinite" specimen, or one in which thickness is large compared to probe spacing; (*b*) four-point probe on a thin layer.

force. The surface of the semiconductor is a plane of symmetry in this problem, and so we may treat, as we choose, either the *semi-infinite* volume suggested in Fig. 3-10*a* or the infinite volume appropriate to the electrostatics problem.

The potential at any position in the field is found in the latter case by a simple summation of $Q_p/4\pi\kappa\epsilon_o r$ for all charges, where Q_p is the value of a given point charge, and r is its distance from the position in question. The positions of interest here are the positions of the inner pair of points, and for these the summations take on a simple and symmetrical form because the problem has, obviously, symmetry about a vertical plane as well as about the horizontal or surface plane.

Proportionality between the electrostatic analogy and the ohmic flow case of immediate interest is readily found by considering a sphere about one of the point sources of almost infinitesimal radius r. In the electrostatics case the flux density (i.e., the field) at the surface of the sphere is given simply by $Q_p/4\pi\kappa\epsilon_o r^2$ for MKS units. In the ohmic flow case the electric field at the surface of the sphere is given, through Ohm's law, by $I\rho/2\pi r^2$. Equating these gives the constant of proportionality which can be factored into the potential difference expression already worked out for the electrostatics case, with the result that resistivity is given by

$$\rho = 2\pi s_p \frac{V}{I} \qquad (3\text{-}17)$$

where s_p is the spacing of the points in cm, and V and I are the values measured at the four-point probe (Fig. 3-10*a*) in volts and amperes, respectively.

Four-point Probe Measurements on Thin Layers. When the sample is reduced from semi-infinite proportions to a thin layer, image charges must be introduced to provide symmetry about the new (bottom) surface. Requiring symmetry about top and bottom surfaces simultaneously leads to an infinite vertical array of image charges. Valdes[7] gave an approximate solution to this kind of problem, and Uhlir[8] gave more exact and more general solutions.

A diffused layer of thickness X on an opposite-type wafer, as shown in Fig. 3-10*b*, qualifies as a thin layer with a nonconducting bottom surface. The criterion for *thinness* here is $X \ll s_p$; most diffused layers qualify easily because X is typically a few microns at most, while s_p is typically of the order of 10^3 microns. The reason that the junction or *bottom surface* of the layer is nonconducting is that lateral voltage drops in the layer reverse-bias the junction slightly. The analysis of this situation gives for the average resistivity $\bar{\rho}$ of the layer

$$\bar{\rho} = 4.5\frac{V}{I}X \qquad (3\text{-}18)$$

Here $\bar{\rho}$ is in ohm cm, V in volts, I in amp, and X in cm. We have used average resistivity here because ρ is a steep function of distance x in a typical diffused layer. It is interesting to notice that confining the current to a thin sheet has caused point spacing s_p to drop out of the resistivity expression.

Sheet Resistance. A quantity known as sheet resistance plays an important role in calculations involving the resistivity of thin layers and the resistance of various

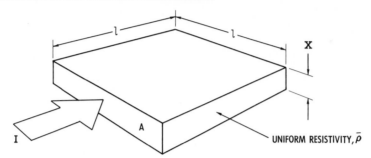

Fig. 3-11   A diagram for visualizing and defining sheet resistance.

shapes cut out of these sheets of resistive material.   Figure 3-11 shows a square of material with a current I flowing through it laterally.   From the familiar $R = \bar{\rho}l/A$ prescription, where in this case we use $\bar{\rho}$ as the resistivity of the sample, we can write for the resistance of this uniform sheet of material

$$R_S = \frac{\bar{\rho}l}{lX} = \frac{\bar{\rho}}{X} \tag{3-19}$$

Note that the absolute value of l is unimportant; so long as a square specimen is employed, the resistance will remain unchanged.   [This gives some insight as to why point spacing s_p does not appear in Eq. (3-18).]   Thus it is that the quotient of bulk resistivity by thickness for a thin uniform layer is frequently employed and is named *sheet resistance*.   It is measured in ohms per square.   The term *square* (like *radian*) is not a true unit in the dimensional-analysis sense, but is usually incorpo-rated in the expression when a sheet resistance value is being named, in order to label the item as such.   The terminology *sheet resistivity* is also used, less frequently but with equal justice, because the quantity in question is intensive (like bulk resistivity, density, etc.) and does not vary with specimen size.   Sheet resistance seems to be the favored terminology, probably because the dimensions truly are ohms.

Equation (3-18) is very conveniently rewritten in terms of sheet resistance R_S:

$$R_S = 4.5\frac{V}{I} \tag{3-20}$$

The sheet resistance concept is convenient because this quantity is directly and simply measured with a four-point probe.   It is important because the end-to-end resistance of a strip of material can be calculated simply by multiplying the num-ber of squares in series by the sheet resistance.   Similarly, the side-to-side resistance of a strip can be calculated by dividing the sheet resistance by the number of squares in parallel.   Calculations like this are common in integrated circuit work.

Diffused Layer Calculations Based on Sheet Resistance.   From Eqs. (3-19), (1-28), and (1-14) it follows that

$$R_S = \frac{1}{q\bar{\mu}\bar{N}}\frac{1}{X} \tag{3-21}$$

where $\bar{N}$ is the average net density of the dominant impurity, and $\bar{\mu}$ is the corre-sponding average carrier mobility.   Thus it is clear that sheet resistance R_S is inversely proportional to the net density of the dominant impurity per unit area of the sheet $\bar{N}X$, assuming complete ionization of the net impurities.

Figure 3-12 shows, with a linear concentration scale, the net impurity concentration in a diffused layer formed in a lightly doped specimen. Once again we have taken the case of n-type impurities diffused into a p-doped crystal. It is apparent here that the net concentration very closely approximates the total diffusant density in the region affected by diffusion. That is, in terms of atoms per unit area, the net concentration represented by the shaded area in Fig. 3-12 approximates Q, the total density (atoms per unit area) assumed to have diffused into the surface. That is to say, $\overline{N}X \simeq Q$. Hence there is an important and simple relation between Q, impurity concentration in atoms per unit area, and R_S, sheet resistance, through Eq. (3-21).

For those gaussian distribution cases in which net and absolute diffusant densities may be regarded as equal, the sheet resistance measurement thus provides a value of Q for use in Eq. (3-13). For the complementary error function distribution the total diffusant density arrived at by integrating the error function complement is given by

$$Q = 1.13 N_o \sqrt{Dt} \qquad (3\text{-}22)$$

Hence, here again the sheet resistance measurement leads directly to a determination of a fundamental quantity such as D, given the values of N_o and t where net and absolute diffusant densities are nearly equal.

In many practical cases, of course, background concentrations are so heavy that $\overline{N}X \neq Q$. That is, the net and absolute diffusant densities cannot be taken as equal. Other important departures from the simple examples just outlined may also enter. For instance, in heavily doped material complete ionization is a poor assumption, as explained in Chap. 1. Furthermore, mobility is lower in heavily compensated material than in lightly compensated material of equal net doping.

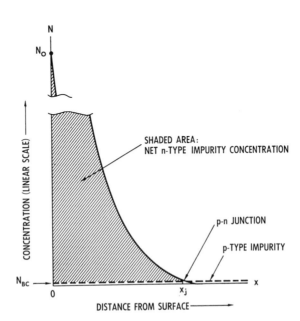

Fig. 3-12 A diffusion situation wherein the net diffusant concentration in the specimen closely approximates the total diffusant concentration.

These and a number of other complications have been considered in a set of extensive calculations carried out by Irvin.[9]   Excerpts from his curves are presented in Figs. 3-13 through 3-16.   As an independent variable in these diagrams he has employed average conductivity $\bar{\sigma}$.   In terms of sheet resistance this is given by

$$\bar{\sigma} = \frac{1}{R_S X} \qquad (3\text{-}23)$$

where X once more is layer thickness.   His ordinate is surface concentration N_o, and a single value of the parameter N_{BC} applies in a given diagram.   We present only the cases $N_{BC} = 10^{15}/cm^3$ and $10^{17}/cm^3$, which have special interest for us.   For generality, Irvin has taken $X = x_j - x$, where x is at some point lying between the surface and the junction.   Thus his curves may be applied to a *subsurface* layer,

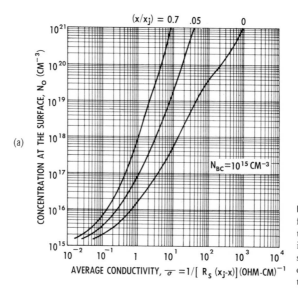

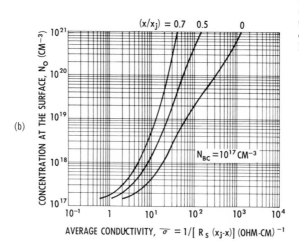

Fig. 3-13 Surface concentration as a function of average conductivity of n-type complementary error function layers in silicon for two values of background surface concentration: (*a*) $N_{BC} = 10^{15}/cm^3$; (*b*) $N_{BC} = 10^{17}/cm^3$. The parameter x/x_j gives the ratio of the depths of two surfaces bounding a subsurface layer (For example, when the average conductivity of a base layer is involved, x is the emitter junction depth and x_j is the collector junction depth.) (*After Irvin.[9]*)

or a region below the surface bounded by two junctions. This situation is approximated by the transistor base layer presented in Fig. 7-3. To convey this information, he has taken the ratio x/x_j as a parameter and has done calculations for values of this parameter ranging from 0 to 0.9. (We have shown curves only for 0, 0.5, and 0.7.) When this ratio is zero we are of course dealing simply with a single diffused layer. Irvin's work covers the cases of both n and p diffused layers, and both error function complement and gaussian distributions. Clearly these curves enable us to arrive easily at reasonably accurate quantitative conclusions about diffused distributions from measurements of sheet resistance and junction depth.

3-4 Diffused Junction Properties

The complementary error function and gaussian distributions differ most from each other in the neighborhood of the surface. In particular, the former always

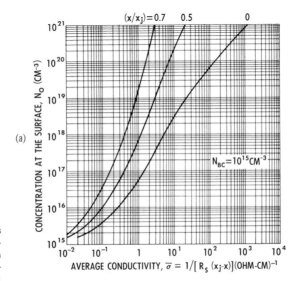

Fig. 3-14 Surface concentration versus average conductivity of p-type complementary error function layers in silicon for two values of background concentration: (a) $N_{BC} = 10^{15}/cm^3$; (b) $N_{BC} = 10^{17}/cm^3$. (*After Irvin.*[9])

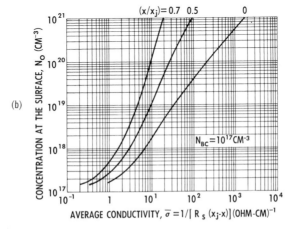

starts out with a nonzero slope, and the latter with zero slope. Away from the surface, however, the two distributions are very similar indeed for equal junction depth and surface concentration. This can be seen in Fig. 3-17, which presents the two distributions in normalized fashion with their common argument as the independent variable. For a junction position reasonably well down on the "tail" of the gaussian curve, for example, it is apparent in this diagram that expanding the horizontal scale for the complementary error function curve to make it pass through the same point would lead to a pair of similar curves.

Another striking feature of the curves in Fig. 3-17 is that they can be approximated with considerable precision by means of simple declining exponential curves (straight lines on the log-linear diagram), at points more than three decades down

(a)

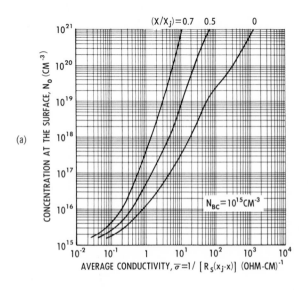

(b)

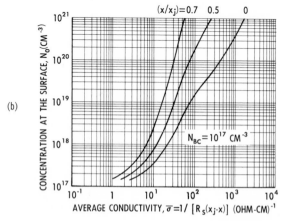

Fig. 3-15 Surface concentration versus average conductivity of n-type gaussian layers in silicon for two values of background concentration: (a) $N_{BC} = 10^{15}/cm^3$; (b) $N_{BC} = 10^{17}/cm^3$. (*After Irvin.*[9])

from the surface concentration. Thus for many purposes we can think in terms of the more familiar simple exponential curve.

Figure 3-18 shows with a linear scale the exponential tail of a diffused distribution. The junction, as always, exists where the diffusant concentration equals the background concentration N_{BC}. That is, the junction is where the two curves cross. On the left, the vertical distance between the exponential n-type concentration curve and the constant p-type background curve gives, of course, the net donor concentration at any value of x. Similarly, on the right the distance from the N_{BC} line down to the exponential curve gives the net acceptor impurity concentration at any position.

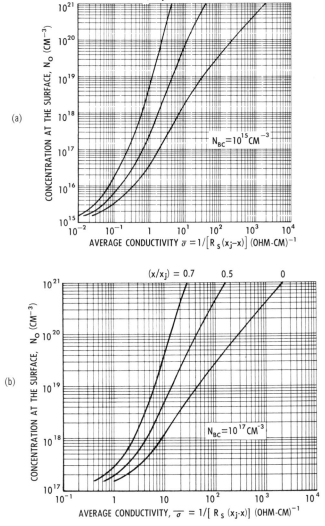

Fig. 3-16 Surface concentration versus average conductivity of p-type gaussian layers in silicon for two values of background concentration: (*a*) $N_{BC} = 10^{15}/\text{cm}^3$; (*b*) $N_{BC} = 10^{17}/\text{cm}^3$. (*After Irvin.*[9])

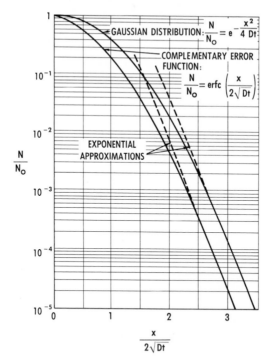

Fig. 3-17   Normalized logarithmic plot of the complementary error function and gaussian distributions. Note the similarity of the curves and the good approximations afforded by simple exponential functions in the deeper portions of the distributions.

The small shaded area on the left side of the junction thus represents the net number of donor atoms per unit of junction area lying between the junction and the left boundary of the interval X_{m1}. Similarly, the small area immediately to the right of the junction represents the net number of acceptor atoms per unit of junction area lying between the junction and the right boundary of the same interval. Now consider X_{m1} to be depletion layer thickness (for an ideally abrupt transition from neutrality to space charge of the sort treated at length in Chap. 2), for some small value of total voltage across the junction. This requires that the two small shaded areas be equal, since a junction always has equal quantities of space charge on the two sides. (Under the customary idealizing assumptions, the space-charge layer and the depletion layer are identical.) It is evident that for such a low-voltage situation, the diffused distribution could be well approximated by the linear tangent to the junction, shown as a short dashed line in Fig. 3-18. This constitutes the linearly graded approximation to a diffused junction. It is also evident that the linear approximation would predict a left-hand (diffused side or surface side) component of the depletion layer which is slightly too thick for the same total voltage on the junction. On the right-hand side, however, the linear approximation would predict too thin a depletion layer. But the *total* depletion layer thickness predicted by the linearly graded approximation is reasonably accurate. It is for this reason that the voltage dependence of capacitance for a diffused junction is well approximated by that of a linearly graded junction ($C \rightarrow V^{-1/3}$) up to surprisingly large voltages. As pointed out in Chap. 2, capacitance is inversely proportional to the spacing of the capacitor plates, or hence to total depletion layer thickness. Conversely, as first emphasized by Pritchard,[10] observation of a $V^{-1/3}$ variation of capacitance is not a reliable indication of linear grading.

Figure 3-18 also shows the depletion layer thickness X_{m2} associated with a total reverse voltage on the junction many times larger than in the example just discussed. The important point here is that the diffused junction can now be reasonably approximated by a step junction. There is a steeply rising concentration to the left with relatively little depletion layer penetration. On the right, however, the depletion layer penetrates appreciably into a region that is almost uniformly doped. Thus, a diffused junction makes a transition as reverse voltage is increased from linearly graded behavior at low voltages to step behavior at high voltages.

The nature of this transition has been calculated and described in considerable detail by Lawrence and Warner.[11] They integrated Poisson's equation analytically for both the gaussian and complementary error functions, and performed a machine solution of the resulting equations. Some of their curves are presented in Figs. 3-19 through 3-21. For reasons outlined earlier in this section, the gaussian and error function complement cases give very similar results, and so only one set of curves is given, and this set may be used for either case.

Part *a* of each figure gives basically capacitance and total depletion layer thickness versus voltage. Dividing voltage by N_{BC} makes each figure serve for a particular value of the ratio N_{BC}/N_o. The parallel portions at the left represent junctions of various gradients in their linearly graded (cube-root) behavior. Obviously each junction depth implies a different gradient. The curves then converge on a steeper

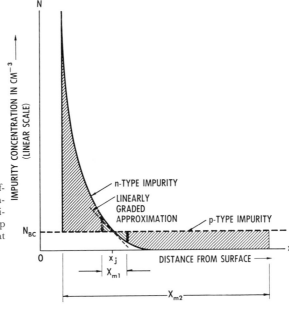

Fig. 3-18 Linear presentation of a diffused distribution illustrating that a linearly graded approximation is appropriate at small reverse voltages while a step approximation is more appropriate at high reverse voltages.

single line at high voltage, representing step (square-root) behavior. There is a single line here because N_{BC} was used to normalize the voltage scale. The region of transition from one mode of behavior to the other occupies about a decade of voltage. Parts *b* of Figs. 3-19 through 3-21 are concerned with *one-sided* properties of diffused junctions, and it is apparent that many more decades of voltage are required for the transition in this case.

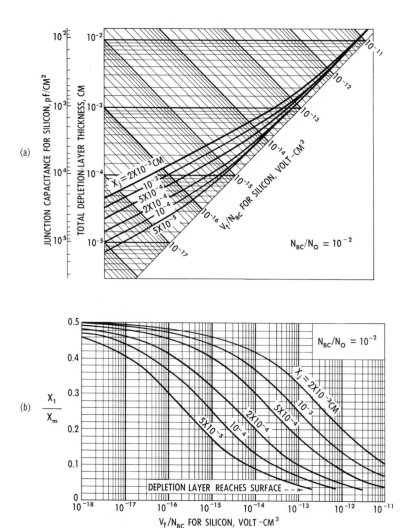

Fig. 3-19   (*a*) Total depletion layer thickness and capacitance per unit area versus total voltage across the junction divided by background concentration. The parameter is junction depth. These curves may be used for either complementary error function or gaussian diffused junctions for N_{BC}/N_o in the range 3×10^{-3} to 3×10^{-2}.   (*b*) Ratio of depletion layer penetration on the side toward the surface to total depletion thickness as a function of total voltage across the junction divided by background concentration, for the same conditions as above.   (*After Lawrence and Warner.*[11])

3-5 Gold Diffusion

To this point we have considered only the diffusion of impurities from groups III and V of the periodic table for the primary purpose of creating p-n junctions. On the other hand, it is sometimes desirable to diffuse other elements into silicon for other purposes. An example of this is gold diffusion for the purpose of "killing" minority-carrier lifetimes in silicon through principles outlined in Chap. 2. This

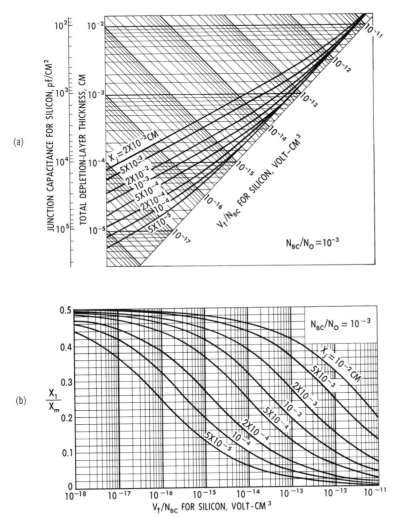

Fig. 3-20 (*a*) Total depletion layer thickness and capacitance per unit area versus total voltage across the junction divided by background concentration. The parameter is junction depth. These curves may be used for either complementary error function or gaussian diffused junctions for N_{BC}/N_o in the range 3×10^{-4} to 3×10^{-3}. (*b*) Ratio of depletion layer penetration on the side toward the surface to total depletion thickness as a function of total voltage across the junction divided by background concentration, for the same conditions as above. (*After Lawrence and Warner.*[11])

unique property of gold is utilized commercially in modifying the characteristics of p-n junctions so that they may be switched rapidly from the conducting state to the nonconducting state. Unlike the group III and V impurities, some of the gold atoms enter the silicon lattice by "squeezing" between the planes of the silicon atoms. Impurities which occupy positions between the planes of the host crystal atoms are referred to as *interstitial*, in contrast to *substitutional* impurities which occupy vacant sites in the silicon lattice. The interstitial atoms of gold diffuse into silicon at a rate several orders of magnitude faster than the group III and V

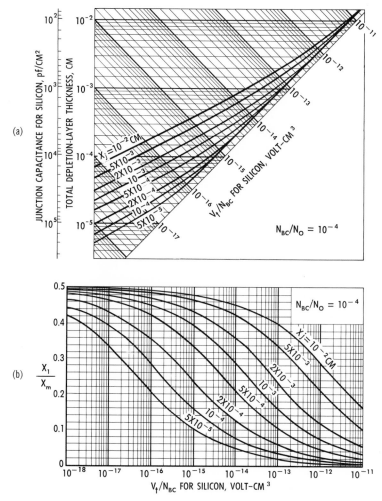

Fig. 3-21 (*a*) Total depletion layer thickness and capacitance per unit area versus total voltage across the junction divided by background concentration. The parameter is junction depth. These curves may be used for either complementary error function or gaussian diffused junctions for N_{BC}/N_o in the range 3×10^{-5} to 3×10^{-4}. (*b*) Ratio of depletion layer penetration on the side toward the surface to total depletion thickness as a function of total voltage across the junction divided by background concentration, for the same conditions as above. (*After Lawrence and Warner.*[11])

impurities. This fact requires that the gold impurity be diffused as the last step in the various heat treatments to which the silicon wafer is subjected. Since interstitial gold diffuses so rapidly, a few minutes at a moderate temperature (i.e., 1000°C) may be considered as an infinite time; hence the gold will be uniformly distributed throughout the wafer at a concentration equal to the solid solubility of gold in silicon at that temperature. The solid solubility of gold in silicon is a strong function of temperature over a rather wide temperature range, as Fig. 3-6 shows. Thus gold has two properties in silicon which make it very important for controlling carrier lifetime: Gold, in the interstitial position, diffuses rapidly, and it exhibits a temperature-dependent solid solubility.

It is important to realize that the solubility of gold in silicon, as shown in Fig. 3-6, is an equilibrium value. That is, if the silicon specimen is heated to 1050°C in the presence of an excess of gold, it will after infinite time (in practice, 30 min can be taken as a reasonable approximation to infinite time) acquire a gold concentration of approximately $2 \times 10^{16}/cm^3$. Increasing the temperature to 1150°C will cause the gold concentration to increase, after a suitable waiting period, to approximately $5 \times 10^{16}/cm^3$. If, now, the temperature is again brought to 1050°C and held there long enough for equilibrium to be approached, the significant gold concentration drops back to about $2 \times 10^{16}/cm^3$. The extra gold (approximately half that present in the crystal at the higher temperature) either diffuses out of the crystal, or precipitates in small clusters scattered throughout the crystal. The precipitated gold is electrically inactive; it can no longer perform the function of aiding carrier recombination. Therefore, to secure an active gold concentration in the lattice characteristic of a given elevated temperature, it is necessary to *quench* the wafers or to cool them quickly from that temperature. In this manner the high gold concentration can be locked in the lattice because the gold is not given time to diffuse. Thus gold doping involves basically a diffusion step in which equilibrium is approached, and a quenching step which departs radically from equilibrium.

Further practical aspects of gold doping are presented in Chaps. 7 and 12. Figure 3-22 is a compilation of currently accepted data on the diffusion constant of gold as a function of temperature.[12-14]

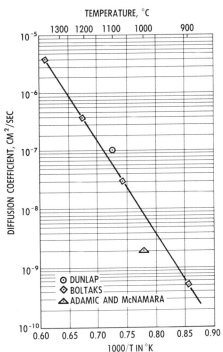

Fig. 3-22 Diffusion coefficient of gold in silicon as a function of temperature.

REFERENCES

1. Fuller, C. S., and J. A. Ditzenberger: Diffusion of Donor and Acceptor Elements in Silicon, *J. Appl. Phys.,* vol. 27, pp. 544–553, May, 1956.
2. Barrer, R. M.: "Diffusion In and Through Solids," Cambridge University Press, London, 1951.
3. Carslaw, H. S., and J. C. Jaeger: "Conduction of Heat in Solids," Clarendon Press, Oxford, 1947.
4. Boltaks, B. I.: "Diffusion in Semiconductors," Academic Press Inc., New York, 1963.
5. Trumbore, F. A.: Solid Solubilities of Impurity Elements in Germanium and Silicon, *Bell System Tech. J.,* vol. 39, pp. 205–234, January, 1960. Fig. 3-6 adapted from the original by permission of the copyright owner, American Telephone & Telegraph Company, and the author.
6. Bond, W. L., and F. M. Smits: The Use of an Interference Microscope for Measurement of Extremely Thin Surface Layers, *Bell System Tech. J.,* vol. 35, pp. 1209–1221, September, 1956.
7. Valdes, L. B.: Resistivity Measurements on Germanium for Transistors, *Proc. IRE,* vol. 42, pp. 420–427, February, 1954.
8. Uhlir, A.: The Potentials of Infinite Systems of Sources and Numerical Solutions of Problems in Semiconductor Engineering, *Bell System Tech. J.,* vol. 34, pp. 105–128, January, 1955.
9. Irvin, J. C.: Resistivity of Bulk Silicon and of Diffused Layers in Silicon, *Bell System Tech. J.,* vol. 41, pp. 387–410, March, 1962. Figs. 3-13 through 3-16 adapted from the originals by permission of the copyright owner, American Telephone & Telegraph Company, and the author.
10. Pritchard, R. L.: Transition Capacitance of P-N Junctions, *Semicond. Prod.,* vol. 2, pp. 31–35, August, 1959.
11. Lawrence, H, and R. M. Warner, Jr.: Diffused Junction Depletion Layer Calculations, *Bell System Tech. J.,* vol. 39, pp. 389–404, March, 1960. *Bell Telephone System Monograph* 3517 contains complete sets of curves. Figs. 3-19 through 3-21 adapted from the originals by permission of the copyright owner, American Telephone & Telegraph Company, and the authors.
12. Dunlap, W. C., H. V. Bohm, and H. P. Mahon, Jr.: Diffusion of Impurities in Silicon, *Phys. Rev.,* vol. 96, p. 822, Nov. 1, 1954.
13. Boltaks, B. I., G. S. Kulikov, and R. Sh. Malkovich: Electrical Transport of Gold in Silicon, *Soviet Phys.–Solid State,* vol. 2, part 2, pp. 2134–2137, April, 1961.
14. Adamic, J. W., Jr., and J. E. McNamara: Studies of the Diffusion of Gold into Silicon and Silicon Dioxide Films, presented at the Semiconductor Symposium of the Electrochemical Society National Meeting, New York, October, 1963.

4

BASIC TRANSISTOR ENGINEERING

The impressive semiconductor circuits and systems in existence today are the tangible results of the cooperation which has developed between the users and the manufacturers of solid-state devices. Implicit in these achievements is the establishment of device criteria which meet the requirements of the circuit designer and guide the semiconductor engineer in his choice of processes and materials. Many of these criteria, originally conceived for junction transistors, are easily extended to apply to integrated circuits.

It is the intent of this chapter to present some of the more important of these design considerations by showing the relationship between the physical properties of the semiconductor device and the familiar electrical specifications from the transistor data sheet. Necessarily, because of the wide scope of this subject, the treatment will be of a cursory nature, with detailed derivations omitted. In place of these derivations, a list of references has been included so that the interested reader can refer to original papers if he so desires.

4-1 The n-p-n Junction Transistor as an Amplifying Device

Figure 4-1a shows the equivalent circuit of a device which has low input resistance R_{in}, high output resistance R_{out}, and near-unity current gain for a load resistance R_L whose value is less than one-tenth of R_{out}. Voltage gain can be realized, using this type of device, since the proper choice of load resistance yields an output voltage $I_{in}R_L$ which is appreciably greater than the input voltage. For the ideal case, the input would approach a short circuit and the output an open circuit, as suggested in Fig. 4-1b.

In order to obtain an amplifying device on the basis of the criteria we have just discussed, viz. (1) low input resistance, (2) high output resistance, and (3) unattenuated current transfer, we may take advantage of the electrical characteristics of p-n junctions as a function of voltage bias. By suitably employing p-n junctions,

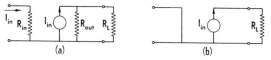

Fig. 4-1   (*a*) Equivalent circuit of a hypothetical amplifier, suggesting realistic properties; (*b*) equivalent circuit of an ideal amplifier.

we can construct an amplifying device in the manner described by Shockley;[1,2] his remarkably detailed analysis given at the very beginning of the junction transistor era has served as a basis for most of the subsequent extended analyses, including the material in this chapter.

A forward-biased p-n junction serves for the input portion of the amplifying device. When a junction is so biased, the junction current increases exponentially with voltage, as was shown in Eq. (2-64), the so-called "rectifier equation." The dynamic resistance of the forward-biased junction thus diminishes with bias and can assume very low values. Figure 4-2*a* illustrates this for an n^+-p junction. For purposes of discussion, the potential of the p region is held fixed at ground potential. The *I-V* characteristic of the forward-biased junction is shown qualitatively at the bottom of Fig. 4-2*a*; it satisfies the first criterion, providing a low resistance for the amplifier input.

In Fig. 4-2*b* a p-n^+ junction is shown in the reverse-biased condition with the application of a positive voltage to the n region. Here again, for the sake of reference, the p region is maintained at ground potential. The current that flows in the circuit is the reverse saturation current which, for the chosen resistivities, consists primarily of the electrons in the p region that diffuse to the junction and are swept

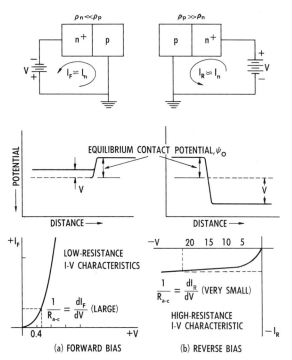

Fig. 4-2   Physical representation, potential diagram, and *I-V* characteristic of a p-n junction, emphasizing dynamic properties: (*a*) Junction under forward bias; (*b*) junction under reverse bias.

into the n region by the applied field. Since n_p is usually quite small, this current is quite small and is also roughly constant with voltage, as shown in the approximate sketch of the *I-V* characteristic. Thus the curve exhibits an extremely large dynamic resistance, which satisfies the second criterion by giving what is required for the output portion of the amplifier.

To construct the amplifier, the obvious procedure would be to combine the p-n junctions as described into a homogeneous structure, in order to obtain the desired characteristics at the input and output terminals. Such a structure would appear as shown in Fig. 4-3, where the p-n junctions are placed back to back, with the p regions common and at ground potential. The bias voltages have been designated V_F and V_R for the forward and reverse biases, respectively. In this model it is assumed that the n regions are of equal and very low resistivity compared to the p region, such that the currents consist predominantly of electron flow. If the thickness X_B of the p region is very much greater than the diffusion length L_n for electrons in that region, the electron current distribution as a function of distance appears as shown by the dashed curve in Fig. 4-3. For the forward-biased junction (at the left), the electron current is shown diminishing in the p region as the electrons recombine with holes. The first loop current I_F flows through the forward-biased junction. The second loop current I_R arises from the concentration of electrons in the p region, which diffuse to the reverse-biased junction (at the right). The important result to note is that since these diffusion mechanisms are remote from each other within the p region, no interactions occur, and the structure behaves just as though the junctions were biased independently.

We may conclude, then, that the structure satisfies the first and second criteria, but not the third, which requires that the input current I_F appear at the output terminals. In Fig. 4-3, the output current I_R is independent of and several orders of magnitude smaller than the input current I_F.

If the structure of Fig. 4-3 is modified by making the thickness X_B of the p region

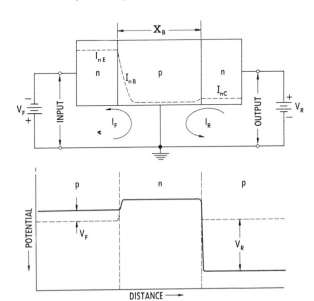

Fig. 4-3 Physical representation and potential diagram of two widely separated p-n junctions placed back to back. No interaction occurs, and hence there is no transistor action.

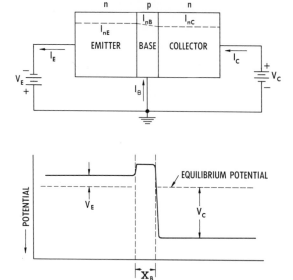

Fig. 4-4 Physical representation and potential diagram of two closely spaced p-n junctions placed back to back. Note that in this case interaction occurs, and hence there is transistor action.

much smaller than the electron diffusion length, an effective means is provided for transmitting the input current to the output. Such a structure is appropriately called a *transistor,* because current is *carried across* the p region in the form of injected minority carrier. In the new structure, shown in Fig. 4-4, where $X_B \ll L_n$, a concentration of electrons will enter the p region from the forward-biased junction and, because of the large concentration gradient in the base region, will diffuse across to the reverse-biased junction. Since the distance is much less than a diffusion length, only a very small fraction of the electrons will recombine with holes in the p region, and most of the electrons will reach the reverse-biased junction. The arriving electrons are then easily swept across this junction, making the electron concentration equal to zero there. The electron current flowing out from the reverse-biased junction is only slightly less than the input value. Thus, we have satisfied the final condition for power gain; the output current is nearly equal to the input current.

In Fig. 4-4, the forward-biased junction is called the *emitter,* since it emits or injects carriers into the p region. In transistor nomenclature, the p region is called the *base,* shown at ground potential in the diagram. The reverse-biased junction is called the *collector,* for reasons that are obvious. Finally, the input and output voltages and currents are called the *emitter and collector voltages and currents,* respectively (V_E, I_E and V_C, I_C). Since some of the injected electrons do not reach the collector because of recombination en route, a *recombination current* must flow into the base region to maintain the hole population in the face of this recombination. In other words, electrons flow outward in the base lead, constituting base current I_B. Figure 4-4 illustrates the *common base* (or *grounded base*) configuration in which the base terminal is common to both the input and output circuits.

The action of the n-p-n junction transistor may also be visualized by referring to the voltage-profile diagram in Fig. 4-4. All the voltages are shown to be constant in the emitter, base, and collector regions; this is so for the assumption that the conductivities of these regions are sufficiently high so that the applied potentials are completely dropped across the junctions only. With the base region fixed at ground potential, the emitter voltage V_E effectively decreases the base-to-emitter potential hill, permitting large numbers of electrons to diffuse into the base. Although some recombination will occur within the base, most of the electrons will reach the collector junction. The collector voltage V_C increases the potential rise from base to collector, thus making it extremely easy for the arriving electrons to fall downhill into the collector region. In other words, the electrons prefer to enter the regions where their potential energy is lowest.

If only the collector voltage V_C were applied to the transistor, so that there was no emitter current I_E, we would still expect a small current to flow in the output circuit. This would be the reverse saturation current of the collector junction; however, it would not be the same as in connection with Fig. 4-3, because the base-region thickness is now much less than the electron diffusion length. This means that the electron concentration throughout the base will be somewhat depressed, including the concentration at the boundary of the emitter junction depletion layer. We saw in Chap. 2 that there is a correspondence between a subnormal carrier concentration at a junction boundary and a reverse bias across the junction. Hence the emitter junction is slightly reverse-biased under the conditions described here.

The fact that the electron concentration throughout the base is depressed means that fewer electrons are available in this case to be collected by the reverse-biased collector junction than in the previous example (Fig. 4-3). Thus the collector *leakage* current with open-circuited emitter I_{CBO} is less than the leakage current of the equivalent isolated junction.

The current I_{CBO} leads to useless power dissipation in the collector circuit of the transistor, but it is typically a very small quantity. When emitter current is fed into the transistor, the output collector current is equal to the sum of the I_{CBO} saturation current and some fraction (close to unity for good transistors) of the emitter current I_E, or

$$I_C = I_{CBO} + \alpha I_E \qquad (4\text{-}1)$$

where α is a measure of the efficiency of transport of carriers through the transistor. Since I_{CBO} is usually very small compared to normal operating values of I_E, Eq. (4-1) simply becomes

$$I_C \approx \alpha I_E \qquad (4\text{-}2)$$

meaning that α is the ratio of the collector current to the emitter current, or the dc current gain for common base operation.

Common Emitter Current-gain Theory. Figure 4-5 illustrates the *common emitter* configuration, or that in which the emitter terminal is common to both the input and output circuits.

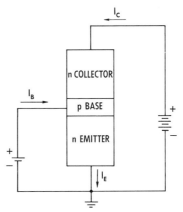

Fig. 4-5 Common emitter (or grounded emitter) configuration. The emitter is common to both input and output circuits.

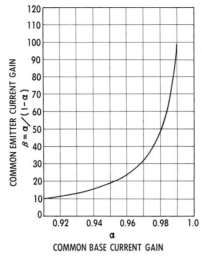

Fig. 4-6 Common emitter current gain versus common base current gain.

(The terminology *grounded emitter* is also used.) In common emitter operation one obtains considerably higher current gain than that of the common base configuration. If the dc collector-to-emitter current gain is α, the dc collector-to-base current gain β (or h_{FE}) is given by

$$\beta = \frac{I_C}{I_B} = \frac{I_C}{I_E - I_C} = \frac{\alpha}{1 - \alpha} \quad (4\text{-}3)$$

In this expression, as α approaches unity, the denominator becomes very small, and β increases rapidly to large values. A useful plot of β as a function of α is given in Fig. 4-6. Common emitter current gain increases by an order of magnitude as α is increased from 0.91 to 0.99.

The small-signal low-frequency common emitter current gain β_o is defined as the ratio of incremental collector current to incremental base current with V_{CB} held constant. Since β as given by Eq. (4-3) involves total currents, it represents an average of β_o over the operating range (i.e., over the collector current range from zero to I_C). For large-signal applications an appropriate average value for current gain is needed. For many operating conditions the average given by Eq. (4-3) is useful. For small-signal applications of the common emitter stage, the β_o corresponding to the bias conditions should be used.

4-2   Relating Current Gain to Transistor Structure

If the emitter current equaled the collector current, then α would be unity and I_B would be zero. In a real transistor there are several mechanisms which contribute to the generation of base current, causing α to be less than unity. These are (1) emitter inefficiency, (2) volume recombination, and (3) surface recombination. As a result of each of these mechanisms, the total base current may be defined as

$$I_B = I_{pE} + I_{vB} + I_{sB} \quad (4\text{-}4)$$

where I_{pE} is the hole current injected into the forward-biased emitter (n-p-n transistor), and I_{vB} and I_{sB} are the recombination currents connected with the volume and surface, respectively, of the base region.

If we assume that the total emitter current is approximately equal to the electron component crossing the junction ($I_{nE} \gg I_{pE}$), then

$$(1 - \alpha) = \frac{1}{\beta + 1} \approx \frac{1}{\beta} \approx \frac{I_{pE}}{I_{nE}} + \frac{I_{vB}}{I_{nE}} + \frac{I_{sB}}{I_{nE}} \quad (4\text{-}5)$$

The ratio of the injected current to the total emitter current is defined as γ. For an n-p-n transistor, the emitter efficiency is

$$\gamma = \frac{I_{nE}}{I_{pE} + I_{nE}} \tag{4-6}$$

Thus, the first term in Eq. (4-5) is the difference between unity and $1/\gamma$. We can write

$$I_{pE} \approx \frac{qA_E D_{pE} p_{nE} e^{qV_E/kT}}{L_{pE}} \tag{4-7}$$

and

$$I_{nE} \approx \frac{qA_E D_{nB} n_{pB} e^{qV_E/kT}}{X_B} \tag{4-8}$$

where X_B is the transistor base thickness, A_E is the emitter area, D_{nB} is the diffusion constant for electrons in the base, and n_{pB} is the equilibrium concentration of electrons in the p-type base. Then

$$\frac{I_{pE}}{I_{nE}} = \frac{1 - \gamma}{\gamma} = \frac{D_{pE} p_{nE}}{D_{nB} n_{pB}} \frac{X_B}{L_{pE}} \approx \frac{\rho_E X_B}{\rho_B L_{pE}} \tag{4-9}$$

The assumption that the mobilities are equal for both holes and electrons on both sides of the junction is implicit in the final form of Eq. (4-9).

The second right-hand term of Eq. (4-5) is the ratio of the rate of electron recombination in the bulk to the rate of electron injection by the emitter. As the electrons diffuse through the base region, some of them will recombine with holes, constituting a small current which is not collected and which flows into the base region. It is of course required that this internal current loss be a minimum, and it is therefore necessary to keep the amount of recombination in the base region as small as possible. Consequently, the base thickness X_B and the electron diffusion length L_{nB} appear in the expression for the base recombination factor. It should be recalled that the diffusion length represents an average distance that a carrier will diffuse before it recombines, and it is equal to $L_{nB} = \sqrt{D_{nB} \tau_B}$. In the case of the transistor, τ_B is the lifetime for carriers in the base. A high-lifetime base region whose thickness X_B is much smaller than L_{nB} then gives a value for the base transport factor very close to unity.

To determine the contribution of volume recombination to base current, we can let the volume recombination current I_{vB} be defined as

$$I_{vB} \equiv \frac{Q \text{ stored}}{\tau_B} = qA_E X_B \frac{n_{pB} e^{qV_E/kT}}{2\tau_B} \tag{4-10}$$

where we have assumed that the electron concentration declines linearly from the emitter junction to the collector junction. Dividing Eq. (4-10) by Eq. (4-8), we obtain

$$\frac{I_{vB}}{I_{nE}} = \frac{X_B{}^2}{2D_{nB}\tau_B} = \frac{1}{2}\left(\frac{X_B}{L_{nB}}\right)^2 \tag{4-11}$$

Thus, if the lifetime were infinite this term would be equal to zero.

The last term of Eq. (4-5) is related to the recombination of carriers at the surface. A semiconductor surface is characterized by a surface recombination velocity s, which was treated in Chap. 2. As pointed out there, a surface may have a low or high recombination velocity, depending on the nature of the surface treatment during the processing of the transistor. From a design standpoint, it is desirable to keep s as small as practicable. In spite of this, some fraction of the carriers injected into the base of a junction transistor will not reach the collector junction, but will be lost by recombination at the surface of the base region. This introduces an additional component of current to the total base current. It must be remembered that the surface recombination current adds directly to the volume recombination current.

Following Eq. (2-12), we may write that the surface component of base current is given by

$$I_{sB} = qsA_s n_{BE} \qquad (4-12)$$

where s is the surface recombination velocity, A_s is the effective area of surface recombination, and n_{BE} is the injected electron density given by $n_{pB} \exp{(qV_E/kT)}$. It is reasonable to use this value in the surface recombination current expression because most of the recombination occurs very close to the edges of the emitter junction. Taking the ratio of Eq. (4-12) to Eq. (4-8), we have, finally,

$$\frac{I_{sB}}{I_{nE}} = \frac{sA_s X_B}{A_E D_{nB}} \qquad (4-13)$$

Therefore we can write

$$\frac{1}{\beta} \simeq \frac{\rho_E X_B}{\rho_B L_{pE}} + \frac{X_B{}^2}{2L_{nB}{}^2} + \frac{sA_s X_B}{A_E D_{nB}} \qquad (4-14)$$

Inspection of Eq. (4-14) indicates that the magnitude for each of the three terms must be kept small in order to maximize β. This implies that (1) all lifetimes should be high, (2) the base thickness should be small, (3) the emitter resistivity should be very low, and (4) surface recombination should be small. Because base thickness X_B plays such an important part in fixing β, factors which tend to alter it will affect β. For example, in a transistor where an increase in collector voltage causes appreciable spreading of the collector junction depletion layer into the base region, X_B will be diminished and β will rise.[3]

Beta Variations with Current. Equation (4-14) shows complete independence of current. However, it is known for silicon transistors that β will fall off at both the low and high values of emitter current. At low currents, β falls off because of the presence of the recombination centers in the emitter-base junction,[4] with the centers near the surface predominating because of their overwhelming numbers. These centers generate a small recombination current I_{RE} which does not contribute to gain. Thus, we must add a term to Eq. (4-14) for the low-current case:

$$\frac{1}{\beta} \simeq \frac{\rho_E X_B}{\rho_B L_{pE}} + \frac{X_B{}^2}{2L_{nB}{}^2} + \frac{sA_s X_B}{A_E D_{nB}} + \frac{I_{RE}}{I_E} \qquad (4-15)$$

I_{RE} might have a value on the order of 1 μA; at an emitter current of 10 μA, β would therefore be less than 10. The recombination current is always present, but is only important when total current is small.

A number of workers have considered the problem of the transistor under conditions of high-level injection,[5-9] and the related one of high-level injection in various diode situations.[4,10-12] The problem is a difficult one, and general agreement has not yet been reached on all of its aspects. The evolution of transistor structure has complicated the matter even more. High-level injection theory began for alloy transistors, which have heavily doped emitters and collectors; integrated circuit transistors, as well as today's discrete high-frequency transistors, have diffused emitter and collector junctions. We will outline a simplified version of the matter and accept its predictions consistently, even though they are not totally verified, concentrating for simplicity on the case of a transistor with a uniformly doped base region.

As an approach, let us first review the case of low-level injection, as depicted in Fig. 4-7a. In the n-p-n structure considered here, the majority carriers in the base are holes, and the minority carriers injected by the emitter are electrons. Once again the concentration of the latter at the base side of the emitter will be denoted by n_{BE}. The low-level case can be described as that wherein $n_{BE} \ll p_p$.

Chapter 2 treated the related problem of an isolated junction under small forward bias. That situation differs in some important details from the transistor case treated here, but the underlying principles are the same. As noted there, near-neutrality requires that the majority-carrier distribution in the base $p(x)$ include an enhancement above the equilibrium distribution which nearly matches the injection-caused enhancement in the minority-carrier distribution $n(x)$. The two small triangles in Fig. 4-7a represent these essentially equal incremental populations. Now electrons move from emitter to collector by diffusion *down* the gradient shown. But a corresponding diffusion of majority holes toward the right takes place simultaneously. There also exists in the picture a very small electric field directed from right to left, which provides a drift counterflow of holes, very nearly balancing the diffusion flow of holes to the right. (Both the hole current into the emitter and the hole recombination current are small, so that net hole current in the base must also be small.) Because the hole population is so large compared to the electron population under these low-level injection conditions, a trifling field is adequate for maintaining the hole counterflow, and hence the field has a negligible effect on electron behavior. Chapter 2 gives a fuller account of this important point. In sum, then, for low-level injection situations, electric field in the base is negligible. The only significant current is the diffusion current of minority carriers (electrons here) from

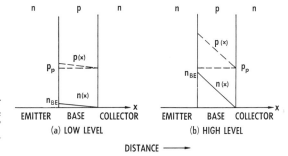

Fig. 4-7 Majority- and minority-carrier concentrations versus distance in the base region of a transistor biased for "active" operation (emitter forward-biased and collector reverse-biased).

emitter to collector. Thus the current-voltage expression for the emitter-base system can be written [(following Eq. (2-64)] as

$$I_E \simeq \frac{qD_{nB}n_{pB}A_E}{X_B} \left(e^{qV_E/kT} - 1\right) \tag{4-16}$$

Here A_E is once more emitter area, and base thickness X_B has been substituted for diffusion length L_n, since the electron gradient at the base side of the emitter junction in the transistor is now determined by the base thickness rather than the diffusion length, which determined it in the case of the isolated junction.

However, for the high-level case the situation is somewhat different, as shown by Fig. 4-7b. Here, n_{BE} may be comparable to, or greater than, p_p. Under these conditions, the electric field required to maintain the majority-carrier counterflow can no longer be neglected. Making the simplifying assumption that carrier concentrations retain their equilibrium values at some plane near the collector junction, and retaining the earlier assumption of near-neutrality in the base, we can readily obtain an analytical expression for the field distribution in the base. Integrating this from emitter to collector yields the voltage drop through the base; in this approximate treatment it is equal exactly to the applied voltage drop on the emitter junction itself. Thus for the composite emitter-base system under high-level injection conditions, the current-voltage expression becomes

$$I_E \simeq \frac{qD_{nB}n_{pB}A_E}{X_B} e^{qV_E/2kT} \tag{4-17}$$

The factor of ½ has entered the exponent because only half the applied voltage appears across the junction. Only the exponential term has been retained since it is large compared to unity in this case. This equation relates emitter current and voltage for high-level conditions.

A simpler but less pictorial description of the high-injection situation notes that when $n_{BE} \gg p_p$, the result is appreciable conductivity modulation, and this in turn means that $n \simeq p$ at the base side of the emitter junction. This can be seen by going to an even more extreme case than that depicted in Fig. 4-7b. Under these conditions it is apparent from Eq. (2-49) that

$$n \simeq p \simeq n_i e^{qV_E/2kT} \tag{4-18}$$

Thus the exponent determining injected minority-carrier concentration increases more slowly with voltage under high-level conditions than under low-level conditions.

The drift field in the base under high-level conditions has a direction which aids minority carriers. Further, it causes a minority drift current equal to the minority diffusion current (since the corresponding components of majority current cancel each other, and since the concentration gradients are approximately equivalent for the two types of carriers). This effect can be described artificially as an apparent doubling of the diffusion constant for the minority carriers, or for the electrons in this case. This is a specific point which lacks firm experimental verification. Nonetheless, as noted at the outset, we will apply it consistently. Accordingly, we should modify Eq. (4-17) by multiplying D_{nB} by 2, to yield

$$I_E \simeq \frac{2qD_{nB}n_{pB}A_E}{X_B} e^{qV_E/2kT} \tag{4-19}$$

For high-level conditions, then, the majority-carrier concentration in the base at the boundary of the emitter junction may be written as

$$p_{BE} = N_A + n_{pB}\, e^{qV_E/2kT} \tag{4-20}$$

But from Eq. (4-19) $\qquad n_{pB}\, e^{qV_E/2kT} = \dfrac{I_E X_B}{2qD_{nB}A_E} \tag{4-21}$

Hence $\qquad p_{BE} = N_A\!\left(1 + \dfrac{I_E X_B}{2qD_{nB}A_E N_A}\right) \tag{4-22}$

With the hole population in the base thus modulated, we must apply a correction factor to the first term of Eq. (4-15) to take account of the corresponding modulation of base resistivity in the region adjacent to the emitter. Furthermore, the second and third terms must be multiplied by ½ because of the effective doubling of the electron diffusion constant mentioned previously. Hence, the final expression for $1/\beta$ for the high-current case is

$$\frac{1}{\beta} \simeq \frac{\rho_E X_B}{\rho_B L_{pE}}\left(1 + \frac{I_E X_B}{2qD_{nB}A_E N_A}\right) + \frac{X_B{}^2}{4L_{nB}{}^2} + \frac{sA_s X_B}{2A_E D_{nB}} \tag{4-23}$$

In summary, then, we see the current dependence of emitter efficiency as the main cause of β falloff at high currents. Note also that the falloff factor is minimized through either heavier base doping or larger junction area.

4-3   Graded-base Current Gain

Thus far we have presented the gain theory for the transistor having a uniformly doped base region. The situation for the diffused-base transistor having a nonuniform base layer is somewhat different. Let us consider an n-p-n transistor model having a step emitter junction and a *graded* base layer given by the impurity distribution $N(x)$. The net impurity concentration as a function of distance along the transistor is given in Fig. 4-8a, where N_{BE} denotes the impurity concentration in the base near the emitter junction.

The energy band diagram for this model at equilibrium is shown in Fig. 4-8b. The Fermi level φ is drawn as a constant-energy reference across the entire length of the transistor structure. The energy bands are shifted in potential to account for the carrier concentrations in the various regions. In the emitter region, which is usually doped very heavily n type, the bottom of the conduction band is drawn very close to the Fermi level. In the collector, which is not quite as n type as the emitter, the conduction band edge is farther away from φ. Within the base region, however, the conductivity is p type, and therefore the bands must shift to bring the top of the valence band closer to the Fermi level. The important point to note is that because

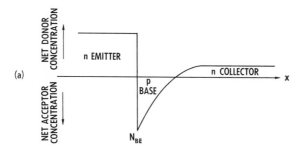

(a)

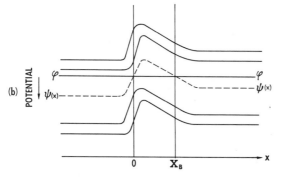

(b)

Fig. 4-8 (*a*) Net impurity concentration versus distance for an n-p-n transistor having a graded-base region; (*b*) band structure diagram for the transistor depicted in *a*.

the carrier concentration in the base is nonuniform according to $N(x)$, the energy bands will bend correspondingly. The base region is bounded by the points where the Fermi level potential φ just equals the intrinsic electrostatic potential ψ. These are the junction positions.

A comparison of Fig. 4-8*b* with an energy diagram for a uniform base clearly shows the effect of the impurity gradient in the base. In the present case the potential ψ is lower at the emitter than at the collector. Because $d\psi/dx$ has a finite value within the base, there is an electric field within the base region. This is a built-in field which gives rise to a drift current in the base—one which is just canceled by diffusion current so that the majority-carrier concentration gradient is maintained. The field, which keeps holes in their place, is in such a direction as to aid the transport of injected electrons. Thus, for the condition of low-level injection, the electrons move by both diffusion and drift. It must be emphasized that all of the above is also applicable to p-n-p structures, wherein the built-in field is in the opposite direction and aids injected holes.

Analysis of current gain for the graded base yields the following expression for β:

$$\frac{1}{\beta} \approx \frac{R_{SE}}{R_{SB}} + \frac{X_B{}^2}{4L_{nB}{}^2} + \frac{sA_sX_B}{A_ED_{nB}} \tag{4-24}$$

where the terms R_{SE} and R_{SB} are the sheet resistances of the emitter and base, respectively. Sheet resistance is defined in Sec. 3-3. R_{SE} must be interpreted as the sheet resistance of an emitter having a uniform resistivity ρ_E and a thickness equal to L_{pE}. R_{SB} is the sheet resistance of a base of thickness X_B whose resistivity $\rho_B(x)$ is a function of distance in the x direction. Note that for the uniform base, $R_{SB} = \rho_B/X_B$, and the first term of Eq. (4-24) simply reduces to the familiar form given by Eq. (4-14). The quantity R_{SB}, base sheet resistance, can be evaluated readily with the aid of Irvin's curves,[13] which are reproduced in part in Figs. 3-13 through 3-16. Section 3-3 explains the basis of these curves and outlines their use.

The second term in Eq. (4-24) has been reduced by a factor of 2 to approximate the effect of the electric field which aids the flow of injected current.

4-4 Base Resistance of Transistors

In the analysis presented so far, no mention has been made of the effects of the inherent resistance of the base region. In the transistor base layer, a fraction $(1 - \alpha)$ of the input emitter current constitutes a small base current I_B, which flows in through the base-region contact. It should be apparent that for any practical transistor geometry wherein ohmic base contacts must be made around and/or along the periphery, the base current must flow parallel to the emitter- and collector-junction planes. Since the base layer has a specific resistivity, this current will develop a transverse voltage drop in the base region, which appears as feedback to the emitter junction. This effect may be represented by an additional term r_B', which is called the *base resistance*.

The base resistance is common to all currents, direct or alternating, producing corresponding voltage drops. From the dc point of view, the base voltage developed can seriously alter the action of the transistor. We recall that for typical operating current bias, the emitter forward potential is quite small, being approximately seven-tenths of a volt for silicon. If either base current or base resistivity is appreciable, it is quite possible that sufficient transverse base voltage may be developed to cut off that part of the emitter junction farthest removed from the contact. For a constant emitter current, this mechanism increases the current density at the emitter, since part of the active emitter area is being blocked off. In other words, since the base region has a finite sheet resistance, there results a finite voltage drop associated with the flow of base current. The maximum potential occurs farthest away from the base contact. Since the external emitter bias voltage may be assumed to be applied uniformly over the entire emitter junction, the effect of the internal base voltage is to reduce the potential applied to those portions of the emitter junction farthest away from the base contact. The net effect is that the injected emitter current density is maximum closest to the base contact, and decreases in some manner as one traverses into the transistor. Thus we have an internal self-bias or "crowding" effect in the base region of a junction transistor; this may be interpreted to be a reduction in the active cross-sectional area. It is best understood by referring to the pictorial illustration of the crowding phenomenon in Fig. 4-9. In this figure, the electron current direction is into the page, and in each case the injected current density increases (darker shading) as the base contact is approached. For the geometries shown, the cutoff effect may be so severe that the injected carrier density near the center of the emitter junction may be practically zero.

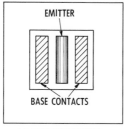

(a) LINEAR TRANSISTOR
GEOMETRY

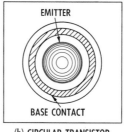

(b) CIRCULAR TRANSISTOR
GEOMETRY

Fig. 4-9 A representation of the emitter current "crowding" effect in transistors. The shading of the emitter regions in these plan-view diagrams is intended to suggest current density differences: (*a*) Linear transistor geometry; (*b*) circular transistor geometry.

From the point of view of practical transistor design, we can take into consideration the effects of base layer crowding by simply assuming that only the *periphery* of the emitter is active; this is particularly true for very small-area high-frequency transistors. On this basis, the current-handling capacity of a transistor becomes proportional to the emitter perimeter rather than the emitter area. Furthermore, with the injected current density concentrated at the edge of the emitter, we can omit the contribution of the base region directly under the emitter in the calculation of base resistance. This leaves that portion of the base between the emitter edge and the base contact as the most important segment affecting r_B'.

GEOMETRY	RESISTANCE
(a)	$R = \dfrac{\rho}{3 X_B} \dfrac{h}{l}$
(b)	$R = \dfrac{\rho}{12 X_B} \dfrac{h}{l}$
(c)	$R = \dfrac{\rho}{X_B} \dfrac{d}{l}$
(d)	$R = \dfrac{\rho}{8 \pi X_B}$
(e)	$R = \dfrac{\rho}{4 \pi X_B} \ln\left(\dfrac{r_2}{r_1}\right)$
(f)	$R = \dfrac{\rho}{2 \pi X_B} \ln\left(\dfrac{r_2}{r_1}\right)$

ARROWS INDICATE DIRECTION OF CURRENT FLOW

Fig. 4-10 A summary of resistance formulas for a number of geometrical elements. These may be used in appropriate combinations to generate approximate expressions for transistor base resistance.

To determine r_B' from the base resistivity, the transistor geometry must be considered. One approach is to visualize the base region as being composed of three-dimensional elements of known resistance. The resistances of these elements are then added in parallel or in series, whichever is appropriate, to obtain a very approximate expression for r_B'.

Figure 4-10 presents a summary of the resistance formulas for a number of three-dimensional elements.[14,15] In the figure, the arrows denote planes through which the current is flowing. Also, the shaded portions represent ohmic base contacts. All the equations are directly proportional to ρ/X_B, which was defined as the base region sheet resistance R_{SB}.

A typical illustration[15] of the use of the formulas in Fig. 4-10 is given in Fig. 4-11, wherein both a linear and a circular geometry are considered. The first term in the r_B' expressions of Fig. 4-11 accounts for the resistance of that portion of the base directly under the emitter junction. If we assume that all the current is injected off the edges of the emitter junction (as is the case for many integrated circuit transistors), then this first term is omitted from each of the equations.

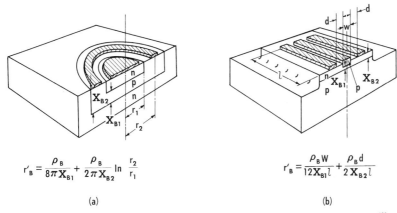

$$r'_B = \frac{\rho_B}{8\pi X_{B1}} + \frac{\rho_B}{2\pi X_{B2}} \ln \frac{r_2}{r_1}$$

$$r'_B = \frac{\rho_B W}{12 X_{B1} l} + \frac{\rho_B d}{2 X_{B2} l}$$

(a)   (b)

Fig. 4-11   Approximate expressions for the base resistance of two transistor structures, illustrating the use of information from Fig. 4-10: (a) Circular transistor geometry; (b) linear transistor geometry.

4-5   Base Input and Collector Saturation Voltages

Of prime importance in switching applications are the input and output voltages of the transistor when it is driven into *saturation* (or more specifically, voltage saturation), when operated in the grounded-emitter configuration. By definition, saturation is the condition in which both the emitter and collector junctions become forward-biased. It will now be explained on a qualitative basis how the collector-junction bias potential switches from a reverse- to a forward-bias condition in the saturation state.

Let us refer to the grounded-emitter n-p-n transistor. The normal region of operation is called the active region. To illustrate operation in the active region, the junction potentials are as indicated in Fig. 4-12a. Let us assume a base current such that the collector current I_C is 5 mA, which places the operating point in the active region. For this condition, $V_{CE} = +5$ volts because of the voltage drop in the load resistor. Furthermore, as shown in Fig. 4-12a, $V_{CB} = 4.5$ volts and $V_{BE} = 0.5$ volt. Thus we see that the emitter is forward-biased and the collector is reverse-biased, as is to be expected.

Now, continuing the illustration, if the base current I_B is increased in order

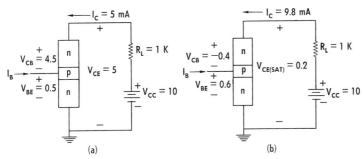

(a)   (b)

Fig. 4-12   Illustration of the effect of base drive on junction potentials: (a) Active region; (b) ON or saturation region.

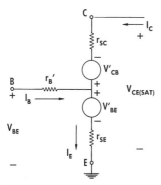

Fig. 4-13 Equivalent circuit for a common emitter transistor in saturation, including emitter and collector bulk resistances.

to achieve a saturation or ON condition, we have the situation shown in Fig. 4-12*b*. For this case we will assume that $I_C = 9.8$ mA, which means that the voltage from collector to emitter when the transistor is saturated, $V_{CE(SAT)}$, equals 0.2 volt; in other words, almost all the battery supply voltage is dropped across the load resistor R_L. To establish the increase in I_C from 5 to 9.8 mA it was necessary to increase V_{BE} from 0.5 to 0.6 volt. Since $V_{CE} = V_{CB} + V_{BE}$, it becomes apparent that V_{CB} must equal -0.4 volt, which is clearly a forward-bias condition for the collector junction. Thus we see that because of the limitations of the external load circuit, the base becomes more positive than either the emitter or collector in saturation. The total voltage from collector to emitter becomes quite small, since it represents the sum of two opposing potentials. This is the collector saturation voltage $V_{CE(SAT)}$.

In our discussion thus far, we have been concerned only with the junction potentials of the transistor in the saturation state. From a practical-device point of view, this is not sufficient to determine the exact saturation voltages. To be complete, it is necessary to include the ohmic body resistance of the collector and emitter regions, since these resistances are directly in series with the junctions. In the grounded emitter configuration the equivalent circuit representation would appear as shown in Fig. 4-13, where the emitter and collector bulk resistances are denoted as r_{SE} and r_{SC}, respectively. In addition, the base resistance r_B' is included in the equivalent circuit. With reference to Fig. 4-13 for current directions and voltage polarities, the following expressions can be written[16] for an n-p-n transistor:

$$V_{BE} = \frac{kT}{q} \ln\left(1 + \frac{I_E - \alpha_i I_C}{I_{EBO}}\right) + I_B r_B' + I_E r_{SE} \tag{4-25}$$

$$V_{CE(SAT)} = -\frac{kT}{q} \ln\frac{\alpha_i[1 - I_C(1 - \alpha)/(I_B\alpha)]}{1 + I_C(1 - \alpha_i)/I_B} + I_C r_{SC} + I_E r_{SE} \tag{4-26}$$

In Eqs. (4-25) and (4-26) α_i is the magnitude of the inverted common base current gain, i.e., the gain with the collector acting as the emitter and vice versa. For a diffused silicon transistor, α_i is usually quite small, being on the order of 0.1. Since $\beta = \alpha/(1 - \alpha)$ and since r_{SE} is usually negligible because of the low resistivity of the emitter region, Eq. (4-26) reduces to

$$V_{CE(SAT)} = -\frac{kT}{q} \ln \alpha_i \frac{(1 - I_C/\beta I_B)}{1 + (I_C/I_B)(1 - \alpha_i)} + I_C r_{SC} \tag{4-27}$$

4-6 Maximum Voltage Characteristics of Transistors

By applying the principles that were developed for the p-n junction in Chaps. 2 and 3, we can readily ascertain the various voltage ratings of the transistor. For example, the avalanche breakdown voltage of the emitter junction, BV_{EBO}, and that of the collector junction, BV_{CBO}, can be estimated through reference to Fig. 2-20. (The subscript O indicates that the third terminal is open-circuited.) For this purpose, we note the impurity concentration on the more lightly doped side of the junction in question, and proceed as for an n^+-p or p^+-n junction. For the emitter, therefore, the doping of the base near the emitter junction is the important quantity. For the collector of integrated circuit transistors or diffused silicon transistors, the doping of the collector body is pertinent. The values so obtained are approximate, but are adequate for most engineering purposes.

In some transistors the upper limit on base-collector voltage is fixed by the phenomenon of *punch-through*. This occurs at the voltage V_{PT} which causes the collector depletion layer to spread through the entire thickness of the base layer. For purposes of explanation, let the base be grounded and the emitter open, and let a positive potential be applied to the collector. With increases in V_{CB}, beyond the punch-through voltage, the emitter floats at a potential differing from the collector potential by very nearly V_{PT}. Thus, it begins to float above ground potential. (If it were *at* ground potential, the emitter junction would be forward-biased.) Consequently the emitter-base junction assumes a reverse bias over part of its area, with the exact area affected depending on the details of transistor design. When the emitter-base junction breaks down by the avalanche mechanism (at BV_{EBO}), then a conducting path is established from base to collector: Avalanching supplies electrons to the emitter from ground, effectively, and these are in turn swept through the punch-through region to the collector. The resulting collector-base *I-V* characteristic exhibits a breakdown or a knee (much like that for the simple collector-junction avalanching). The breakdown voltage for the punch-through-limited device may thus be written as

$$BV_{CBO} = V_{PT} + BV_{EBO} \qquad (4\text{-}28)$$

Punch-through voltage can be predicted, given the proposed transistor profile, by consulting Fig. 2-18 for a step-junction situation, or Figs. 3-19 through 3-21 for a diffused collector junction. The latter case is, of course, most probable in present integrated circuit transistors. To use these curves for the determination of V_{PT} it is necessary to employ a trial-and-error approach, arriving at the voltage required to make X_1 equal to the base thickness.

We must now turn our attention to the grounded emitter configuration to determine collector-to-emitter breakdown relationships, viz., BV_{CES} and BV_{CEO}. BV_{CES} is the collector-to-emitter breakdown voltage measured when the base is short-circuited to the emitter. If BV_{CBO} for the transistor is limited by avalanche effects,

$$BV_{CES} = BV_{CBO} \qquad (4\text{-}29)$$

If BV_{CBO} for the transistor is limited by voltage punch-through,

$$BV_{CES} = V_{PT} \qquad (4\text{-}30)$$

This is apparent from Eq. (4-28) since BV_{EBO} is equal to zero when the emitter-base junction is short-circuited.

The remaining grounded emitter property is BV_{CEO}, which is the collector-to-emitter breakdown voltage with the base open-circuited; i.e., $I_B = 0$. Under these conditions, the voltage applied across the transistor to reverse-bias the collector junction also acts to forward-bias the emitter junction. It is interesting to note the current that flows under these conditions. Since

$$I_C = I_{CBO} + \alpha I_E \tag{4-31}$$

then during the measurement of BV_{CEO}, $I_C = I_E = I_{CEO}$ and $I_{CEO} = I_{CBO} + \alpha I_{CEO}$, or

$$I_{CEO} = \frac{I_{CBO}}{1 - \alpha} \tag{4-32}$$

This equation indicates that the grounded emitter reverse current is larger than I_{CBO} by a factor approximately equal to the β of the transistor at that current level. This result is understandable from a physical point of view, since the emitter is injecting additional minority carriers into the base. As the applied voltage is increased, however, I_{CEO} will begin to increase because the current gain α must be multiplied by the factor M, which we repeat for convenience.

$$M(V) = \frac{1}{1 - (V/V_B)^n} \tag{2-83}$$

The exponent n has values ranging from 2 to 4 in silicon. When the α term in Eq. (4-32) is multiplied by Eq. (2-83), there exists some value of V for which $\alpha M = 1$ and I_{CEO} goes to infinity. This is the breakdown condition where $V = BV_{CEO}$ or

$$M = \frac{1}{\alpha} = \frac{1}{1 - (BV_{CEO}/BV_{CBO})^n} \tag{4-33}$$

Solving for BV_{CEO}, we obtain

$$BV_{CEO} = BV_{CBO}(1 - \alpha)^{1/n} \tag{4-34}$$

Since n varies from 2 to 4 in silicon, we can use as a rough rule of thumb for a silicon transistor

$$BV_{CEO} = \frac{BV_{CBO}}{\sqrt[3]{\beta}} \tag{4-35}$$

4-7   Transistor Frequency Response

Up to this point only the dc characteristics of transistors have been considered. We will now turn our attention to some of the ac characteristics. Therefore we will now be concerned with the ac current gains. These are

$$\alpha = \frac{dI_C}{dI_E}\bigg|_{V_{CB}} \tag{4-36}$$

for the common base case and

$$\beta = \frac{dI_C}{dI_B}\bigg|_{V_{CE}} \tag{4-37}$$

for the common emitter case. Furthermore, in the following α and β will signify the current gain of the entire device (including parasitics) rather than the current gain of the active base region only.

The magnitude of the small-signal short-circuit common base current gain α is a decreasing function of frequency as shown in Fig. 4-14. The α cutoff frequency f_α is defined as the frequency at which the magnitude of α is below its low-frequency value by a factor of $1/\sqrt{2}$ (or by 3 db). The four most important factors that determine f_α are discussed below.

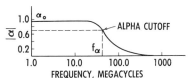

Fig. 4-14 Frequency dependence of common base current gain α.

The frequency response of the active base region is obtained from the continuity equation. In view of the distributed nature of the base region, an infinite number of time constants are required to describe the frequency response of the base. Pritchard[17] shows that the intrinsic cutoff frequency of the base region for uniform doping is approximately

$$\omega_B = \frac{2.43D}{X_B{}^2} \tag{4-38}$$

where X_B is the base thickness and D is the diffusion constant for minority carriers in the base (D_{nB} for n-p-n transistors). Increasing the collector bias decreases the base thickness, which increases ω_B. Graded-base transistors have a higher value of ω_B. Typically, the constant multiplier in Eq. (4-38) is increased to about 5 for a transistor with a graded base.

For high-frequency transistors with extremely thin bases, the measured cutoff frequency is considerably less than that predicted by the analysis of the base region. This indicates that additional mechanisms are important in determining cutoff frequency. The collector and emitter junction capacitances are two important factors here. The collector junction capacitance C_{TC} and the bulk resistance of the collector region r_{sc} establish the time constant.

$$\frac{1}{\omega_C} = r_{sc}C_{TC} \tag{4-39}$$

Emitter series resistance is very low because of heavy emitter doping, and may thus be neglected. The emitter junction capacitance C_{TE} is in parallel with the dynamic emitter-junction resistance r_e. The emitter time constant is

$$\frac{1}{\omega_E} = r_eC_{TE} = \frac{kT}{qI_E}C_{TE} \tag{4-40}$$

The forward-biased emitter junction exhibits a transition capacitance per unit area which may be approximated by

$$C_{TE} \approx 4A_EC_T(0) = 4A_E\sqrt{\frac{q\kappa\epsilon_o N_B'}{2\psi_o}} \tag{4-41}$$

A_E is the emitter area, $C_T(0)$ is based on Eq. (2-78), with ψ_o being the built-in voltage of approximately ½ volt, and N_B' is the impurity concentration near the base side of the emitter junction.

If the collector depletion layer thickness is appreciable, we must consider the transit time necessary for the carriers to cross it. In the presence of an electric field the carriers travel with an average scattering-limited velocity v_{sc}. The average collector depletion layer transit time is

$$t_d = \frac{X_m}{v_{sc}} \tag{4-42}$$

where X_m is the total thickness of the depletion layer. For silicon, v_{sc} is approximately 8×10^6 cm/sec.

A comparison of the above quantities indicates which frequency-determining mechanisms are important for a given transistor. A rough estimate of f_α for a typical graded-base transistor is

$$\frac{1}{2\pi f_\alpha} = \frac{1}{\omega_\alpha} \approx \frac{1}{\omega_B} + \frac{1}{\omega_C} + \frac{1}{\omega_E} + t_d \tag{4-43}$$

or

$$\frac{1}{\omega_\alpha} \approx \frac{X_B^2}{5D} + r_{sc}C_{TC} + r_e C_{TE} + \frac{X_m}{v_{sc}} \tag{4-44}$$

The constant multiplier of 5 used here for ω_B is appropriate for a typical graded-base transistor.

In terms of the complex plane (the frequency domain), the Laplace transform of α has an infinite number of poles, or zeros of the denominator, spaced on the negative real axis. Typically, the second pole is two to nine times as far from the origin as the first. Then for low enough frequencies the first pole is dominant; i.e., the frequency dependence of α is almost completely determined by the first pole for low frequencies, and α can be approximated by a one-pole expression

$$\alpha = \frac{\alpha_o \omega_\alpha}{s + \omega_\alpha} \tag{4-45}$$

where $s = \sigma + j\omega$ is the complex-frequency variable. (For purely sinusoidal frequencies $s = j\omega$; in the time domain s can be interpreted as the operator d/dt.) The most important effect of the nondominant poles is to add more phase shift than would be obtained from a one-pole function. The difference between the actual phase shift and the phase shift of a one-pole function will be termed *excess phase*. Since a two-pole function has more phase shift, a better approximation of α is[18,19]

$$\alpha = \frac{\alpha_o \omega_1 \omega_2}{(s + \omega_1)(s + \omega_2)} \tag{4-46}$$

Because the excess phase of α is nearly a linear function of frequency, another good approximation is[20]

$$\alpha = \frac{\alpha_o \omega_\alpha e^{-(m/\omega_\alpha)s}}{s + \omega_\alpha} \tag{4-47}$$

where m is the excess phase at $\omega = \omega_\alpha$. The range of validity for Eq. (4-47), which depends on the location of the nondominant poles, is roughly $\omega < \omega_\alpha/2$. Equation (4-46) should be valid for somewhat higher frequencies.

The choice between expressions (4-46) and (4-47) is dictated by the particular usage of the model. In Eq. (4-47) there is unlimited freedom in matching excess phase, whereas Eq. (4-46) has a maximum phase shift of 180° at $\omega = \infty$. On the other hand, the two-pole α has some advantages over (4-47) when used in circuit analysis because of the transcendental nature of the latter. In addition, by appropriately selecting ω_1 and ω_2, a closer fit to the variation of the magnitude of α with frequency may be obtained with (4-46) than with (4-47).

It should be pointed out that for a uniform base the excess phase m is about 0.22 rad (13°). The excess phase is higher for a graded base. If the excess phase is to be zero, the base must be graded in the opposite direction so that the minority carriers see a retarding field in the base region.

Frequency Variation of Beta. The cutoff frequency of the small-signal short-circuit common emitter current gain β is much less than f_α. If we consider only the active base region, β is given by

$$\beta = \frac{\alpha}{1 - \alpha} \tag{4-48}$$

This expression is also approximately correct for the overall transistor, and will be used in the following discussion. Referring to Fig. 4-15, it can be seen that as the phase angle θ increases, the magnitude of $(1 - \alpha)$ increases rapidly which in turn reduces the magnitude of β.

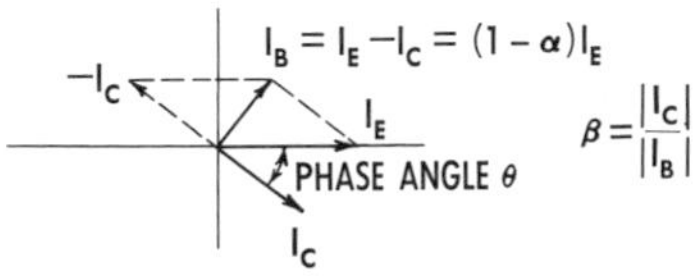

Fig. 4-15 Effect of phase shift on the magnitude of $(1 - \alpha)$.

When Eq. (4-47) is substituted into Eq. (4-48), β is found to be

$$\beta = \frac{\alpha_0 \omega_\alpha e^{-ms/\omega_a}}{s + \omega_\alpha - \alpha_0 \omega_\alpha e^{-ms/\omega_a}} \tag{4-49}$$

If $m = 0$,

$$\beta = \frac{\alpha_0 \omega_\alpha}{s + (1 - \alpha_0)\omega_\alpha} \tag{4-50}$$

and the β cutoff frequency is

$$\omega_\beta \bigg|_{m=0} = (1 - \alpha_0)\omega_\alpha \tag{4-51}$$

In the frequency range where $|ms/\omega_\alpha| \ll 1$, the exponential term in the denominator can be expanded in a power series. If the first two terms are retained the result is

$$\beta(s) = \frac{\alpha_0 \omega_T e^{-ms/\omega_a}}{s + (1 - \alpha_0)\omega_T} \tag{4-52}$$

where

$$\omega_T = \frac{\omega_\alpha}{1 + \alpha_0 m} \approx \frac{\omega_\alpha}{1 + m} \tag{4-53}$$

A typical value of m is 0.4 rad. Then if $|s| < \omega_\alpha/2$, $|ms/\omega_\alpha| < 0.2$, and the two-term expansion is reasonably accurate. The cutoff frequency is

$$\omega_\beta = (1 - \alpha_0)\omega_T = \frac{(1 - \alpha_0)\omega_\alpha}{1 + m} \tag{4-54}$$

The excess phase reduces the β cutoff frequency by a factor of $1/(1 + m)$.

The frequency at which the magnitude of β is equal to unity for $s = j\omega$ is called the *(current) gain-bandwidth product*. If we use Eq. (4-52) to find the frequency at which $|\beta(j\omega)| = 1$, we obtain

$$\omega|_{|\beta|=1} = \sqrt{2\alpha_o - 1}\, \omega_T \approx \omega_T \tag{4-55}$$

Thus, to the accuracy of our approximations, ω_T is the gain-bandwidth product.

The following simple procedure can be used to measure ω_T. For $s = j\omega$ and $\omega > (1 - \alpha_o)\omega_T$, the magnitude of Eq. (4-52) becomes

$$|\beta(j\omega)| = \frac{\alpha_o\omega_T}{\omega} \approx \frac{\omega_T}{\omega} \tag{4-56}$$

or

$$\omega_T = \omega|\beta(j\omega)| \tag{4-57}$$

In this frequency range the magnitude of β has a slope of -6 db/octave, and the gain-bandwidth product is constant (and equal to ω_T). For example, a β of 4 at 100 Mc corresponds to an $f_T(= \omega_T/2\pi)$ of 400 Mc, provided 100 Mc is in the 6-db/octave region. Figure 4-16 illustrates the relationships of f_β, f_T, and f_α for a representative transistor. Note that the magnitude of the current gain is expressed in decibels (i.e., 20 log β).

In the foregoing it has been assumed that Eq. (4-52) is valid for frequencies near f_T. At frequencies near $f_T/2$, its accuracy may become questionable, depending on the location of the nondominant poles. In particular, the slope of $|\beta|$ may approach -12 db/octave (a two-pole response). In this case ω_T is only an *apparent* gain-bandwidth product. The actual gain-bandwidth product will be smaller because of the steeper slope. The above expressions are valid if the magnitude of β decreases at -6 db/octave or less, or, typically, for frequencies near $f_T/2$ or less.

In summary, the gain-bandwidth product can be estimated from

$$\frac{1}{f_T} = 2\pi(1 + m)\left(r_eC_{TE} + \frac{X_B^2}{5D} + \frac{X_m}{v_{sc}} + r_{sc}C_{TC}\right) \tag{4-58}$$

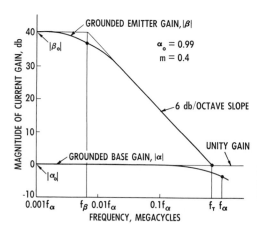

Fig. 4-16   Frequency dependence of common emitter and common base current gain, illustrating the relationships among f_T, f_α, and f_β.

In most high-frequency diffused transistors having very thin bases, the first term $r_e C_{TE}$ is significant in affecting frequency response. Thus, it is important to maintain the emitter area as small as possible. However, we saw that base layer crowding causes the current rating to be proportional to the perimeter of the emitter. Thus, the optimum design for a transistor is one incorporating a high perimeter-to-area ratio for the transistor emitter. Such a geometry is a long thin stripe. If $r_e C_{TE}$ is predominant in determining f_T, then by increasing the stripe length n times, we can still achieve the same f_T simply by increasing the current n times. Thus, f_T is approximately a constant for a given perimeter-area ratio provided that the current is adjusted accordingly. It is for this reason that high-frequency power transistors may be designed simply by scaling up small geometries.

High-frequency Power Gain. A very approximate analysis of a grounded emitter bandpass transistor amplifier with a matched source and load gives the power gain as[21]

$$G_e \approx \frac{f_T}{8\pi f_o{}^2 r_B' \, C_{TC}} \tag{4-59}$$

for

$$f_o > (1 - \alpha_o) f_T$$

where f_o is the center frequency. In the analysis the f_T of the active base region was used. When the value of f_T given by Eq. (4-58) is used, a more pessimistic estimate is obtained for G_e.

The highest frequency at which power gain can be obtained from a bandpass amplifier $f_{\max}$ is found by setting $G_e = 1$.

$$f_{\max} \approx \sqrt{\frac{f_T}{8\pi r_B' \, C_{TC}}} \tag{4-60}$$

The frequency $f_{\max}$ is also the maximum frequency of oscillation of the transistor.

For most transistors $f_{\max}$ is greater than f_T. The analysis used to obtain the power gain requires essentially the same assumptions needed to obtain Eq. (4-52). Therefore the accuracy of the analysis is questionable at frequencies above, say, $f_T/2$. This would cause Eq. (4-60) to predict a somewhat higher value than the measured $f_{\max}$. Use of the overall f_T given by Eq. (4-53) rather than the f_T of the active base region will help reduce the calculated $f_{\max}$ to a more reasonable value.

4-8 Switching Characteristics of Transistors

In addition to its use as an amplifier, the transistor serves as an excellent switching device, since it can go from an open-circuit OFF condition to almost a short-circuit ON condition with great speed and minimal power.

In transistor switching circuits, the grounded emitter configuration is by far the most widely used. For this arrangement, we shall be concerned with the collector output characteristic, since this will enable us to understand clearly the mechanism of switching from one state to another. A typical I_C-V_{CE} characteristic for an n-p-n

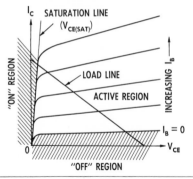

REGION OF OPERATION	EMITTER BIAS	COLLECTOR BIAS
OFF	REVERSE	REVERSE
ACTIVE	FORWARD	REVERSE
ON	FORWARD	FORWARD

Fig. 4-17 Output *I-V* characteristics for a common emitter transistor, illustrating the three operating regions.

junction transistor is given in Fig. 4-17. Examining this figure, we see that the output characteristic is divided into three regions of operation. These are: the OFF region, the active region, and the ON region. Each of these regions will be described separately.

The OFF region is defined as that region of operation in which both the emitter and collector junctions are reverse-biased. In this region the device has very high input and output impedances. Figure 4-18 shows a sketch of the minority-carrier concentration in the base layer for each of the three regions of operation. For the OFF condition, since both junctions are reverse-biased, the electron concentration is zero at the junctions, as shown.

The boundary between the OFF and active regions is the curve for $I_B = 0$. In the active region we have the normal mode of operation for the junction transistor; that is, the emitter is forward-biased, and the collector is reverse-biased. In switching from OFF to ON, the active region is traversed with a speed which is a function of the gain and frequency response in that region. The minority-carrier concentration for the active region, as shown in Fig. 4-18, is the familiar form discussed previously.

The last of the three regions of operation is the ON region, which is often referred to as the *saturation* region. In this mode, the collector bias reverses polarity so that both emitter and collector junctions are forward-biased. The saturation line drawn in Fig. 4-17 is a linear version of the results of Eq. (4-27) for saturated operation. This straight line is a good approximation and leads to the concept of saturation resistance, viz., the inverse of the slope of the saturation line. The minority-carrier concentration in the base and collector layer for the ON condition is also included in Fig. 4-18. At the collector junction, the minority-carrier concentration increases significantly because of the forward-bias condition at the collector.

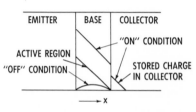

Fig. 4-18 Minority-carrier concentrations versus distance for the three different operating conditions.

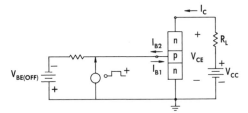

Fig. 4-19 Basic common emitter transistor switching circuit.

The next section will present a physical description of the mechanisms that take place as the transistor is switched through the three regions of operation just defined.

4-9   Qualitative Description of Switching Process

Before we present specific mathematical expressions for the switching transistor, it would be appropriate to present a qualitative description of the physical events that occur when a transistor is switched from OFF to ON and then to OFF again. Let us refer to the basic switching circuit shown in Fig. 4-19, in which the transistor is driven by a constant base-current source. The potential $V_{BE(OFF)}$ holds the transistor in the OFF state because of the reverse-biased emitter. The generator in the base circuit is a pulse generator and is assumed to generate an ideal step-function input pulse which turns the transistor on. For this circuit, the waveforms that are observed for the base and collector current pulses, respectively, are as shown in Fig. 4-20. We observe that the output collector pulse is far from being an exact replica of the input base pulse. The reasons for these particular waveshape discrepancies will be explained in the paragraphs to follow.

At time t_0, the pulse generator delivers a step base current to the transistor. At this instant, the transistor is in the OFF condition because of the emitter reverse-bias voltage $V_{BE(OFF)}$. The collector current that is flowing is extremely low (on the order of I_{CBO}); since this is negligible, the voltage across the collector junction is equal to the sum of the supply voltage V_{CC} and the turn-off voltage $V_{BE(OFF)}$. After t_0, the base current rises immediately to I_{B1}, but it is observed that the collector current does not begin to increase until t_1. The time between t_0 and t_1 is

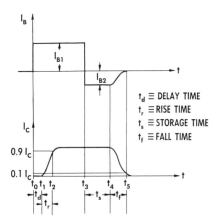

Fig. 4-20 Current versus time at the input (base) and output (collector) terminals of a common emitter transistor switch, illustrating the definitions of several switching times.

called the *delay time* t_d and is defined as the time required to bring the transistor from the initial OFF condition to the edge of conduction, i.e., to the beginning of the active region. This may be defined as that instant of time t_1 at which the applied base-to-emitter voltage is zero. Physically, the finite time required for t_d comes about because of the reverse bias on both the emitter and collector junctions. As the effective base-to-emitter voltage goes from $V_{BE(OFF)}$ to zero, the depletion layers on both junctions must reduce in thickness accordingly. The delay time is the time required to charge these capacitances to the new voltage level. (Because these capacitances are voltage-dependent, their values also increase in this process.) It should be apparent that if $V_{BE(OFF)} = 0$, then $t_d = 0$.

At time t_1, the operating point of the transistor is at the beginning of the active region, in which the emitter starts to become forward-biased and begins to inject electrons into the base. Now the collector current begins to increase toward its saturation value, corresponding approximately to V_{CC}/R_L. However, rather than increasing instantaneously at t_1, it requires a finite time to reach 90 per cent of the final value. This occurs at time t_2; the time interval $(t_2 - t_1)$ is defined as the *rise time* t_r of the collector current pulse. Rise time is partly due to the frequency dependence of β, discussed earlier. It should be recognized that neither the gain nor the frequency response remains constant through the active region. The dc β will vary with current for the reasons already discussed and may pass through a maximum value, depending on the $\beta(I_C)$ characteristic and the magnitude of current to be switched. Also, the effective base thickness increases as the collector voltage decreases from the supply value to the saturation value. This, in turn, causes f_T to decrease.

During the same active switching interval, both the emitter and collector transition capacitances must be discharged to account for the depletion layer changes with voltage. In the emitter, the capacitance increases because forward-bias is applied; in the collector, the capacitance also increases and must be discharged through the collector series resistance, which is predominantly the external load resistor R_L. All these effects take place simultaneously, and collectively determine rise time.

The transistor will remain in the ON state as long as the input base current I_{B1} is maintained. With reference to Fig. 4-20 again, at time t_3 the base input pulse steps off immediately; however, it is observed that the collector pulse does not respond until time t_4. The time interval between t_3 and t_4 is referred to as the storage time t_s and is attributed to a basic storage phenomenon in the collector and base. The storage time is a measure of the time required for the minority carriers in the base and collector to return to the level corresponding to the boundary between the active and saturation regions. These excess carriers are introduced because the collector junction becomes forward-biased when the base current I_{B1} is greater than the I_B necessary to produce I_C; that is, $I_{B1} > I_C/\beta$. Thus, storage time is related to a carrier-recombination process and is a measure of the minority-carrier lifetime in the base and collector regions.

Finally, at time t_4, the transistor comes out of saturation, and the operating point traverses the load line again through the active region into the OFF state. This is the turn-off portion of the collector waveform; the time interval between t_4 and t_5

is defined as the *fall time* t_f. At t_5, the collector current has reduced to $0.1I_C$. The description of the switching process for fall time is similar to that for rise time, except that the active region is traversed in the reverse direction.

In summary, we see that in response to a step input of base current, the collector current requires a total *turn-on time*, which is

$$t_{ON} = t_d + t_r \tag{4-61}$$

Also, when the base current is removed as a step, the collector current requires a total *turn-off time*, which is

$$t_{OFF} = t_s + t_f \tag{4-62}$$

It can be shown that for a diffused base n-p-n transistor[22-36]

$$t_d \approx \frac{2C_{TE}}{I_{B1}}[(V_{BE(OFF)} - \psi_o)^{1/2} - |\psi_o|^{1/2}] + \frac{C_{TC}}{I_{B1}}(V_{BE(OFF)}) \tag{4-63}$$

$$t_r \approx \beta\left(\frac{1}{\omega_T} + 1.7R_LC_{TC}\right)\ln\frac{\beta I_{B1}}{\beta I_{B1} - 0.9I_C} \tag{4-64}$$

$$t_f \approx \beta\left(\frac{1}{\omega_T} + 1.7R_LC_{TC}\right)\ln\frac{I_C - \beta I_{B2}}{0.1I_C - \beta I_{B2}} \tag{4-65}$$

$$t_s \approx \tau_s \ln\frac{I_{B1} - I_{B2}}{(I_C/\beta) - I_{B2}} \tag{4-66}$$

where

β = dc beta at edge of saturation

ψ_o = contact potential of base-emitter junction [negative quantity in Eq. (4-63)]

C_{TE} = emitter transition capacitance measured at $|V_{BE(OFF)} - \psi_o| = 1$ volt

C_{TC} = collector transition capacitance measured at V_{CC} (assuming V_{CC} is much greater than $V_{BE(OFF)}$ or $V_{BE(ON)}$)

$V_{BE(OFF)}$ = off voltage, base to emitter [a positive quantity in Eq. (4-63)]

$V_{BE(ON)}$ = base-emitter voltage in the active region (approximately 0.7 volt for silicon)

τ_s = storage time constant

ω_T = angular gain-bandwidth product measured at edge of saturation

Expressions (4-63) through (4-66) can be applied to p-n-p transistors if the appropriate changes in polarities are made. Note that for an n-p-n transistor I_{B2} is a negative quantity in Eqs. (4-65) and (4-66).

REFERENCES

1. Shockley, W.: The Theory of p-n Junctions in Semiconductors and p-n Junction Transistors, *Bell System Tech. J.,* vol. 28, pp. 435–489, July, 1949.
2. Shockley, W.: "Electrons and Holes in Semiconductors," D. Van Nostrand Co., Inc., Princeton, N.J., 1950.

3. Early, J. M.: Effects of Space-charge Layer Widening in Junction Transistors, *Proc. IRE,* vol. 40, pp. 1401–1406, November, 1952.

4. Sah, C. T., R. N. Noyce, and W. Shockley: Carrier Generation and Recombination in P-N Junctions and P-N Junction Characteristics, *Proc. IRE,* vol. 45, pp. 1228–1243, September, 1957.

5. Webster, W. M.: On the Variation of Junction-transistor Current-amplification Factor with Emitter Current, *Proc. IRE,* vol. 42, pp. 914–920, June, 1954.

6. Rittner, E. S.: Extension of the Theory of the Junction Transistor, *Phys. Rev.,* vol. 94, pp. 1161–1171, June 1, 1954.

7. Misawa, T.: Emitter Efficiency of Junction Transistor, *J. Phys. Soc. Japan,* vol. 10, pp. 362–367, May, 1955.

8. Misawa, T.: A Note on the Extended Theory of the Junction Transistor, *J. Phys. Soc. Japan,* vol. 11, pp. 728–739, July, 1956.

9. Matz, A. W.: A Modification of the Theory of the Variation of Junction Transistor Current Gain with Operating Point and Frequency, *ATE J.,* vol. 16, pp. 96–109, January–July, 1960.

10. Hall, R. N.: Power Rectifiers and Transistors, *Proc. IRE,* vol. 40, pp. 1512–1518, November, 1952.

11. Kleinman, D. A.: The Forward Characteristic of the PIN Diode, *Bell System Tech. J.,* vol. 35, pp. 685–706, May, 1956.

12. Ladany, I.: DC Characteristics of a Junction Diode, *Proc. IRE,* vol. 47, p. 589, April, 1959.

13. Irvin, J. C.: Resistivity of Bulk Silicon and of Diffused Layers in Silicon, *Bell System Tech. J.,* vol. 41, pp. 387–410, March, 1962.

14. Early, J. M.: Design Theory of Junction Transistors, *Bell System Tech. J.,* vol. 32, pp. 1271–1312, November, 1953.

15. Phillips, A. B.: "Transistor Engineering," p. 216, McGraw-Hill Book Company, New York, 1962.

16. Ebers, J. J., and J. L. Moll: Large-signal Behavior of Junction Transistors, *Proc. IRE,* vol. 42, pp. 1761–1772, December, 1954.

17. Pritchard, R. L.: Frequency Variations of Current-amplification Factor for Junction Transistors, *Proc. IRE,* vol. 40, pp. 1476–1481, November, 1952.

18. Hamilton, D. J., F. A. Lindholm, and J. A. Narud: Large-signal Models for Junction Transistors, University of Arizona Engineering Research Laboratories Report, Tucson, pp. 81–83.

19. Narud, J. A., W. C. Seelbach, and C. S. Meyer: Microminiaturized Logic Circuits: Their Characterization, Analysis and Impact upon Computer Design, 1963 IEEE International Convention.

20. Chow, W. F., and J. J. Suran: Transient Analysis of Junction Transistor Amplifiers, *Proc. IRE,* vol. 41, pp. 1125–1129, September, 1953.

21. Drouilhet, P. R., Jr.: Predictions Based on the Maximum Oscillator Frequency of a Transistor, *IRE Trans. Circuit Theory,* vol. CT-2, pp. 178–183, June, 1955. The same expressions were given earlier by R. L. Pritchard: Frequency Response of Grounded-base and Grounded-emitter Transistors, AIEE Winter Meeting, New York, January, 1954.

22. Anderson, A. E.: Transistors in Switching Circuits, *Proc. IRE,* vol. 40, pp. 1541–1558, November, 1952.

23. Moll, J. L.: Large-signal Transient Response of Junction Transistors, *Proc. IRE,* vol. 42, pp. 1773–1784, December, 1954.

24. Beaufoy, R., and J. J. Sparkes: The Junction Transistor as a Charge-controlled Device, *ATE J.,* vol. 13, pp. 310–324, October, 1957.

25. Baker, A. N.: Charge Analysis of Transistor Operation, *Proc. IRE,* vol. 48, pp. 949–950, May, 1960.

26. Ekiss, J. A., and C. D. Simmons: Calculation of the Rise and Fall Times of an Alloy Junction Transistor Switch, *Proc. IRE,* vol. 48, pp. 1487–1488, August, 1960.

27. Cho, Y.: Calculation of the Rise and Fall Times in the Alloy Junction Transistor Switch Based on the Charge Analysis, *Proc. IRE,* vol. 49, pp. 636–637, March, 1961.

28. Severin, E.: Switching Time Formulae for Single Diffused Mesa Transistors, *Semicond. Prod.,* vol. 4, pp. 37–42, June, 1961.

29. Easley, J. W.: The Effect of Collector Capacity on the Transient Response of Junction Transistors, *IRE Trans. Electron Devices,* vol. ED-4, pp. 6–14, January, 1957.

30. Simmons, C. D.: Hole Storage Delay Time and Its Prediction, *Semicond. Prod.,* vol. 1, pp. 14–18, May-June, 1958.

31. Lax, B., and S. F. Neustadter: Transient Response of a p-n Junction, *J. Appl. Phys.,* vol. 25, pp. 1148–1154, September, 1954.

32. Grinich, V. H., and R. N. Noyce: Switching Time Calculations for Diffused Base Transistors, *IRE WESCON Conv. Record,* part 3, Electron Devices, pp. 141–147, August, 1958.

33. Sparkes, J. J.: A Study of the Charge Control Parameters of Transistors, *Proc. IRE,* vol. 48, pp. 1696–1705, October, 1960.

34. Simmons, C. D.: High-speed Switching Transistors, *Elec. Design News,* vol. 5, pp. 39–47, September, 1960.

35. Hwang, Y. C., D. S. Cleverley, and D. J. Monsour: Transistor Switching Speed from Base Storage Charges and Their Lifetimes, *Electron. Design,* part I, pp. 52–55, March, 1961, part II, pp. 50–53, April, 1961.

36. Phillips, A. B.: *op. cit.,* pp. 327–349.

Part 2

INTEGRATED CIRCUIT DESIGN PRINCIPLES

5

FUNDAMENTALS OF MONOLITHIC
AND HYBRID CIRCUIT DESIGN

Let us establish from the outset that it is possible and practical, with the present state of the integrated circuits art, to design and manufacture integrated circuits for a wide variety of applications. These applications encompass the digital field, where off-the-shelf devices are already available to cover virtually the entire range of required circuit functions in a variety of basic circuit designs. They include also the field of linear amplifiers, where the greater range of circuit design requirements essentially prohibits standardization, and demands design and production facilities capable of producing, with a reasonably short delivery cycle, custom circuits on an economically competitive basis.

These requirements have led to the development of two distinctly different integrated circuit technologies, which are referred to here as the monolithic technology and the hybrid technology. (See A Note on Terminology in the front matter of the book.)

The monolithic integrated circuit (Fig. 5-1) is one in which all circuit components are manufactured into or on top of tiny blocks of silicon, normally referred to as *dice* (singular, *die*). Interconnections between the component parts within a given die are made by means of metallization patterns, and the individual parts are not separable from the complete circuit. Hence, the monolithic circuit is often referred to as a *fully integrated* circuit.

The monolithic circuit is particularly attractive for applications where identical circuits are required in relatively large quantities. For such applications it is this technology that provides the lowest per-unit cost and potentially the highest order of reliability.

The hybrid circuit is one in which separate component parts are attached to a ceramic substrate and interconnected by means of either a metallization pattern or wire bonds, as in Fig. 5-2. It is evident that the hybrid circuit bears some resemblance to the conventional discrete-component circuit, except that the individual parts consist of unencapsulated diffused or thin-film components and that the complete circuit is very small.   However, it is quite possible for a hybrid circuit to contain one or more monolithic dice in its makeup.   Thus, whether an integrated circuit consists solely of individual component parts, or of a monolithic circuit surrounded by individual component parts, or of two or more monolithic circuits, so long as these are housed in a single package the device is called a hybrid circuit.

Fig. 5-1 Photomicrograph of a monolithic integrated circuit.

Fig. 5-2 Photomicrograph of a hybrid integrated circuit.

The hybrid technology, at present, is more adaptable to small-quantity custom circuits.   It is entirely conceivable that, as the state of the art progresses, this technique will be supplanted entirely by monolithic processes.   At this time, however, and for the immediately foreseeable future, it provides an important tool for the development of practical integrated circuits.   This portion of the book, therefore, is devoted to the discussion of integrated circuit design principles for both monolithic and hybrid devices.

5-1 Basic Processes

For the fabrication of integrated circuits four basic processing techniques have emerged as predominant—the hybrid technique, the thin-film technique, the monolithic technique, and the "compatible" technique.   Basically, a thin-film integrated circuit consists of microscopically thin films of material deposited (by sputtering, vacuum deposition, etc.) on a ceramic substrate to form the passive components (resistors, capacitors, inductors) of the circuit.   Metallized interconnecting patterns are used and active components (transistors, diodes, etc.) must be added in discrete form to the thin-film passive networks.   Thus, the formation of fully integrated circuits, wherein all parts are manufactured and interconnected simultaneously and inseparably, is not possible with the thin-film technique alone at this time.

With the monolithic technique, all parts, including both active and passive components, are formed within a single block of silicon. This technique involves the use of proved semiconductor processes such as solid-state diffusion and epitaxial growth, and permits the simultaneous fabrication of all circuit elements with approximately the same number of process steps required to manufacture a single transistor. The design of the series of sequential photographic masks needed to fabricate, isolate, and interconnect the various parts on a single silicon substrate (as in a monolithic circuit) is quite critical and relatively expensive. Although, once the masks are designed, this technique lends itself quite well to low-cost mass production. The range of passive component values, their tolerances, and their temperature coefficients is somewhat more limited than with thin-film processes, although quite adequate for many circuits. In fact, a large number of off-the-shelf digital integrated circuits as well as numerous "custom" circuits for large-quantity production contracts are manufactured in this manner.

In addition to the exclusively thin-film and semiconductor techniques, there exists today a compatible capability which combines the advantages of both thin-film and semiconductor processes. A compatible integrated circuit is one in which the active components are formed within a silicon die, and the passive component pattern is deposited by thin-film techniques on top of the silicon dioxide passivating layer covering the active circuit. Compatible circuits, therefore, are an extension of the monolithic art. They utilize the advantages of both semiconductor and thin-film processes—combining the features of a truly monolithic circuit with the greater design freedom offered by thin-film passive components. Compatible circuits, however, do require additional manufacturing steps, as compared with monolithic semiconductor circuits, and are, therefore, somewhat more expensive to produce.

The design considerations for active and passive components associated with various types of integrated circuits will be treated in detail in Chaps. 7 through 10. In the following sections of this chapter the basic overall design concepts for integrated circuits will be discussed.

5-2 Fundamentals of Hybrid Integrated Circuit Design

Hybrid integrated circuits, like their conventional counterparts, are frequently constructed of individual transistors, diodes, resistors, and capacitors. However, their resistors and capacitors are not conventional. And further, the components are interconnected in a different way and are packaged differently. Conventional transistor and diode dice are commonly used, mounted together with the resistors and capacitors on a common header.

Although some of the components in a hybrid circuit resemble those of conventional circuits, there are important differences between the two with respect to assembly methods. Hybrid circuits require *die bonding* to mount each separate semiconductor piece on a header or substrate. And they employ *wire bonding* to achieve interconnections with very light gauge wire (e.g., diameter = 0.001 in.).

Since the hybrid integrated circuit resembles a conventional circuit in many respects, few problems of a fundamental nature are encountered in converting a conventional circuit breadboard design to the finished microminiaturized design for a hybrid circuit. The most significant consideration is that which must be given to the parasitic elements associated with some of the resistors and capacitors for integrated circuits. Because of their design these have inherent parasitic resistances and capacitances besides the resistance or capacitance for which they were designed, and allowance for these effects must be made in any circuit which is to be integrated. The nature and magnitude of these parasitic effects are considered in detail in Chap. 10. Still it should be emphasized that the hybrid circuit designer can choose components which lead to a circuit having parasitic effects equal to or less than those of a conventional discrete-component circuit.

5-3   Fundamentals of Monolithic Design

The root of the term *monolithic* may be traced to the Greek: *mono*—meaning single, and *lithos*—meaning stone. A monolithic circuit, literally speaking, means a circuit fabricated from a *single stone,* or single crystal. Monolithic circuits are, in fact, made in a single piece of single-crystal silicon.

Ideally, it would be desirable to fabricate a complete integrated circuit with the same number of process steps required for the most complex component in the circuit. In most instances, this is the three-layer two-junction transistor structure;[1] with a semiconductor monolithic integrated circuit it is possible to approximate this ideal. Two diffusions are necessary to fabricate the base and emitter, respectively, of the integrated transistor. With the monolithic semiconductor circuit, it is possible to utilize these diffusion cycles also to produce the diffused resistors and capacitors. Hence no additional steps are necessary for the fabrication of these components. The only added processes, therefore, are those required for electrical isolation of the various parts of a given circuit and those for interconnecting the components of the circuit. It can be seen, then, that transistor fabrication represents the basis for the manufacturing of monolithic integrated circuits.

The conventional planar or annular transistor structure consists of three separate semiconductor layers. The parent material of the wafer, called the *substrate,* represents the collector region into which, by consecutive masked etching and diffusion processes, the base and emitter regions are fabricated. In this fabrication procedure, all transistors on a wafer have a common collector—a procedure which is perfectly permissible since the wafer will subsequently be cut apart into individual transistor dice.

With monolithic integrated circuits, where additional component parts occupy the same die as the transistor, a common substrate is intolerable since the various parts must be electrically isolated from one another. This isolation has been accomplished by electrically isolating the substrate from the active circuit by means of p-n junctions.[2]

The transistor for monolithic semiconductor circuits (Fig. 5-3) thus differs from its conventional counterpart in that it contains three junctions and four semiconductor layers. The extra layer, or region, is the substrate which the monolithic transistor shares with other integrated circuit components. The p-n junction formed by the transistor collector region and the substrate represents a diode which, when held in a reverse-biased state, isolates the transistor from the other parts.

This form of diode isolation is illustrated in Fig. 5-4, where the cross-sectional view of a silicon die containing two transistors is shown, together with the equivalent circuit. Here, it is seen that, as long as the p-type substrate is held at a more negative voltage than either or both transistor collector regions, the transistors are separated by the high dc resistance of a back-biased diode. There is, however,

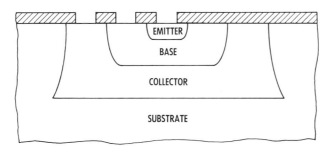

Fig. 5-3 Cross-sectional diagram of a transistor for monolithic integrated circuits. Note that it contains three junctions and four semiconductor layers.

a capacitive coupling between the components because of the capacitance associated with the isolating p-n junctions. This form of diode isolation is used between elements of many types of monolithic circuits. An isolation scheme using silicon dioxide altogether is rapidly coming into favor. This system will undoubtedly supplant junction-type isolation in numerous instances because it diminishes isolation parasitic capacitance by a large factor, raises isolation breakdown voltage, and diminishes isolation leakage current to vanishingly small values.

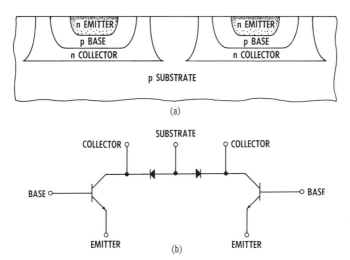

Fig. 5-4 Isolation of monolithic transistors by means of back-to-back diodes: (*a*) Cross-sectional diagram showing two monolithic transistors isolated by back-to-back p-n diodes; (*b*) the equivalent circuit for monolithic transistor isolation.

5-4   Basic Monolithic Structures

Three basic processes by which a monolithic circuit may be constructed are (1) the epitaxial-diffused process, (2) the diffused-collector process and, (3) the triple diffusion process.   All these have in common the four-layer, or isolated-transistor, structure which forms the basis of the monolithic circuit.   Primary differences are in the steps by which this structure is achieved, and the resulting circuit characteristics.

Of the three, the epitaxial-diffused system is, at present, in general use because of a number of inherent advantages.   In the following discussion, this system is described qualitatively in detail, followed by brief discussions of the other methods.

Epitaxial-diffused System.   Fabrication of an epitaxial-diffused integrated circuit begins with a wafer of p-type silicon.   Upon this wafer is grown an epitaxial film (approximately 25 microns thick) of n-type silicon, which ultimately becomes the collector region of transistors or an element of the diodes and diffused capacitors associated with the circuit.   Remaining elements of transistors, diodes, and capacitors, as well as resistors, are formed by subsequent diffusion processes.   The sequence of processes and some of the considerations attending each step are given in the following pictorial representation (Figs. 5-5 to 5-15).

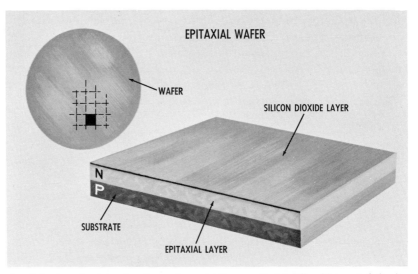

Fig. 5-5   An epitaxial wafer, the starting point for an epitaxial-diffused integrated circuit.

The basic silicon wafer in Fig. 5-5 may contain up to several hundred potential dice, each one containing a complete integrated circuit, as represented by the black square of the checkerboard pattern drawn on the wafer.   The cross section of a future die shows a p-n structure consisting of a p-type substrate and an epitaxially grown n-type layer.

A thin (5,000 Å) film of silicon dioxide has been thermally grown over the epitaxial layer.   This film will serve as the vehicle for the photolithographic masking process necessary for the formation of integrated circuits and will act as a passivation for the junctions formed.

The substrate must be thick enough to be handled without excessive breakage, yet not so thick as to prevent clean separation of dice after scribing. Its resistivity must be high in order to obtain a high breakdown voltage and low capacitance across the p-n junction. Commonly used substrates are p-type silicon 6 to 8 mils thick with a resistivity of approximately 10 ohm cm.

The epitaxial layer is n-type silicon, approximately 1 mil thick, with a resistivity on the order of 0.5 ohm cm. This represents a practical compromise between the high resistivity needed for high breakdown voltage and low junction capacitance (collector-base junction) and the low resistivity desired for low $V_{CE(SAT)}$ and high-frequency response for the transistors to be fabricated in it (see Chap. 7).

The SiO_2 film is grown following the epitaxial growth cycle by exposing the wafer to an oxygen atmosphere while heated to about 1000°C. The thickness of the film is governed by time, temperature, and moisture content of the atmosphere. For practical devices, film thicknesses range from 3,000 to 7,000 Å.

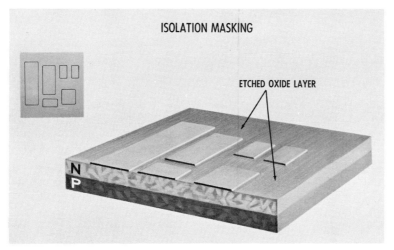

ISOLATION MASKING

ETCHED OXIDE LAYER

N
P

Fig. 5-6 The wafer with the isolation masking pattern etched into the SiO_2 layer.

The epitaxial wafer is prepared for an "isolation" diffusion step by means of a photolithographic process.[3] In the process, the wafer is covered with a uniform film of photosensitive emulsion (e.g., a compound such as Kodak Thin Film Resist or the former Kodak Metal Etch Resist, sometimes generically termed *photo resist*). Unless polymerized, this material is quite readily soluble in certain liquids. Polymerization of the photo resist can be accomplished by exposure to ultraviolet light. By exposing it to ultraviolet light through an appropriate photographic mask, the polymerization can be made to take place only in the desired areas. The unpolymerized film is readily removed, leaving a polymer which covers selected areas and which is highly resistant to corrosive etches. An etchant containing hydrofluoric acid can then be used to remove the SiO_2 layer where the unpolymerized emulsion had been, leaving untouched the SiO_2 in the areas covered by the polymerized emulsion (see Sec. 5-7).

The remaining SiO_2 serves as a mask for the diffusion step which follows. As discussed in Chap. 12, the commonly used diffusants, in this case boron, diffuse much more slowly in SiO_2 than in silicon; hence the boron will penetrate into the silicon only in those areas in which the SiO_2 was removed by the etchant. The areas under the SiO_2 will not be exposed to the diffusant. This principle is the basis for all "masked diffusions," which are the heart of monolithic integrated circuit technology.

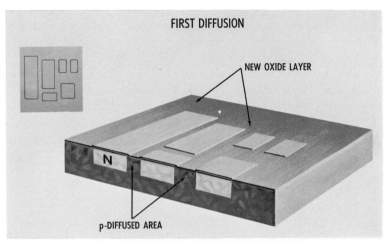

Fig. 5-7   The wafer after the first (a p-type) diffusion.

The wafer is now subjected to a p-type diffusion, during which the impurities enter the silicon only where the silicon dioxide has been removed. A time and temperature cycle is used which will ensure that the p-type impurities diffuse through the epitaxial layer to the p-type substrate. The areas that remained covered with silicon dioxide are now isolated islands of n-type silicon surrounded by p-type. Isolation results because of the n-p junction formed around each n region, and between any two n regions these junctions result in back-to-back diodes, so that no matter what polarity voltage might appear between the two "islands," there is always a back-biased diode between them.

During the diffusion cycle, a new layer of silicon dioxide grows over the diffused p-type region, and the preexisting oxide over the n regions grows thicker.

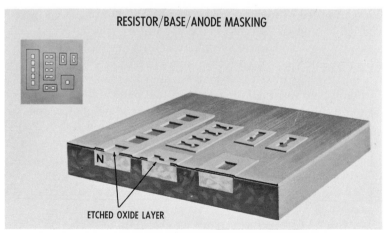

Fig. 5-8   The wafer with the second pattern etched into the oxide layer.

A second pattern, to form the transistor base regions, resistors, and the anode elements of diodes and junction capacitors, is etched in the silicon dioxide layer, using the photolithographic process previously described.

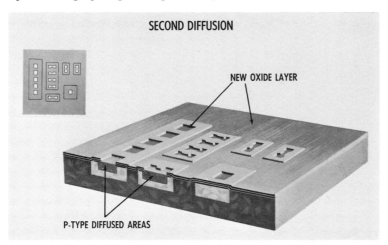

SECOND DIFFUSION

NEW OXIDE LAYER

P-TYPE DIFFUSED AREAS

Fig. 5-9   The wafer after the second (again p-type) diffusion.

p-type impurities, such as boron, are again diffused through the openings into the islands of n-type epitaxial silicon.   The depth of this diffusion is controlled so that it is quite shallow and does not penetrate through to the substrate.   A layer of silicon dioxide is again grown over the diffused p-type regions.

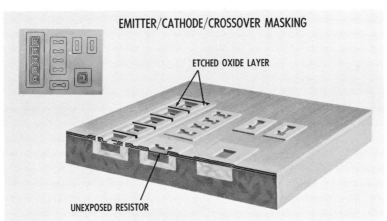

EMITTER/CATHODE/CROSSOVER MASKING

ETCHED OXIDE LAYER

UNEXPOSED RESISTOR

Fig. 5-10   The wafer with the emitter/cathode/crossover pattern etched into the SiO_2 layer.

The oxide coating is again selectively etched to open windows in the base regions, to permit the diffusion of phosphorus for the formation of transistor emitters, and cathode regions for diodes and capacitors.

Windows are also etched into n regions, particularly those with a low surface concentration, where contact is to be made to the n-type layer, and phosphorus is diffused into these regions simultaneously with the emitter diffusion.   This is necessary because aluminum is used as the contacting and interconnecting material.

Aluminum is a p-type impurity in silicon, with a maximum solubility of 2×10^{19} atoms/cm^3. Hence, a large surface concentration of phosphorus in the n region is required to prevent the formation of a p-n junction when the aluminum is alloyed in, to form the contact.[4] Experience shows that in order to assure a good ohmic contact, it is desirable to have the phosphorus surface concentration under the aluminum contacts in excess of 2×10^{20} atoms/cm^3. (An *ohmic* contact, which obeys Ohm's law, is contrasted here with a *rectifying* contact, which results when a p-n junction is formed in the process of making contact to the semiconductor material.)

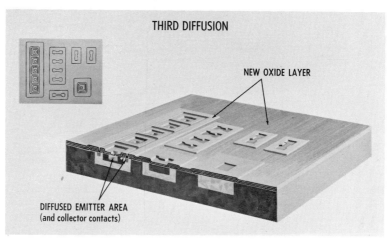

Fig. 5-11   The wafer after the third (n-type) diffusion.

Phosphorus, with a high surface concentration, producing an n$^+$ region, is diffused to form the transistor emitter area, cathode region for diodes and capacitors, and contacts to the n-type areas. As before, a layer of silicon dioxide is grown over the diffused regions. At this point, the junction formation in the monolithic circuit is complete.

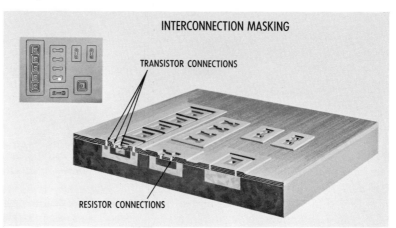

Fig. 5-12   The wafer with openings etched into the SiO$_2$ layer to permit electrical contact to the various components of the integrated circuit.

In order to permit interconnection between the various components of the monolithic circuit, a fourth set of windows is etched in the silicon dioxide layer at the points where contact is to be made to each of the various components of the integrated circuits.

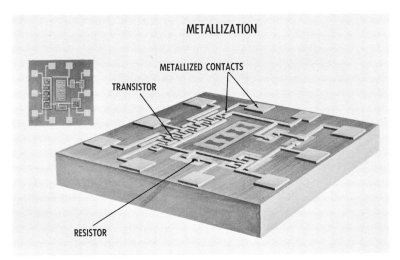

Fig. 5-13 The wafer with the metallized contacts deposited.

A thin, even coating of aluminum is vacuum-deposited over the entire surface of the wafer. The interconnection pattern between components in the monolithic circuit is then formed by photo-resist techniques. The undesired aluminum areas are etched away leaving a pattern of interconnections between transistor, resistors, diodes, and other circuit elements. Some areas of metal may be left to form the top plates of silicon oxide–metal capacitors.

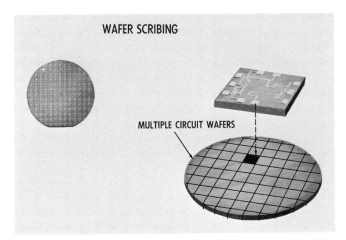

Fig. 5-14 Separation of the wafer into the individual circuits by scribing.

The wafers are now scribed with a diamond-tipped scribing tool and separated into individual circuits.

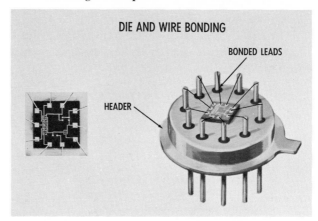

DIE AND WIRE BONDING

BONDED LEADS

HEADER

Fig. 5-15 The individual circuit mounted on the header with the leads bonded in place.

After separation into individual circuits, the die may be mounted on a ceramic wafer, and then to a suitable header by means of a high-temperature eutectic solder. Or the die can be mounted in an all-ceramic flat package. Wires only 0.001 in. in diameter are bonded from the circuit to the proper package leads. This completes the fabrication of a monolithic epitaxial-diffused integrated circuit.

Diffused-collector Process. The diffused-collector process consists of three sequential diffusion cycles to form the three junctions in a monolithic die.

As before, the substrate is a p-type silicon wafer, upon which a layer of silicon dioxide is thermally grown. The silicon dioxide layer is selectively etched, utilizing a photolithographic process to expose specific areas into which an n-type impurity is to be diffused.

The wafer is then subjected to an n-type phosphorus diffusion. This diffusion step forms the isolated collectors of the transistors, as well as isolated n-type islands, into which resistors and elements of diodes and capacitors can be diffused. During the diffusion cycle, a new layer of silicon dioxide is grown over the wafer.

The process then proceeds as previously described for the epitaxial-diffused process. This process is shown diagrammatically in Fig. 5-16.

Triple-diffused Process. This process, like the diffused-collector process, utilizes three successive diffusion cycles, as shown in Fig. 5-17. However, in this case the substrate is n type and serves to form the collector regions of devices. As with the epitaxial-diffused process, the choice of collector doping level is a compromise. Also, as with both other processes, the substrate (n type in this instance) is covered by a thermally grown layer of silicon dioxide. The first photo-resist masking operation removes the silicon dioxide in all regions except those which are to remain n type. These n-type areas will become the collectors of the finished integrated circuit transistors.

The wafer is then subjected to a heavy predeposition of a p-type impurity, such as boron. This p-type impurity is introduced into both sides of the wafer, with only one side masked by the silicon dioxide layer. The p-type impurity then diffuses from both sides of the wafer until the two diffusion fronts meet in the center of the wafer. The regions covered by silicon dioxide then become isolated n-type islands in an otherwise p-type diffused wafer. The thickness of the n region, the collector, is approximately half the thickness of the original wafer. The sheet resistance of the collector R_{SC} thus becomes ρ_C/X_C, where ρ_C is the resistivity of the original wafer, and X_C is the thickness of the collector. A new layer of silicon dioxide grows over the isolation-diffused region after the diffusion.

The remainder of the process proceeds in a manner similar to that previously described for the epitaxial-diffused process.

5-5   Advantages and Disadvantages of Each Process

As shown in the graphs of Figs. 5-18 through 5-20, the emitter and base impurity distributions for all of the three processes are essentially alike. The differences between structures show up in the collector and substrate regions, and it would be accurate to assume that it is in those regions that the electrical differences occur. The overall benefits of the epitaxial-diffused process can best be appreciated by first examining the disadvantages and virtues of the other two processes.

The major drawback in the diffused-collector structure is that the collector has a negative impurity gradient; i.e., the number of impurities in the collector decreases as the collector-substrate junction is approached. This is exactly opposite to the desired condition. Collector-to-base capacitance is determined primarily by the doping level in the collector immediately adjacent to the collector-base junction. Although the collector-base junction will be graded, i.e., a gradual transition from p type (base) to n type (collector), the collector doping is near a maximum at the collector-base junction, making this capacitance value a maximum, as can be seen from the consideration of junction capacitance in Sec. 2-5. The collector-base breakdown voltage is also reduced by the comparatively high surface concentrations on either side of the junction as compared to that attained in the other two processes discussed.

Series collector resistance is hardly optimized, since the base is diffused into the collector region having the greatest conductivity. It has been pointed out that one variable governing the final surface concentration of impurities following a diffusion cycle is the background concentration and its uniformity. Since the collector background is graded, the base region, which must have a carefully controlled gradient, is diffused into a background concentration which varies with distance from the surface of the wafer. This situation can present problems in controlling the surface concentration of the base region.

One possible advantage may arise from having a graded collector region. By referring to Fig. 5-21, it can be seen that the substrate, collector, and base regions constitute a p-n-p transistor. Although this is a highly compromised p-n-p device (low β), of the three structures discussed, this one will provide the best p-n-p device without resorting to special processing techniques.

Triple-diffused Process. The triple-diffused structure has the advantage of having a uniformly doped collector region, which obviates the voltage and capacitance compromise at the collector-base junction of the diffused-collector structure.

The doping level of the collector can be chosen to minimize the collector-to-base capacitance and maximize the collector-to-base breakdown voltage, within the re-

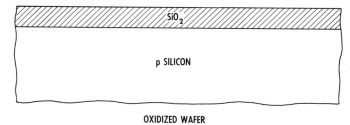

OXIDIZED WAFER

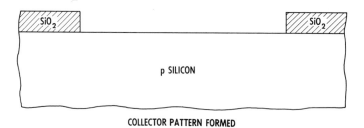

COLLECTOR PATTERN FORMED

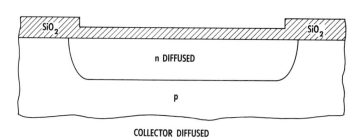

COLLECTOR DIFFUSED

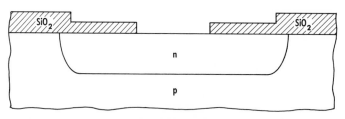

BASE PATTERN FORMED

Fig. 5-16   Diagrammatic representation of the process steps used for the production of an integrated circuit by means of the diffused-collector process.

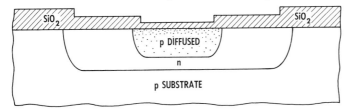

BASE DIFFUSED WAFER

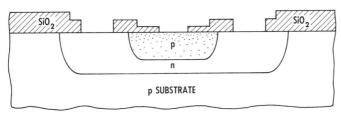

EMITTER PATTERN FORMED

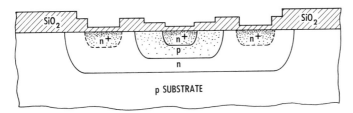

EMITTER DIFFUSED WAFER

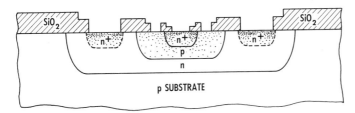

PRE-OHMIC PATTERN FORMED

Fig. 5-16 (continued) Diagrammatic representation of the process steps used for the production of an integrated circuit by means of the diffused-collector process.

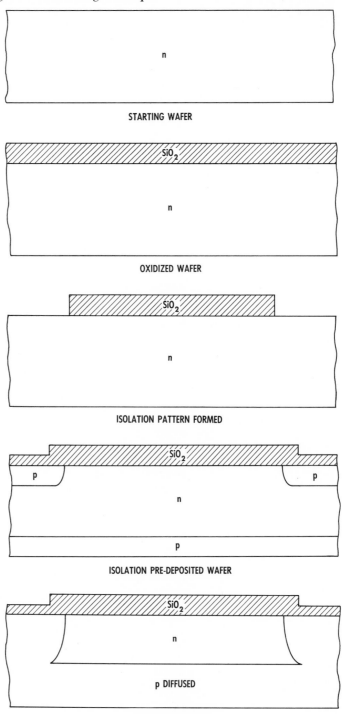

Fig. 5-17   Diagrammatic representation of the process steps used for the production of an integrated circuit by means of the triple-diffused process.

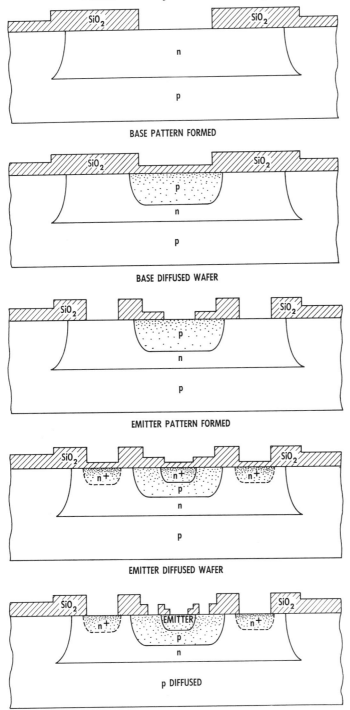

BASE PATTERN FORMED

BASE DIFFUSED WAFER

EMITTER PATTERN FORMED

EMITTER DIFFUSED WAFER

PRE-OHMIC PATTERN FORMED

Fig. 5-17 (continued) Diagrammatic representation of the process steps used for the production of an integrated circuit by means of the triple-diffused process.

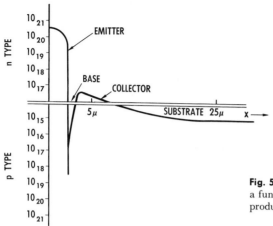

Fig. 5-18 Approximate impurity distribution as a function of distance into wafer for a transistor produced by the diffused-collector process.

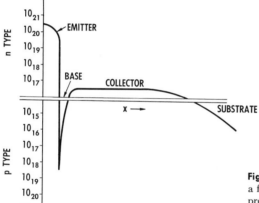

Fig. 5-19 Approximate impurity distribution as a function of distance into wafer for a transistor produced by the triple-diffused process.

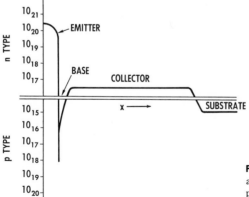

Fig. 5-20 Approximate impurity distribution as a function of distance into wafer for a transistor produced by the epitaxial-diffused process.

striction of maintaining low collector sheet resistance in order to obtain low $V_{CE(SAT)}$.

However, the triple-diffused structure does have two inherent limitations. Since the substrate is diffused, the collector region is the most lightly doped side of the collector-substrate junction. Therefore, the collector-to-substrate capacitance will be determined by the doping level in the collector. Since permissible collector sheet resistance will impose a minimum collector doping level, collector-to-substrate capacitance can never be fully eliminated.

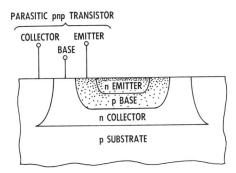

Fig. 5-21 Cross-sectional diagram of monolithic n-p-n transistor, showing the parasitic p-n-p transistor.

The p-type diffusion performed for purposes of isolation must diffuse through half the thickness of the wafer; therefore, the thickness of the wafer must be limited in order to maintain a reasonable diffusion time cycle. A deep diffusion of this type performed at 1250°C, for example, using boron as an impurity source, would require 35.8 hr to penetrate half the thickness of a 150-micron-thick wafer. One other factor which will limit the thickness of the wafer is illustrated in Fig. 5-22. Since the diffusion of these impurities, either n type or p type, is isotropic in nature, the diffused layer will diffuse under a masking oxide to approximately the same distance as the depth of diffusion. It can be seen that this underdiffusion will reduce the usable area of each isolation region. The greater the thickness of a wafer, the larger the inactive area of each isolation region.

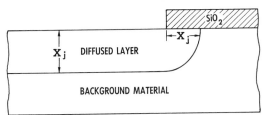

Fig. 5-22 Diffusion of impurities under the masking oxide.

Epitaxial-diffused Process. The epitaxial-diffused process has all of the advantages of the triple-diffused structure and none of its limitations.

There are no wafer thickness limitations upon the epitaxial-diffused system. The thickness of the n-type collector-epitaxial region is independent of the thickness of the p-type substrate. Since the parent material is the p-type substrate, its doping level may be chosen such that the collector-to-substrate capacitance is independent of the doping level of the collector region. Thus, this parasitic capacitance may be minimized without influencing other device parameters.

5-6   Formation of p-n-p—n-p-n Structures

Any one of the three processes discussed will yield an integrated circuit with both p-n-p and n-p-n devices on the same monolithic wafer. A p-n-p transistor may be formed by utilizing the base, collector, and substrate areas of the n-p-n transistor.[5] Alternatively, an additional diffusion cycle may be used on any of these processes to obtain improved electrical characteristics for the p-n-p transistor. This entails diffusing a deep, heavily doped p layer, using an impurity such as boron, into the wafer prior to the base diffusion. This will form an efficient p-n-p emitter and provide a thin base for the p-n-p device without degrading the collector characteristics of the n-p-n transistor. This structure is illustrated in Fig. 5-23. If more than one p-n-p device is included in the circuit, the collectors will not be isolated, making the usefulness of this structure somewhat limited.

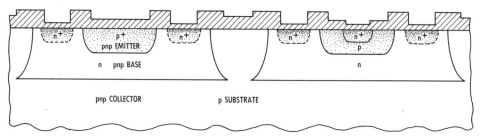

Fig. 5-23 Four-layer structure which will provide a p-n-p transistor and an n-p-n transistor on a monolithic integrated circuit die.

In order to form a structure containing electrically isolated n-p-n and p-n-p transistors, a five-layer device is required. This type of monolithic structure may assume two basic forms, as illustrated in Fig. 5-24a and b. A process sequence for the structure shown in Fig. 5-24b is illustrated in Figs. 5-25 through 5-27. In this type of construction, the collector of the n-p-n and the base of the p-n-p are diffused in two different operations. The diffusion cycle forming the base of the n-p-n may then be used to form the emitter of the p-n-p.

Optimized Epitaxial-diffused Structure. In order to build transistors in a monolithic integrated circuit having ac and dc characteristics equivalent to those of a discrete epitaxial transistor (e.g., with respect to BV_{CBO}, $V_{CE(SAT)}$, and collector time constant), it is necessary to modify the epitaxial-diffused process. As will be discussed in Chap. 7, the required thickness of n-type silicon in the collector is quite small, and is dependent upon the maximum collector voltage needed versus the extent of the depletion layer in the collector at this voltage.

Since the collector current path in a monolithic transistor is transverse, or parallel to the surface, the series collector resistance is dependent upon the geometry, spacing, and dimensions of the collector, base, and emitter contacts and the sheet resistance of the collector. To reduce the effective sheet resistance in the collector without degrading the collector voltage and capacitance characteristics, a localized, heavily doped n-type region may be placed in the collector of the device, as shown in Fig. 5-28. This region may be formed by a selective diffusion of n-type impurities, such as arsenic, before the epitaxial growth of the n-type collector region. The effective sheet resistance of the collector region is reduced to the parallel combination of the sheet resistance of the lightly doped n-type epitaxial region and that of the heavily doped n-type diffused region.

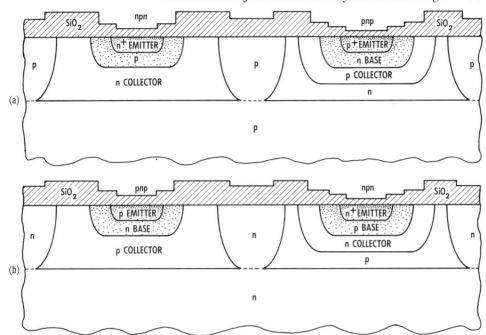

Fig. 5-24 Five-layer structures which will provide isolated p-n-p and n-p-n transistors on a monolithic integrated circuit die: (*a*) Using a p-type substrate; (*b*) using an n-type substrate.

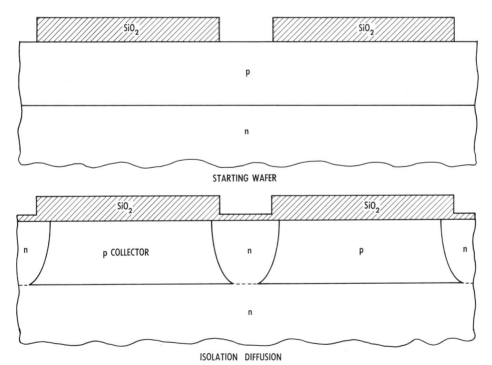

Fig. 5-25 Process sequence for the production of the n-p-n–p-n-p transistor pair of Fig. 5-24*b*, showing the starting p or n epitaxial wafer and the isolation diffusion.

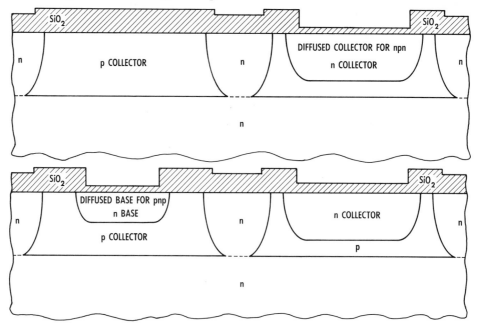

Fig. 5-26   Process sequence for the production of the n-p-n–p-n-p transistor pair of Fig. 5-24*b* (continued), showing the diffusions of the n-p-n collector and the p-n-p base.

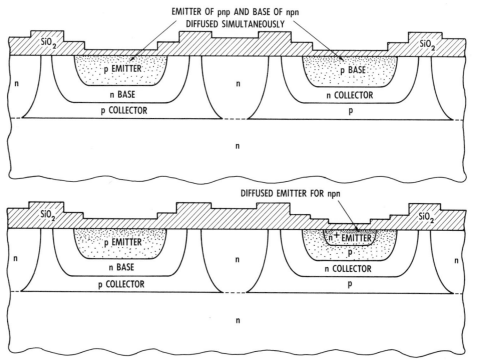

Fig. 5-27   Process sequence for the production of the n-p-n–p-n-p transistor pair of Fig. 5-24*b* (concluded), showing the simultaneous diffusion of the p-n-p emitter and the n-p-n base, followed by the diffusion of the n-p-n emitter.

Arsenic is selected as the impurity for this region because this region must remain localized during subsequent process steps. To meet this requirement the n-type impurity used must have a low diffusion coefficient compared to that of boron and phosphorus. The impurity must also dope silicon in excess of 10^{19} atoms/cm^3 in order to form a region of low sheet resistance. As shown in Fig. 3-7, arsenic has

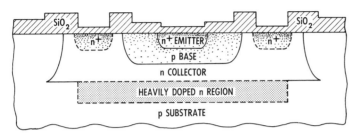

Fig. 5-28 Use of a heavily doped buried n region to improve $V_{CE(SAT)}$, BV_{CBO}, and collector time constant.

a diffusion coefficient an order of magnitude lower than that of boron and phosphorus, and as shown in Fig. 3-6, arsenic has a solid solubility in silicon in excess of 10^{21} atoms/cm^3.

Another method by which this localized n$^+$ region may be formed is by a selective epitaxial growth cycle. This process is illustrated in Fig. 5-29. The p-type

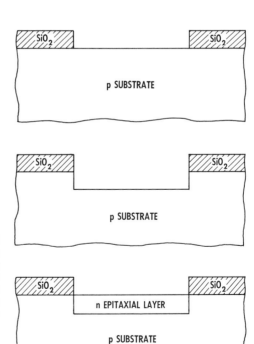

Fig. 5-29 Production of a heavily doped buried n region by epitaxial methods. Here, the silicon dioxide and then a shallow region are selectively removed from the substrate. An epitaxial growth cycle follows, which refills the region with n-type silicon. The silicon dioxide is removed from the surface of the wafer, which then receives the normal epitaxial-diffused processing cycle.

substrate has a layer of silicon dioxide grown upon it. The silicon dioxide is selectively removed in a pattern conforming to that desired for the n^+ layer. A shallow region of silicon is removed from the substrate in the pattern. An epitaxial growth cycle is performed in order to refill the region with n-type silicon. The silicon dioxide is removed from the surface of the wafer, and the wafer receives the normal epitaxial-diffused processing cycle.

It can be seen, then, from the foregoing discussion that the epitaxial-diffused process will provide the most flexible monolithic structure available. In cases requiring optimum transistor characteristics, the process may be modified to satisfy these requirements.

5-7 Photo-resist Process

All integrated circuit processes are dependent upon the use of masked etching techniques, which in turn depend on light-sensitive organic compounds, generally known as *photo resists*. The use of photo resist in conjunction with a photographic mask will provide the various patterns required upon a semiconductor wafer. The photo mask carries a pattern which is to be reproduced photographically upon another surface by contact printing. The surface upon which these images are to be reproduced is in this case either a semiconductor, an oxide on the semiconductor, or a metal film covering the semiconductor. The photo-resist process consists of the following basic operations:

1. Making the substrate a photographic plate by coating with the light-sensitive photo-resist emulsion.
2. Aligning the photo mask with respect to the substrate or images previously placed upon the substrate.
3. Exposing the emulsion to intense ultraviolet light.
4. Developing the image of the mask in the emulsion. In this, the emulsion is removed in the areas not exposed to light, leaving the substrate bare in those areas.
5. Fixing the emulsion which was not removed in development so that it will be resistant to corrosive etches, etc.
6. Performing an operation such as etching on the substrate in the locations determined by the image formed in the emulsion.
7. Stripping the emulsion and cleaning up the wafer for the next process step.

The image formed in the photo resist can be no more perfect than the photo mask used to reproduce it. Therefore, the important characteristics which the image must possess are:

1. The image must be dimensionally correct.
2. The photo mask must possess dimensional stability with respect to temperature and humidity.
3. The image must have uniform density in both clear and opaque areas.
4. There must be sharp definition between clear and opaque areas.

In nearly all applications, more than one image is formed on a photo mask. In small-geometry transistors, more than 1,000 images may be placed upon a single photo mask. These multiple images are produced with a given center-to-center spacing, in order to form a coherent array of images upon the semiconductor wafer. Also, in most applications, more than one photo mask is required to produce a finished semiconductor device. Since these masks are used sequentially, the image produced by the second mask must conform to the image formed by the first photo mask with respect to center-to-center spacing between patterns. (A *set* of photo masks is the entire sequence of photo masks required to complete a given semiconductor device or integrated circuit.)

5-8   Photo-mask Fabrication

The general sequence of operations in making a photo mask is as follows:

1. Preparation of initial artwork
2. First or intermediate reduction
3. Multiple-image formation
4. Second or final reduction

The formation of multiple images may precede, coincide with, or follow the final image reduction, depending upon the technique employed.[6]

The equipment required for this type of photography consists of a copyboard, a lens system, and a film holder. The photographic system must be mounted rigidly upon a solid base, and be isolated from shock and vibration.

Preparation of Initial Artwork. The larger the size of the initial artwork, the more accurate the final image. However, the scale of the initial artwork is determined by several factors. The physical size of the copyboard employed enforces a maximum dimension, while a minimum dimension is imposed by the line resolution capability of the camera. The interaction of these two factors may be minimized by making more than one reduction. A more basic limitation is the ratio of the finest line width to the overall dimension (or center spacing) of the artwork. For example, assume that the overall dimension of the final image is to be 0.1 by 0.1 in., and that the finest line width encountered on the final image is 0.0005 in. At a scale of 250:1, the finest line width on the initial artwork would be 0.125 in. wide, and the copyboard required would be 25 by 25 in. It can be seen that if we wish to make the size of the finest line of the initial artwork any larger, a proportionate increase in the size of the copyboard will be necessary.

If the artwork is to involve reflected light, ink drawings should be used because they provide smooth edges and solid blacks. In order to maintain contrast in the image, the blacks should be uniformly dark upon a clean white background.

For mask-making photography it is necessary to have as much contrast between the light and dark areas as possible. One way to accomplish this is to transmit the light through the original copy. Under these conditions, the artwork should not consist of line drawings, but of alternate clear and opaque regions on a dimensionally stable medium. One such medium is a Mylar laminate known as Ruby Studnite, which is a clear Mylar with a peelable opaque overlay. By cutting the overlay with a knife edge, it may be removed to form clear areas in an opaque background.

One problem with a transmitted light copyboard is light intensity falloff near the edge of the artwork. This problem is compounded by the greater distance from the edge of the copyboard to the center of the lens system. Obtaining a photograph of uniform density from center to edge requires a copyboard which is uniformly illuminated.

Whether the initial artwork is a line drawing or is cut in peelable Mylar, the accuracy of line placement must exceed that attainable by hand drafting. A type of drafting table known as the *coordinatograph* is commonly used. It can accurately locate a point within its working area to 0.001 in. The point may be referenced to linear as well as angular position. With this minute error introduced in the original artwork, the dimensional error in the final image is reduced by a factor equal to the overall reduction. Assuming an overall reduction of 250:1, the error in the final image would be 4 by 10^{-6} in., which is of course negligible.

Artwork Reduction. Once the initial artwork is prepared, the single image is reduced in the first reduction by 2:1 to 40:1, depending upon center spacing and line width in the initial artwork. The image formed in the first reduction must be an extremely accurate reproduction of the initial artwork. When a multiple array of images is to be formed before the final reduction, the first reduction is repeatedly contact-printed on accurate spacings with what is known as a *step-and-repeat* machine. The terminology arises from the fact that the image is contact-printed at a point, and then moved from that point to another point at a fixed center spacing and the process repeated. This continues until the entire array is formed. The multiple images formed are then reduced to the final desired size by producing a microphotograph of the print from the step-and-repeat machine. The final reduction is formed by a process similar to that used in the first reduction.

The spacing between images is produced mechanically, and errors in image placement may result. However, these errors are minimized by producing the multiple image before the final reduction. The error is reduced by the ratio of the final reduction to the first reduction. Disregarding spacing, the image resolved is an extremely accurate reproduction of the original artwork.

If the formation of a multiple array of images is deferred until the final reduction stage, placement errors become large compared to those in which multiple-image formation and final reduction are separate processes. These errors are larger by a factor equal to the final reduction ratio.

The advantages of using the step-and-repeat process are (1) very accurate final image size, and (2) excellent resolution in the final image. The disadvantages of this process are that (1) image-positioning errors are introduced mechanically by the step-and-repeat machine, and (2) the step-and-repeat process itself is laborious and time-consuming. The image-positioning errors are random in nature in this process, and because each mask set is stepped and repeated at a different time, the positioning errors are potentially cumulative. But it is usually necessary for the pattern produced by a given mask to fall completely within that produced by the preceding mask in the set, or else to surround it completely. Thus, a certain tolerance must be provided in mask design to assure that this will occur. Further, the random nature of the positioning errors places a lower limit upon this tolerance.

The Multiple-lens Camera. If the camera for the first reduction has a separate lens system for each image required at the desired center spacing, random spacing errors between images in a mask set can be greatly reduced. Moreover, a camera of this type eliminates the tedious and lengthy process of mechanically stepping and repeating each image for each mask. For example, consider an image to be placed on 0.050 in. centers. If the scale of the initial artwork is 100:1, and the first reduction 5:1, the first reduction produces images on 1.0 in. centers. The lenses in the multiple lens camera therefore must also be approximately on 1.0 in. centers. These lenses must be of the highest optical quality and uniformity. Also, the lens plane of all the lenses must be uniform and parallel to the film plane and the artwork plane. Each lens must produce a sharp image on the film plane.

It is obvious that a line perpendicular to the center of the artwork and film planes can pass through the axis of only one lens. To reduce the angular displacement from the axes of lenses, the initial artwork should be as far from the lens board as is practical. Any spacing error in the lens system will be uniformly repeated from mask to mask; therefore, image alignment is no longer a function of these spacing errors, as long as a single camera is used for the production of all the masks of a set. Thus the image displacement associated with the multiple-lens camera is not objectionable if it is not excessive; however, image distortion is objectionable, and the lenses must be chosen to be as distortion-free as possible.

The final reduction of the multiple image is produced by a single-lens camera, in a manner similar to the final reduction following the step-and-repeat process. The result of the final reduction is a *master*. The master will be the negative of the final mask, so that the copies may be produced by simply contact-printing the master. The contact printing must be very carefully performed in order to avoid problems arising from dust and other factors which prevent intimate contact between print and master, leading to "specks," Newton's rings, and other defects. Figure 5-30 shows the sequence of mask making.

5-9 Monolithic Layout Considerations

The devices which constitute a monolithic circuit may include:

1. Transistors
2. Diodes
3. Other active devices
4. Junction capacitors
5. Thin-film capacitors
6. Diffused resistors
7. Thin-film resistors

These devices and their limitations will be discussed in following chapters. A monolithic circuit consisting of these devices has definite performance limitations imposed by parasitic factors. The electrical performance of a monolithic circuit may be optimized by minimizing these parasitic effects through judicious physical layout of the integrated circuit.

With reference to Fig. 5-3, it is evident that a monolithic transistor bears a resemblance to either a four-layer diode or a p-n-p-n controlled rectifier.[7] Indeed,

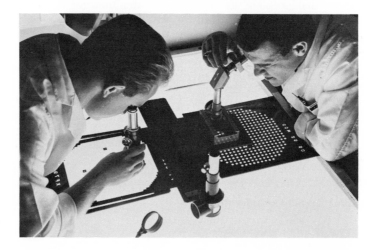

Fig. 5-30   Mask-making sequence showing the initial artwork, the intermediate reduction, and the final mask.

it is quite possible to obtain four-layer switching action from such a device under appropriate conditions of voltage and current.

In order to keep the device from acting as a four-layer switch, the collector-substrate junction must always be kept in a reverse-biased condition, to prevent it from acting as an emitter. In a monolithic circuit this is accomplished by connecting the p-type substrate to the most negative voltage present in the circuit.

Parasitic Capacitance. A four-layer transistor in a monolithic circuit has a parasitic capacitance that is not associated with a three-layer transistor. That parasitic capacitance is of course the collector-substrate capacitance, which appears in parallel with the collector-base junction capacitance.

In the monolithic structure, the junction depth of the collector-substrate junction may be appreciable. In calculating the value of this capacitance, two portions of the junction must be considered:

1. The bottom portion of the junction parallel to the surface of the wafer
2. That portion of the junction constituting the "sidewalls" of the diffusion

This is illustrated in Fig. 5-31. The capacitance per unit area for each component may be calculated, using the equations and figures in Chaps. 2 and 3. It should be noted that the area of the sidewall component is approximately the area of a quarter of a cylinder whose radius is the junction depth. The capacitance associated with this portion of the junction is that of a diffused junction, and may be determined approximately from Fig. 3-21a. In the epitaxial-diffused structure, the capacitance of the bottom component is that of a step junction, and Eq. (2-79) may be used in its calculation.

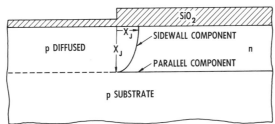

Fig. 5-31   Cross section of a monolithic wafer, showing the two components associated with the collector-substrate capacitance.

Metal-over-oxide Capacitance. The metal strips which interconnect elements on a monolithic wafer pass over the silicon dioxide covering the monolithic structure, and a parasitic capacitance is formed between the silicon and the interconnection paths, with the silicon dioxide acting as a dielectric. The thickness of the silicon dioxide also varies from region to region over the monolithic wafer.

For example, the capacitance per unit area associated with a 10,000-Å-thick silicon dioxide layer is approximately 0.02 pf/mil^2. The capacitance is distributed between terminals of a resistor, which is the resistance of the silicon layer appearing beneath. However, for the sake of convenience, the capacitance may be lumped at one terminal or the other.

This parasitic capacitance may be kept small enough to be negligible compared to the parasitic junction capacitances associated with the components in a monolithic circuit, by keeping the physical dimensions of the metal interconnection strips as small as possible.

5-10 A Monolithic Layout Example

The first consideration to be resolved in a monolithic design is to determine the number of isolation regions required. In review, an isolation region is an n-type region corresponding to the collector of a transistor. The region is isolated from other similar n-type regions by reverse-biased diodes. The regions are electrically isolated from one another so that these various n-type regions may assume different levels of potential. The number of isolation regions required is determined by the number of collector regions which must assume different voltage levels. The size of these isolation regions should be kept to a minimum if circuit performance is adversely affected by parasitic capacitance from a collector node to the substrate.

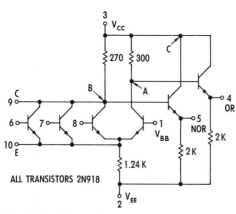

Fig. 5-32 Schematic diagram of a typical three-input current-mode logic gate.

A current-mode logic circuit is shown in Fig. 5-32. The monolithic form of this circuit is illustrated in Fig. 5-33. There are three isolation regions in this circuit, labeled A, B, and C. From the schematic in Fig. 5-32, it is seen that the three input transistors have a common collector. The voltage level of this common collector region is fixed by connecting it through an emitter follower to the output on pin 5.

The transistor whose input appears at pin 1 also has its collector connected through an emitter follower to a complementary output on pin 4. It can be seen that the common collector point at B and the collector point at A must be electrically isolated in order to prevent the shorting of the two outputs. Separate isolation regions, B and A, must be provided for the three input transistors, and for the fixed-bias transistor, respectively.

Since outputs are taken off both collector nodes, A and B, transient response measurements may be made at either or both outputs. The total parasitic capacitance appearing at A or B will affect the transient response at its corresponding output. In order to equalize the transient response values measured at the two outputs, the parasitic capacitances appearing at A and B must be equal-

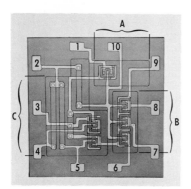

Fig. 5-33 Photomicrograph of the current-mode logic gate shown in Fig. 5-32. The three isolation regions labeled A, B, and C and the pin numbers correspond to those shown in Fig. 5-32.

ized. This is accomplished by reducing the area at region B to a minimum, and making region A equal in area to region B, since for equivalent junction profiles, capacitance is proportional to area.

The collector regions of the emitter-follower transistors are held at V_{CC}, the most positive voltage appearing in the circuit. Since V_{CC} is a voltage level different from that appearing at either point A or B, a third isolation region, C, is provided for the emitter-follower transistors.

The resistor in a monolithic circuit is normally formed by the same diffusion operation which forms the base of the transistor. One characteristic of a diffused layer which may be measured directly is its sheet resistance R_S. The value of a diffused resistor may be determined from

$$R = R_S \frac{l}{w} \qquad (5\text{-}1)$$

where l and w are the length and width of the diffused area (top view).

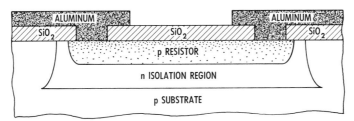

Fig. 5-34 Cross-sectional view of a diffused resistor for a monolithic integrated circuit.

It can thus be seen that the resistance of a resistor utilizing the base diffusion will be determined by two factors:

1. The sheet resistance of the base-diffused region
2. The length-width ratio of the region which forms the resistor

Figure 5-34 illustrates the actual construction of a diffused resistor in a monolithic circuit. The equivalent circuit of a diffused resistor is shown in Fig. 5-35.

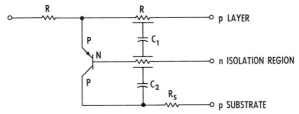

Fig. 5-35 The equivalent circuit of a diffused resistor, illustrating the parasitic elements associated with it.

(For a more complete discussion of resistance, see Chap. 10.) It can be seen that a parasitic p-n-p transistor exists with the resistor as its emitter, the isolating n region as its base, and the substrate as its collector. The most negative voltage present in the circuit must be connected to the substrate in order to prevent four-layer switching in the transistors of the monolithic circuit. This voltage condition presents the resistor's parasitic p-n-p transistor with a reverse-biased collector region. Thus it is apparent that the diffused resistor junction must also be kept reverse-biased for the double purpose of maintaining the integrity of the resistor and of keeping the parasitic p-n-p transistor off. This desired end may be accomplished here by connecting the n-type isolation region surrounding the resistor to the most positive voltage present in the circuit. This will ensure that both junctions are reverse-biased under all circuit conditions. To ensure that the resistor isolation regions are connected to the most positive circuit voltage for all resistors, one simply places all the resistors in a common isolation region. The resistors are electrically isolated from one another by the back-to-back junctions between resistors.

The resistors and the emitter-follower transistors may all be placed in isolation region C, because the voltage level required for the collectors of the emitter followers is the same as that for the n-type isolation region of the resistors. The parasitic capacitance of this type of common isolation region appears as a capacitance from the power supply to ground. The only case in which a resistor and a transistor may appear in a common isolation region is that in which the collector of the transistor and the isolation region of the resistor may be at the same voltage level. In any other case, the resistor and the transistor must be isolated from each other.

Isolation region considerations may be summarized in this way:

1. All n-type collector regions which assume different potentials must be isolated.

2. The areas of those isolation regions affected by parasitic capacitance from the isolation region to ground should be minimized.

3. The isolation region containing resistors should be connected to the most positive voltage available in the circuit. These resistors may be in a common isolation region.

4. The minimum area for a given isolation region will be determined by the size of the components contained within it. The physical size of components will be determined by the circuit function performed. The isolation region for a transistor with a current-carrying capacity of 1 amp must be much larger than that for a transistor carrying 10 mA.

5. All n-type isolation regions must be reverse-biased with respect to the substrate in order to avoid clamping to the substrate voltage.

Since the current-mode logic circuit discussed contained neither diodes nor capacitors, we will consider these as a separate case. The usefulness of a collector-base diode is normally quite limited. Consider again the equivalent circuit shown in Fig. 5-35. The collector-base diode cannot be forward-biased because of the shunting action associated with the parasitic p-n-p transistor. However, the emitter-base diode has no such restriction if properly interconnected. In order to use the emitter-base diode under forward-bias conditions, the base constituting the anode of the diode must be shorted to the collector or isolation region in which it is located. This condition fixes the potential of the collector with respect to the base, eliminating any spurious p-n-p or n-p-n action due to induced potentials on the collector. This structure is illustrated in Fig. 5-36. In using this diode structure, the potential of the anode of the diode must be considered in determining isolation regions, since the anode (or base) and collector are shorted. These must be considered in addition to the factors discussed in Chap. 7.

Since the emitter-base junction has the largest value of capacitance per unit area associated with it of any junction on a monolithic wafer, this junction should be used in forming junction capacitors. This value of capacitance per unit area may be increased by externally shorting the emitter to the collector. In this fashion, the collector-base junction capacitance and the emitter-base junction capacitance appear in parallel. In this type of junction capacitor, the base must always have more negative voltage applied to it than the collector-emitter regions, to avoid forward conduction. The isolation region considerations for this type of capacitor involve maintaining a positive voltage on the collector, or isolation region of the capacitor.

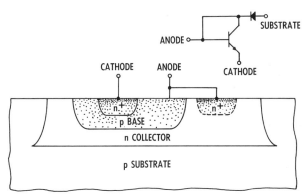

Fig. 5-36   Diode for monolithic integrated circuit utilizing the emitter-base junction.

The silicon dioxide capacitor discussed in Chap. 10 is also used in monolithic circuits. The n-type isolation region in which it is formed must have a positive voltage applied to it in order to avoid conduction to the substrate, which has a negative voltage applied to it. For example, if the substrate-collector diode is forward-biased by a negative voltage appearing at the collector side of the capacitor, that point of the circuit will drop to the substrate voltage.

Die Size. The minimum die size in a monolithic circuit is determined by:

1. The aggregate area of the isolation regions
2. The minimum area required for bonding pads on the edge of the die
3. The area required to run metal strips over the silicon dioxide to interconnect the components in the isolated regions

The area of isolation regions will be determined by the physical dimensions of the components enclosed in the isolation region. For example, the area occupied by a resistor with a line width of 0.003 in. will be nine times as great as that of a resistor with a line width of 0.001 in. The larger the line width of a diffused resistor, the more accurate the control over its absolute value. This control factor is dominated by the accuracy to which a resistor pattern may be etched in the silicon dioxide. The physical size of a diffused resistor will involve a compromise between a large pattern with an easily controllable value, and a small pattern which will occupy a smaller area and have a less predictable value.

The area of isolation regions for transistors and diodes will be determined by the physical size of the transistor or diode involved. The physical dimensions of a transistor or diode are determined by the electrical characteristics of the device, which are in turn dictated by circuit performance requirements.

In order to facilitate wire bonding of leads to the die, bonding pads are provided on the edge of the wafer, as shown in Fig. 5-33. The size of each of these particular pads is 0.003 by 0.005 in. Such pads may be as small as 0.003 by 0.003 in. and still be readily bondable. The maximum size of the pads will be limited by the amount of space available on the die.

The area covered by the interconnecting metal strips which run between components and bonding pads must also be minimized. The line width of these interconnecting strips should be equal to or less than 0.001 in., and the spacing between strips should be equal to or greater than 0.001 in. The minimum interconnection strip width on the circuit shown in Fig. 5-33 is 0.0005 in. This narrow strip is required between one of the emitter-follower transistors and pin 4. All other metal strips are 0.001 in. wide. The die size of this particular circuit is 0.050 by 0.050 in.

The die size must be maintained at a minimum for two reasons:

1. The number of circuits produced per wafer increases with decreasing die size.
2. Past experience has shown that the probability of random defects on a semiconductor die increases with increasing area.

Pin Connections. The pin connections of a monolithic circuit are usually determined by requirements imposed by the system in which the circuits are used. However, careful consideration must be given to the relationship of pin connection requirements and the interconnection of components. Consider once more the monolithic circuit shown in Fig. 5-33. The OR and NOR outputs appear at pins 4 and 5. If these two pins were reversed, the layout of the circuit would have to be completely redone, and complexity of the layout would be increased. Examination of the schematic will show that logic design has not been compromised on this circuit. All power supply leads are grouped together on adjacent pins: 1, 2, and 3. The outputs are together at pins 4 and 5. The inputs follow each other on pins 6, 7, and 8. Pins 9 and 10 are common emitter and collector tie points for expansion of inputs.

The problem of interconnecting components in a monolithic circuit can be approached as shown in the schematic diagram of Fig. 5-37. This schematic is the current-mode logic circuit of Fig. 5-32, redrawn with the pins in their proper order and sequence; thus any problems encountered in interconnecting the circuit become apparent. Note that each line which crosses a resistor also crosses that resistor in the monolithic layout. Redrawing the schematic in this form is an initial step toward designing a monolithic layout.

Crossovers. Any resistor may be used as a crossover point in a monolithic layout. If the layout is so complex that additional crossover points are required, a diffused conductor may be added to the layout. A structure which is essentially a diffused conductor is shown cross-sectionally in Fig. 5-38. It can be seen that this structure is similar to the ohmic contact region of a collector. The collector of a transistor may be extended in a fashion similar to that shown in Fig. 5-38, so that wires may be passed over it. This does increase series collector resistance r_{sc} and parasitic collector-to-substrate capacitance.

This type of crossover will require a separate isolation region and will depend upon the voltage level of the metal strip.   A crossover should be avoided if at all possible for the following reasons:

1. The complexity of the circuit is increased by the addition of an isolation region.

2. The minimum die size must be increased to accommodate the extra isolation region.

3. A parasitic capacitance will be added to that part of the circuit to which the crossover is connected.

4. The finite resistance value introduced by a crossover will shift all the voltage levels in a circuit; thus a crossover should never be introduced in a power supply lead.

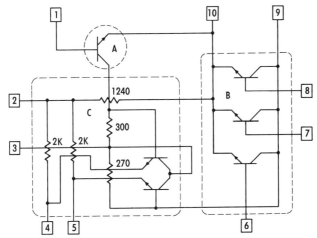

Fig. 5-37 Schematic of the current-mode logic gate shown in Fig. 5-32, redrawn so as to show the pins in proper order and with the components grouped together for isolation. Redrawing the schematic in this form is the first step toward designing a monolithic layout.

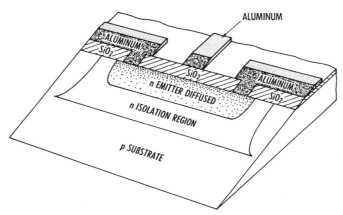

Fig. 5-38 Cross-sectional view of a diffused conductor which provides a crossover point. This type of structure should be used only when absolutely necessary, and even then, never in a power supply lead.

Summary. The rules for a monolithic layout may be summarized as follows:

1. Determine the number of isolation regions.

2. Draw the schematic of the circuit, with the leads in the sequence and order appearing at both the bonding pads and the external pins.

3. Eliminate crossovers wherever possible.

4. Minimize the area of those isolation regions which are performance-sensitive to capacitive loading.

5. Determine the component geometry by circuit performance requirements.

6. Connect the resistor isolation region to the most positive voltage in the circuit. The resistors may appear in a single isolation region.

7. Connect the substrate to the most negative voltage present in the circuit to eliminate four-layer action.

8. Maintain a minimum die size in view of (*a*) the number of isolation regions, (*b*) the area of the isolation regions, (*c*) the area required for bonding pads, and (*d*) the area required for component interconnection.

9. Determine the pin connections not only by logic design but also by monolithic interconnection considerations.

Figures 5-39 through 5-43 illustrate the fabrication of the monolithic circuit shown in Figs. 5-32 and 5-33 at various stages in the processing, from the diffusion of the isolating regions to the completed circuit.

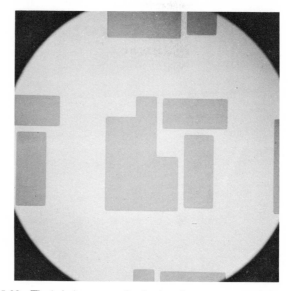

Fig. 5-39 The isolation pattern for the three-input current-mode logic gate.

5-11 Conclusion

The various processes which may be used in fabricating a monolithic circuit have been briefly reviewed. The advantages and disadvantages of each process have

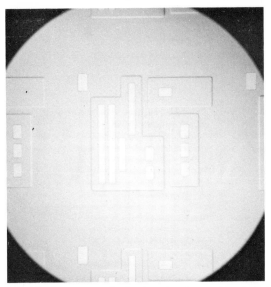

Fig. 5-40   The base pattern for the three-input current-mode logic gate.

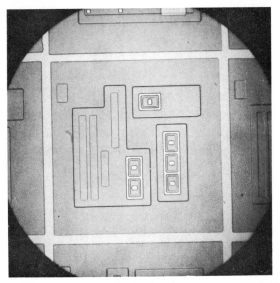

Fig. 5-41   The emitter pattern for the three-input current-mode logic gate.

been enumerated. The epitaxial-diffused process offers the optimum junction-isolated monolithic structure available. Monolithic structures have been presented encompassing both n-p-n and p-n-p transistors.

Several photo-mask-making systems have been presented, which illustrate the various steps encountered in mask making. The multiple-aperture system appears to be the most desirable from the standpoint of image alignment and the speed with which a photo-mask set may be made.

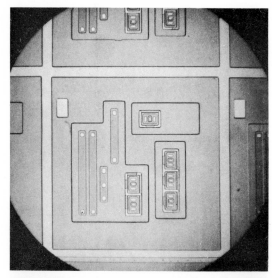

Fig. 5-42 The preohmic pattern for the three-input current-mode logic gate.

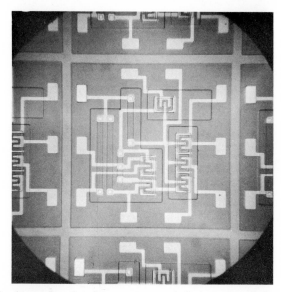

Fig. 5-43 A complete three-input current-mode logic gate ready for separation into dice and mounting in a package.

The parasitic effects which adversely affect circuit performance have been enumerated. These include four-layer action, isolation-junction capacitance, metal-over-oxide capacitance, and parasitic transistor action.

A particular monolithic layout, a current-mode logic gate, has been analyzed in detail. Considerations determining the number of isolation regions required have been given for both the general case and the current-mode logic circuit. A monolithic circuit has been shown as it proceeds through the various fabrication steps until a finished circuit is obtained. Factors affecting die size and pin connections have been reviewed. Finally, a summary of the general rules applied to a monolithic layout have been enumerated. These rules were general rather than specific for the following reasons:

1. The active and passive components of the monolithic device will be determined by the circuit function.

2. There are always a number of monolithic layouts for a given circuit which will function correctly in every way, yet be quite different in terms of physical design.

There are a large number of variations possible in a monolithic layout, and within the limitations of good semiconductor component design, these variations are at the disposal of the designer.

REFERENCES

1. Phillips, A. B.: "Transistor Engineering," p. 5, McGraw-Hill Book Company, New York, 1962.
2. King, D. S., G. R. Madland, and W. J. Corrigan: Methods of Isolation of Active Elements in Integrated Circuits, Professional Group on Electron Devices, Washington, D.C., October, 1962.
3. Kodak Photosensitive Resists for Industry, Eastman Kodak Company, Rochester, N.Y.
4. Hunter, L. P.: "Handbook of Semiconductor Electronics," p. 7-4, McGraw-Hill Book Company, New York, 1956.
5. DeBoice, W. F., and J. F. Bowker: Designing a Microelectronic Differential Amplifier, *Electron. Prod.*, pp. 34–37, July, 1962.
6. Fromm, H. J.: The Production of Photographic Microimages, unpublished work of Eastman Kodak Research Laboratories, Rochester, N.Y.
7. Moll, J. L., M. Tannenbaum, J. M. Goldey, and N. Holonyak: P-N-P-N Transistor Switches, *Proc. IRE*, vol. 44, pp. 1174–1182, September, 1956.

6

MULTIPHASE MONOLITHIC INTEGRATED CIRCUITS

In previous chapters, attention was given to two types of integrated circuit structures. The hybrid structure contains two or more *separate* specimens of silicon. Within each of these discrete pieces are contained localized regions doped with selected impurities so as to yield desired electronic functions. Each silicon specimen is physically connected to other pieces within the integrated circuit.

The monolithic structure consists primarily of a *single* specimen of silicon. Within this block of silicon are fabricated the various regions designed to perform specific electronic functions.

As was discussed in the previous chapter, it is necessary to provide electrical isolation between the various active and passive elements of the circuit; this is commonly accomplished by means of the back-to-back diodes produced by an isolation diffusion process. This is clearly illustrated in Fig. 5-4. This system, though effective, has some significant drawbacks. Perhaps the most significant among these is the parasitic capacitance of the junction between an active element and the substrate. As will be seen in Chap. 7, this capacitance has a very detrimental effect on the speed or frequency response of the monolithic circuit. Other detrimental features of this method for electrical isolation are the parasitic active elements associated with the extra junctions. The integrated circuit designer must constantly avoid four-layer switching effects in the active elements; and he must avoid the possibility of having the parasitic p-n-p transistor turn on, thus shunting signals or currents to the substrate.

It should be pointed out here that the entire body of the monolithic block consists of a continuous uninterrupted array of silicon atoms. Specific kinds of impurities are concentrated in localized regions of this array of silicon atoms. Thus, in an n-p-n transistor region, the silicon near the top surface contains a net concentration of an n-type impurity such as phosphorus, while the base region contains a net concentration of an impurity such as boron. As has been pointed out in previous chapters, the plane within the material where the concentration of the n-type impurity is equal to the concentration of p-type impurity constitutes the electrically all-important p-n junction. From a material and structural standpoint it is important to keep in mind that the p-n junction does not represent any change in the basic physical continuity of the silicon lattice. Recalling that at most p-n junctions the total impurity doping level is of the order of 10^{16} to $10^{18}/cm^3$, and that this represents an extremely dilute impurity concentration in silicon, it can be seen that from a material standpoint the p-n junction is not a region of profound metallurgical or chemical changes. Thus, the monolithic circuits which have been described in the previous chapters consist of a continuous orderly array of silicon atoms (in other words, a single phase) containing localized regions doped with various but minute amounts of n- or p-type impurities.

The above discussion pertains to the body of the monolithic circuit. At the surface of the monolithic block, of course, are different phases of material. These various phases perform one of two basic functions. For example, the silicon dioxide regions perform the function of passivating or protecting the top surface of the monolithic block from a potentially hostile environment. This protective function is particularly critical over these regions of the top surface which contain a p-n junction. A secondary function of the passivating regions is to provide a source of impurities during the actual manufacture of the integrated circuit. However, once the integrated circuit has been fabricated, the function of this region becomes solely one of passivation.

In addition to the protective function accomplished by a phase such as silicon dioxide, a second function is performed by metallic regions which enable electrical contact to be made to the various regions within the block of the monolithic circuit.

Thus, from a structural standpoint the conventional monolithic integrated circuit may be thought of as a block of single-crystal silicon containing a "roof" of two materials—one for protecting the inside of the "house" from the foreign elements, and the other providing the means for accomplishing electronic contact with the interior of the house. While different electronic functions may occur within the house, from a structural standpoint the conventional monolithic integrated circuit contains no interior "walls" or "floors."

We have made the point that the different regions of the monolithic block are not isolated from one another in the sense that there is a region of different material separating the localized elements which are to be isolated. If we could fabricate an integrated circuit structure in which electrical isolation within a given block could be achieved by the use of discrete layers of some electrically inert material, then the integrated circuit designer would have considerably more design freedom. In addition, the introduction of a different phase of material within the body of the integrated circuit would also result in a *physical* barrier as well as an electrical barrier between the different regions of the monolithic block. There are many instances in integrated circuit structures where the presence of such a layer could be used to advantage.

Such a structure is the one shown in cross section in Fig. 6-1. In this structure, unlike the conventional monolithic circuit, the orderly array of the single-crystal silicon phase is interrupted by the presence of a thin region of dielectric material

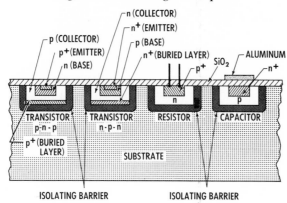

Fig. 6-1 A multiphase structure for integrated circuits. Note presence of isolating barrier separating the elements of the integrated circuits from the substrate both electrically and physically.

located within the body of the monolithic integrated circuit. To return to our analogy of the house given above, we have now incorporated, within the structure, materials which will form the interior walls and floors. In this structure the monolithic block no longer consists of only a single material phase; rather we have a multiphase system within the monolithic block. In contrast, the conventional monolithic circuit can be thought of as being a single-phase system. Both structures contain a roof of such materials as silicon dioxide and electrical conductors. As can be seen from Fig. 6-1, in the multiphase structure the isolation regions actually join the passivation regions present on top of the integrated circuit.

By use of such a multiphase monolithic structure, then, there will be a significant reduction in the parasitic capacitance between the substrate and the active and passive elements of the integrated circuit. In addition, the extra junction normally associated with conventional diode isolation has been eliminated, removing the problem of parasitic transistor action and four-layer switching.

Another advantage of this type of structure may also be realized: If the isolating phase is properly chosen, it will also act as a barrier to impurity diffusion. Thus the semiconductor device engineer has an additional degree of freedom in the fabrication of the multiphase monolithic integrated circuit.

In the following sections, we will consider in some detail one process* by which the manufacturer of integrated circuits can realize such a multiphase structure. After consideration of the process, attention will be given to the specific design advantages to be gained from the multiphase structure.

6-1   Fabrication of Multiphase Monolithic Integrated Circuits

To understand the basic principles underlying the multiphase monolithic approach, let us consider the step-by-step construction of a typical structure. The starting point would be a wafer of single-crystal silicon. Typical dimensions for such a wafer are a diameter of 1 in. and a thickness of 6 to 8 mils. The wafer could have

---

* The EPIC (trademark registered by Motorola Inc.) process provides an example of a specific procedure leading to the desired multiphase result.

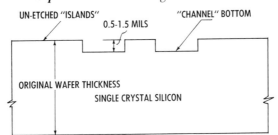

Fig. 6-2 Isolation "channels" etched into single crystal in preparation for fabricating of a multiphase structure.

been fabricated from either Czochralski or float-zone silicon. Typically, the wafer is uniformly doped with an n-type impurity to a resistivity of 0.5 ohm cm.

The first process step in the construction of the multiphase integrated circuit involves the growth of a thermal oxide on the surface of the wafer. Using standard photo-resist techniques, predetermined areas of the oxide are removed, thus exposing the underlying silicon on one of the major surfaces.

After removal of all the photo-resist materials, the wafer is then subjected to an etching procedure in which a chemical medium is used that selectively attacks the silicon and not the silicon dioxide. The result of this treatment, which we refer to as the isolation channel etching, is to produce a structure as shown in Fig. 6-2. For reasons which will become more apparent later, the depth of the etch channel is typically 0.5 to 1.5 mils. A number of specific etching procedures can be used for isolation etching. The basic requirements for all such procedures are twofold. First, the procedure must give controlled depth of etching so that the depth of the isolation channel is reproducible to at least ± 10 per cent. The second basic requisite is that the channel have a flat bottom.

After the formation of the isolation channels, the wafer is then subjected to a process in which the etched surface (i.e., the top surface in Fig. 6-2) is covered with a layer of the material to be used for electrical and chemical isolation. A typical material for this purpose is silicon dioxide which has both the low dielectric constant and the low chemical reactivity required in many multiphase integrated circuit structures. Formation of a thin film of silicon dioxide can be accomplished in a number of ways. For example, if an oxide thickness of only 10,000 to 15,000 Å is desired, then standard thermal oxidation techniques can be employed to produce the isolation layer. Should thicker layers be required, then a number of well-known deposition methods can be utilized. For example, the channel-etched silicon could be placed in an epitaxial furnace and exposed to a gas mixture consisting of hydrogen, silicon tetrachloride, and carbon dioxide. At suitable temperatures these three gaseous substances react with one another and produce a deposit of silicon dioxide.[1] Other methods utilize the decomposition of various organosilane compounds.[2] The method used must be capable of producing a *continuous* film of silicon dioxide, free of such defects as pinholes, which would result in the loss of electrical isolation in the final multiphase integrated circuit structure.

The wafer containing the thin film of silicon dioxide over the channel-etched surface is placed in an epitaxial furnace. Utilizing appropriately modified conventional epitaxial technology, silicon is deposited over the entire surface of the wafer.

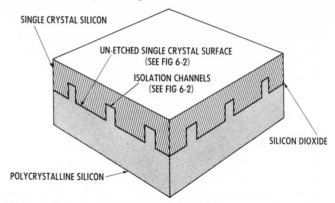

Fig. 6-3 Multiphase structure after growth of isolating layer and polycrystalline layer.

The final structure after this step is shown in Fig. 6-3. This final silicon phase, though apparently a continuous structure upon casual examination, is actually a random array of microscopic particles of single-crystal silicon. In conventional epitaxial deposition of silicon on silicon, the deposit is a single-crystal structure. The reason for the polycrystalline deposition in the multiphase structure is that the material on which the silicon is deposited is not single-crystal material. However, the function of the polycrystalline layer is to provide a support for the single-crystal regions which will compose the functional phase of the integrated circuit. Typical thicknesses of the polycrystalline silicon range from 4 to 6 mils. The determining factor here is the minimum thickness required to ensure efficient mechanical handling in subsequent operations without undue breakage.

The sandwich structure shown in Fig. 6-3 is mounted on a suitable mechanical polishing instrument with the polycrystalline surface against the abrasive. A small amount of the polycrystalline material is lapped from the sample. The wafer is then remounted with the single-crystal phase in contact with the lapping or polishing material. As the lapping and polishing proceed, successive layers of the single-crystal silicon are removed. As can be seen from Fig. 6-4, when the polishing has removed the fourth layer, the silicon dioxide phase is exposed on those portions of the surface not containing the single-crystal islands. Further polishing will result in the removal of the silicon dioxide from the top surface, thus exposing the underlying polycrystalline silicon. At this point, the wafer may be considered to consist of a relatively large "sea" of polycrystalline material, in which float indi-

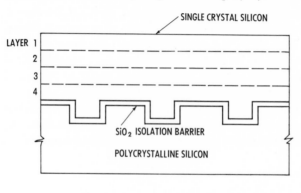

Fig. 6-4 Cross-sectional view of multiphase structure while in process, showing schematically the removal of single-crystal material.

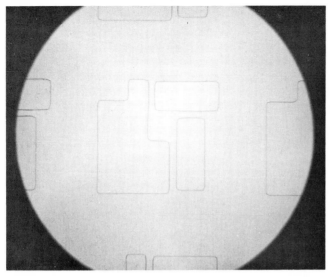

Fig. 6-5 Photomicrograph of a multiphase wafer after lapping and polishing.

vidual islands of single-crystal silicon, isolated from the underlying support material by the silicon dioxide phase. A picture of a portion of such a wafer is shown in Fig. 6-5. Note the thin line tracing the outline of the silicon dioxide isolation phase.

After this point in the process, the multiphase structure can be processed by the same basic procedures employed for the single-phase structure. Thus the top surface will be subjected to the usual passivation procedure, followed by diffusion, metallization, scribing, die bonding, and final assembly. A cross section of a typical final multiphase integrated circuit was shown in Fig. 6-1. A top view of a finished EPIC* circuit is shown in Fig. 6-6.

The above discussion relates to a basic structure in which the starting material consists of a uniformly doped wafer. By now the reader can appreciate that this starting material, when subjected to the process described above, will result in a transistor structure in which the collector region is uniformly doped. For starting materials of a resistivity high enough to give typically desired collector breakdown voltages, the resistance in the underlying regions adversely affects $V_{CE(SAT)}$. To maintain the desired collector breakdown and yet lower $V_{CE(SAT)}$, the above procedure can be altered in one of two ways.

In the first method, the starting wafer, instead of being a uniformly doped sample, can contain a thin highly doped epitaxial layer on the top surface, i.e., the surface which later becomes the bottom of the island. During conventional processing following fabrication

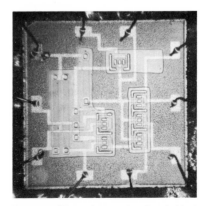

Fig. 6-6 Photomicrograph of a finished EPIC circuit.

* Trademark registered by Motorola Inc.

of the n-p-n structure, the impurity in the epitaxial film will diffuse upward in the direction of the collector-base junction. This diffusion may be controlled so that the diffusing impurity atoms do not approach the collector junction, but yet lower the collector resistance to give the desired $V_{CE(SAT)}$.

An alternative to the above method consists of incorporating the desired diffusant impurity into the silicon dioxide isolation phase. As in the epitaxial layer source, subsequent high-temperature processing will result in diffusion of the impurity into those portions of the body of the collector region which are near the silicon dioxide.

6-2 Advantages of Multiphase Monolithic Integrated Circuits

The technology described above yields important performance improvements in monolithic structures. As has been previously shown, in normal monolithic structures isolation is achieved by using back-to-back junctions. A typical value of capacitance per unit area for one of these junctions is 0.12 pf/mil². The use of silicon dioxide as an isolation medium essentially eliminates this parasitic capacitance. The polycrystalline substrate may be left floating. The only capacitive coupling existing here and not present in a discrete equivalent circuit is the series capacitance between isolation regions, and this can be made very small.

The parasitic p-n-p transistor consisting of the base-collector-substrate regions in a conventional monolithic circuit is completely eliminated.

The most dramatic improvement in circuit performance may be realized in diode-transistor logic circuits, such as illustrated in Fig. 6-7. One severe limitation is placed upon this type of circuit in conventional monolithic form. As in any saturating logic circuit, lifetime control is required to minimize minority-carrier charge-storage effects in Q_1.

However, charge-storage characteristics are desirable in diodes D_3 and D_4. When a diode is biased in the forward direction, an excess of minority carriers forms on either side of the junction. When the diode is switched from a state of forward conduction to a reverse-biased state, there is a finite delay time during which the diode is unable to block reverse current. In other words, a low reverse imped-ance occurs in the switching interval, as shown in Fig. 4-20. The flat portion of the upper curve represents a delay connected with the time required for the excess minority carriers on either side of the junction to recombine or to be swept out. Usually this represents the minority-carrier storage effects in the most lightly doped region of the diode, i.e., that portion of the diode with the longest lifetime. There-

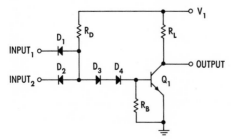

Fig. 6-7 Schematic diagram of a typical DTL cir-cuit which benefits from the use of EPIC.

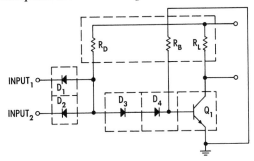

D₁ & D₂   COLLECTOR-BASE DIODES – GOLD DIFFUSED

D₃ & D₄   COLLECTOR-BASE DIODES – NON GOLD DIFFUSED

Q₁   TRANSISTOR – GOLD DIFFUSED

R_D, R_B & R_L   RESISTORS – NON GOLD DIFFUSED

6 ISOLATION REGIONS REQUIRED

Fig. 6-8 Schematic diagram of DTL circuit shown in Fig. 6-7 indicating the six isolation regions required for EPIC fabrication of the circuit.

fore, the precondition that D_3 and D_4 conduct strongly for a short period to remove the excess charge from Q_1 is met as long as D_3 and D_4 exhibit minority-carrier storage effects. This condition conflicts with the lifetime requirements of Q_1.

In junction-isolated monolithic circuits, this lifetime control is usually achieved by diffusing gold into the *entire* silicon wafer. In junction-isolated circuits, some measure of selectivity in diffused-gold placement can be achieved by localized gold deposition.[3] Still we are fundamentally limited by the fact that the circuit is a single phase. In the multiphase monolithic structure, it is possible to control lifetime more completely on a selective, local basis because the isolation medium, silicon dioxide, acts as a diffusion mask against gold. In this structure, isolated components are completely surrounded by a silicon dioxide barrier. By introducing gold into selected isolation regions, the lifetime may be radically reduced in those particular areas. In those other isolation regions which are not gold-doped, the lifetime remains high. As shown in Fig. 6-8, there are six isolation regions required for EPIC fabrication of the DTL circuit under consideration. The isolation regions containing D_1, D_2, and Q_1 require lifetime reduction. Therefore, gold is introduced and diffused into these regions.

Thus, it can be seen that although the multiphase monolithic technology is still in its infancy, it promises to revolutionize the entire monolithic integrated circuit concept.

REFERENCES

1. Steinmaier, W., and J. Bloem: Successive Growth of Si and SiO₂ in Epitaxial Apparatus, *J. Electrochem. Soc.,* vol. 111, pp. 206–209, February, 1964.
2. Klerer, J.: A Method for the Deposition of SiO at Low Temperatures, *J. Electrochem. Soc.,* vol. 108, pp. 1070–1071, November, 1961.
3. Adamic, J. W., Jr., and J. E. McNamara: Studies of the Diffusion of Gold into Silicon and Silicon Dioxide Films, presented at the Semiconductor Symposium of the Electrochemical Society National Meeting, New York, October, 1963.

7

TRANSISTORS AND DIODES FOR
MONOLITHIC CIRCUITS

With the assumption that the reader is now familiar with the basic theory and technology involved in semiconductor devices, we can proceed to delve into the design aspects of the diode and transistor as they appear within the monolithic integrated circuit. The characteristics and design features that will aid the designer in selecting the components to satisfy his circuit requirements prior to the establishment of the actual monolithic layout will be presented in detail in this chapter. The differences between the integrated circuit transistor and the discrete passivated epitaxial transistor will be pointed out. These differences fall into the categories of both structure and electrical properties. Further, it will be seen that because of the four-layer aspects of the integrated circuit transistor, its electrical characteristics can vary considerably, depending upon the connection arrangement, particularly when it is connected as a diode. These various combinations and their properties are of extreme importance to an integrated circuit designer, in order that he may select the best arrangements compatible with his circuit requirements. The design formulas that were developed in Chap. 4 will be applied to the integrated circuit structure wherever possible. This applies to diodes as well as transistors. The design calculations will serve as an illustrative application of the theory of semiconductor devices. Along with these calculations, there will also be discussions of the necessary design compromises that must be made.

7-1 Structural Description of the Monolithic Integrated Circuit Transistor

As pointed out in Chap. 4, we can determine the electrical characteristics of the structure, provided we can specify the impurity profile and the geometry of a semiconductor device. Therefore it is essential that the physical model of the structure be completely specified before any analysis is attempted.

In order to isolate the various components of a monolithic circuit from one another electrically, it has been common practice to employ a four-layer structure. The treatment to follow will be restricted only to the epitaxial process for making monolithic circuits. This method is an optimum one from the points of view of design flexibility and manufacturability. Rather than attempt to cover the numerous design possibilities for an integrated circuit transistor, we will use as the basis of analysis a design that is typical in terms of impurity profile and geometry.

The process begins with the growth of an n-type epitaxial layer 25 microns thick (1 mil) on a p-type substrate. The substrate resistivity is 10 ohm cm, which corresponds to an acceptor concentration of $1.4 \times 10^{15}/cm^3$. The epitaxial layer is grown with a resistivity of 0.5 ohm cm, n-type, corresponding to a donor concentration of $1.2 \times 10^{16}/cm^3$. Figure 7-1 illustrates how the epitaxial layer is divided into isolated n-type regions through the use of a deep p-type isolation diffusion. The integrated circuit wafer is oxidized, and a specific pattern is cut in the oxide by means of the photo-resist technique, which establishes the size of the isolated islands; the p-type diffusion extends through the epitaxial layer and joins the substrate. These n-type areas are electrically isolated from one another by the p-n junctions that are formed between them. The integrated circuit transistors or diodes will be formed within one or more of these isolated regions.

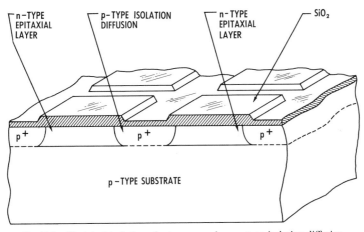

Fig. 7-1   Electrical isolation of n-type areas by a p-type isolation diffusion.

Figure 7-2 is a cross-sectional view of an isolated integrated circuit transistor showing all four layers. From the top, these are the diffused emitter, the diffused base, the epitaxial collector, and the substrate. This is the complete cross-sectional view, which will be used as the typical model throughout the rest of this chapter. Note that the base is formed by a p-type diffusion into the 0.5-ohm-cm epitaxial collector, and the emitter is an n-type region that is diffused into the p-type base. Connections to the collector region are provided for simultaneously with the diffusion of the emitter, by diffusing n-type impurities into the collector. This will establish an ohmic contact to that region. Electric contact to the emitter, base, and collector regions, respectively, is made with the use of aluminum metallizing, as shown in Fig. 7-2.

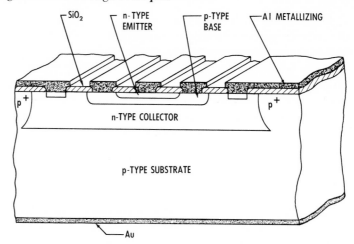

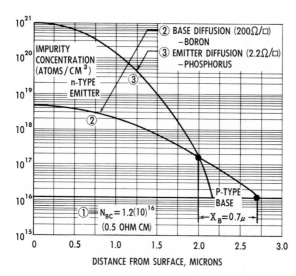

Fig. 7-2 Cross-sectional view of an isolated monolithic integrated circuit transistor.

The impurity profiles that result from the diffusion processes as discussed are shown in Fig. 7-3. The background line corresponds to the impurity level of the epitaxial collector. It is seen that this is a level of $1.2 \times 10^{16}/cm^3$ (curve 1). Curve 2 shows a plot of the impurity concentration as a function of distance into the epitaxial collector from the top surface of the transistor. This profile represents the diffusion of boron to form the p-type base. The boron concentration at the surface starts at $5 \times 10^{18}/cm^3$ and is diffused in to a depth of 2.7 microns. This impurity function is shown as a gaussian distribution, although in actual practice it is a complex combination of this function and the complementary error function (erfc). The curve is concave down on a logarithmic plot, but the "tail" of the curve is concave up on a linear plot, and strongly resembles a simple decaying exponential function. A typical value of sheet resistance for the layer formed by

Fig. 7-3 Typical impurity profiles for a monolithic integrated circuit transistor.

the boron diffusion is 200 ohms per square. This is related to the number of net impurities in the layer represented by the region between curves 1 and 2. Curve 3 is the profile for the emitter diffusion. This is a much heavier concentration of impurity, which starts from a surface concentration of about $10^{21}/cm^3$ and is diffused to a junction depth of about 2.0 microns. The emitter sheet resistance is approximately 2.2 ohms per square. As practically measured, this corresponds to the region between curves 2 and 3, but the number of impurities represented by this region differs by less than 1 per cent from the number represented by the region between curves 1 and 3.

The two curves intersect each other at a distance of 2.0 microns, which represents the position of the emitter-base junction. Therefore, we observe a physical base thickness of 0.7 micron, which is the difference between the two curves at their respective crossover points, denoted by the heavy dots in Fig. 7-3. In the analysis to follow, it will be assumed that the emitter-base junction is a step junction, even though the impurity profile in Fig. 7-3 shows a graded transition. Actually, this is a reasonably good approximation since the emitter is diffused from an impurity concentration several orders of magnitude higher than that of the base.

Monolithic Transistor Layout. The geometry of a typical integrated circuit transistor, looking at the top surface of the structure, is illustrated in Fig. 7-4. The emitter consists of a diffused rectangle measuring 1 by 1.5 mils. The emitter is diffused into a 2.5- by 4.0-mil base region. The ohmic contact to the base consists of two metallized stripes on either side of the diffused emitter. Completely surrounding the diffused collector-base junction is a rectangular metallized stripe, which is the ohmic contact to the collector region. Finally, completely surrounding this structure is the outermost rectangle, which is the edge of the original silicon oxide that was used to mask the p-type isolation diffusion.

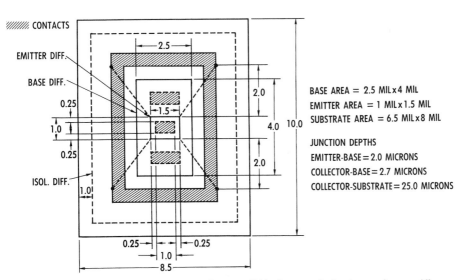

Fig. 7-4 Double-base-stripe geometry for monolithic integrated circuit transistors. All dimensions are in mils. All clearances are 0.5 mil. Dashed lines denote trapezoids for r_{sc} calculation.

As pointed out above, the isolation diffusion was deep enough to join the substrate, located approximately 1 mil below the surface of the structure. Since diffusion is a three-dimensional process, the impurities diffuse laterally as well as downward, as described in Chap. 2. The lateral diffusion distance is therefore approximately 1 mil. This is shown by the large dotted rectangle in Fig. 7-4, and this determines the actual size of the isolation island or, more specifically, the area of the p-n junction formed between the n-type epitaxial collector and the p-type substrate. In other words, the actual size of the isolated junction is 6.5 by 8 mils, whereas the size of the oxide mask is 8.5 by 10 mils.

The emitter contact is made with aluminum metallizing which is 0.5 mil wide, leaving a narrow clearance of 0.25 mil on either side. All other spacings between contacts and diffused junctions are held to a minimum of 0.5 mil.

It was stated previously that this particular geometry is only a typical one to be used as a basis for discussion. Since these patterns are established by photographic processes, the designer has complete freedom to utilize any combinations of patterns or dimensions. For example, the designer may make the emitter as long as is necessary to handle the intended current. Emitter width is a fundamental limiting dimension, however, with 1 mil being a practical minimum value. Another option which may be considered is a transistor design incorporating only one base stripe and hence having potentially smaller junction areas. The geometry of a single-base-stripe transistor is shown in Fig. 7-5.

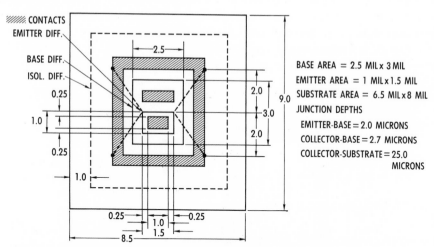

Fig. 7-5 Single-base-stripe geometry for monolithic integrated circuit transistors. All dimensions are in mils. All clearances are 0.5 mil. Dashed lines denote trapezoids for r_{sc} calculation.

In summary, we may say that the optimum geometry for an integrated circuit transistor consists of a 1-mil-wide emitter stripe which has a length l and is flanked by either one or two base contacts. All junction-to-junction and contact-to-junction separations are 0.5 mil, save in the case of the emitter. The significance of these geometrical considerations will be treated again later on. In the transistor discussion to follow, we will use two base contacts as our model, since this provides a more nearly optimum geometry when we consider applying a transistor to both switching and amplifier functions.

Comparison with Discrete Passivated Epitaxial Transistors. The cross-sectional view of the integrated circuit transistor just discussed is repeated in Fig. 7-6 to illustrate how it differs from a conventional discrete passivated epitaxial transistor, which is also shown in the figure. In the integrated circuit device, the epitaxial collector is isolated within a p-type substrate, and the ohmic contact to the collector is made on the top side. In the discrete transistor, the epitaxial collector is not isolated but rests on an n^+ substrate which simply serves as an ohmic extension of the collector, so that ohmic contact is made on the bottom side. This is by far the most striking difference between the two structures. This structural difference manifests itself in the form of two parasitic elements which are characteristic of integrated circuit devices. First, contact to the top of the collector introduces additional series resistance r_{SC}, thereby increasing the $V_{CE(SAT)}$ of the device. Second, the integrated circuit transistor embodies an additional capacitance, which is of course the collector-to-substrate capacitance.

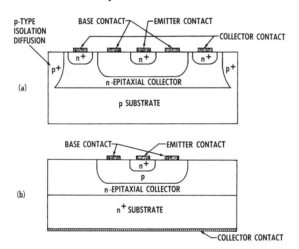

Fig. 7-6 Comparison of cross sections of (*a*) monolithic integrated circuit transistor with (*b*) discrete planar epitaxial transistor.

Two Types of Monolithic Transistors. The four-layer semiconductor structure described by Figs. 7-2 through 7-5 will now be discussed; this is the form of the transistor which appears in a monolithic integrated circuit. For this particular geometry, two types of impurity profiles will be treated in the analysis to follow. One is for a gold-doped transistor, and the other is for a non-gold-doped transistor. The principles underlying gold diffusion as a means of carrier lifetime control are treated in Chaps. 2 and 3, while gold diffusion practice is taken up in Chap. 12.

The non-gold-doped transistor has a collector resistivity of 0.5 ohm cm or an impurity atom concentration of $1.2 \times 10^{16}/\text{cm}^3$. The other transistor is gold-doped in order to reduce carrier lifetime. The collector resistivity for this structure is 0.1 ohm cm for design compromise reasons, which will be treated later in this chapter, corresponding to an impurity concentration of $8.6 \times 10^{16}/\text{cm}^3$. These impurity profiles are summarized in Fig. 7-7. In both cases we have a physical base thickness of 0.7 micron, corresponding to the difference between the 2.7-micron base diffusion and the 2.0-micron emitter diffusion. In both cases we are assuming a base diffusion sheet resistance of 200 ohms per square, and 2.2 ohms per square emitter sheet resistance. It should be noted that in going from a 0.5-ohm-cm background for the non-gold-doped transistor to a 0.1-ohm-cm background for the gold-doped transistor, the collector impurity level is increased almost an order of magnitude. Thus, for the 0.1-ohm-cm gold-doped transistor, there must be a greater total amount of impurity diffused into the structure during base diffusion, in order to achieve an equivalent sheet resistance.

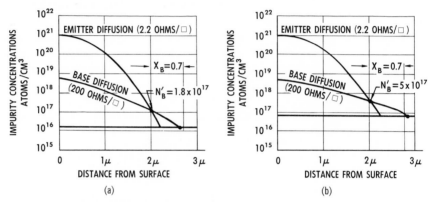

Fig. 7-7 Impurity profiles for two types of monolithic integrated circuit transistors: (*a*) Non-gold-doped transistor; (*b*) gold-doped transistor.

In the sections to follow, the theoretical characteristics for the double-base-stripe geometry and each of the aforementioned impurity profiles will be calculated. The intent is to show on a comparative basis the important differences between a transistor designed for amplifier applications and one designed for switching applications. At the appropriate points, we will also consider special cases of a single-base-stripe version of this particular structure. Similarly, we will consider, where applicable, longer emitter-stripe geometries in order to achieve suitable operation at higher currents.

7-2 Breakdown Voltage Characteristics

The avalanche breakdown voltage of a step junction is strictly a function of the high-resistivity side of the junction. The transistor with a 0.5-ohm-cm collector (Fig. 7-7*a*) has a collector junction which is closer to step-junction behavior than to linearly graded junction behavior. At this impurity concentration (1.2×10^{16}/cm^3) the BV_{CBO} as read from Fig. 2-20 is approximately 55 volts.

For a 0.1-ohm-cm structure the collector junction can be approximated well by a linearly graded junction. An additional factor which enters is that the gold doping tends to raise background resistivity through compensation. The resulting value of BV_{CBO} is approximately 25 volts.

The emitter-base breakdown voltage BV_{EBO} is primarily a function of the doping level just at the base side of the emitter junction. Note, however, that this background can no longer be characterized by a single concentration as it could for the collector junction. At the surface of the silicon, the emitter diffusion proceeds laterally into the material with an impurity concentration in the neighborhood of $5 \times 10^{18}/cm^3$ in both transistors. Therefore the observed values of BV_{EBO} are not very different for the two; approximately 7 volts is obtained in the non-gold-doped transistor, and 5 volts in the gold-doped transistor.

The avalanche breakdown voltage of the junction formed between the collector and substrate, BV_{CS}, is determined primarily by the very graded junction between the epitaxial-collector region and the deep p-type isolation diffusion. This deep, graded junction exhibits a breakdown voltage higher than that read from Fig. 2-20, which applies to step junctions or shallow, steeply graded diffused junctions. Thus for the non-gold-doped transistor BV_{CS} is approximately 75 volts, and for the gold-doped transistor BV_{CS} is in the neighborhood of 25 volts.

The collector-to-emitter breakdown voltage BV_{CEO} is given by the following expression:

$$BV_{CEO} \simeq \frac{BV_{CBO}}{\sqrt[n]{\beta}} \qquad (7\text{-}1)$$

Here, n is the Miller exponent [see Eq. (2-83)], approximately equal to 4 for n-type silicon. The appropriate value of β is that which applies at the current level chosen for measuring BV_{CEO}. For the non-gold-doped transistor with a β of approximately 30 at 0.1 mA, and a BV_{CBO} of 55 volts,

$$BV_{CEO} \simeq \frac{55}{\sqrt[4]{30}} = 23 \text{ volts} \qquad (0.5 \text{ ohm cm}) \qquad (7\text{-}2)$$

For the gold-doped transistor, the β at low currents is considerably lower because of the presence of the gold recombination centers in the emitter junction. Assuming a β of 10,

$$BV_{CEO} \simeq \frac{25}{\sqrt[4]{10}} = 14 \text{ volts} \qquad (0.1 \text{ ohm cm}) \qquad (7\text{-}3)$$

These calculated values are reasonably close to those actually measured in monolithic transistors of this geometry.

7-3 Leakage Current Characteristics

The leakage current of a silicon p-n junction is attributed to the generation of charge from recombination centers within the depletion layer of the junction. For this case, the current that flows under the reverse-bias condition is given by Eq. (7-4):

$$I_g = qgX_mA \qquad (7\text{-}4)$$

where g is the generation rate of carriers, and X_m is the thickness of the depletion layer at the particular reverse voltage. For a non-gold-doped structure, such as the transistor with the 0.5-ohm-cm collector, the junction leakage currents are in the order of 1 nanoampere. For the gold-doped transistor having the 0.1-ohm-cm collector, the charge generation current would normally be proportional to the increase of the generation rate g. This may be as much as a factor of 10. However, this is offset by the reduced thickness of the depletion layer X_m, as one goes from a high resistivity to a lower value. Since X_m varies (approximately) inversely as the square root of the impurity concentration, then the I_{CBO} for the gold-doped transistor may be calculated to be approximately four times higher than that of the non-gold-doped value. Similarly, the I_{EBO} for the gold-doped transistor is calculated to be approximately six times higher than that for the non-gold-doped transistor. These ratios are determined simply by dividing the factor of 10 (for generation rate increase) by the square root of the appropriate impurity ratios. In other words, for I_{CBO}, the X_m change is related to the impurity shift from $1.2 \times 10^{16}/\text{cm}^3$ to $8.6 \times 10^{16}/\text{cm}^3$ (N_{BC}). Likewise, for I_{EBO}, the X_m variation is related to the change in N_B', which goes from $1.8 \times 10^{17}/\text{cm}^3$ to $5 \times 10^{17}/\text{cm}^3$. In any event, the leakage currents are seen to be less than 10 nA.

7-4 Monolithic Transistor Capacitances

In this section the various emitter, collector, and substrate capacitances will be calculated for the double-base geometry transistor. As before, the comparison between transistors with 0.5- and 0.1-ohm-cm collectors will be made. The relative merits of the single-base geometry will also be illustrated.

An approximate expression for the emitter capacitance of a transistor under forward-bias conditions was given in Chap. 4 as

$$C_{TE} \approx 4A_E C_T(0) = 4A_E \sqrt{\frac{q\kappa\epsilon_o N_B'}{2\psi_o}} \qquad (4\text{-}41)$$

Here N_B' is the impurity concentration at the base side of the emitter junction, A_E is the total area of the emitter including sidewall components, and ψ_o is the built-in voltage of approximately ½ volt. Referring to Fig. 7-4, we see that the total emitter area is as follows when the sidewall is assumed to be 0.08 mil high:

$$A_E = 1 \times 1.5 + 5 \times 0.08 = 1.9 \text{ mil}^2 \qquad (7\text{-}5)$$

We will use for the value of N_B' the value of one-half the total base diffusant concentration at the emitter junction in this calculation. (The *net* impurity concentration at the junction, by definition, is zero.) This value will probably be too high for the calculation of the bottom component and too low for that of the sidewall. However, this semiarbitrary selection will yield a satisfactory engineering approximation.

Using the values for $N_B'/2$ of 9×10^{16} and 2.5×10^{17} for the non-gold-doped and gold-doped transistors, respectively, we obtain for $C_T(0)$ the values of 1.25×10^5 and 2.1×10^5 pf/cm² by means of Fig. 2-18. Thus for the non-gold-doped transistor,

$$C_{TE} = 4 \times 1.9 \text{ mil}^2 \times 6.45 \times 10^{-6} \text{ cm}^2/\text{mil}^2 \times 1.25 \times 10^5 \text{ pf/cm}^2 = 6 \text{ pf} \qquad (7\text{-}6)$$

For the gold-doped transistor,

$$C_{TE} = 4 \times 1.9 \text{ mil}^2 \times 6.45 \times 10^{-6} \text{ cm}^2/\text{mil}^2 \times 2.1 \times 10^5 \text{ pf/cm}^2 = 10 \text{ pf} \qquad (7\text{-}7)$$

It should be noted that these are the approximate capacitances under forward-bias conditions. The equilibrium capacitance $A_E C_T(0)$ at a nominal contact potential of 0.5 volt would be one-fourth of the calculated values, or 1.5 and 2.5 pf, respectively.

The second junction capacitance to be calculated is that of the collector-base junction under normal reverse-bias voltage of 5 volts. Because the base diffusion penetrates a uniformly doped (epitaxial) background, this is a graded junction which can be treated by using the Lawrence and Warner curves (see Sec. 3-4) as a basis for calculation:

$$\frac{N_{BC}}{N_o} = \frac{1.2 \times 10^{16}/\text{cm}^3}{5 \times 10^{18}/\text{cm}^3} = 2.4 \times 10^{-3} \qquad (7\text{-}8)$$

$$\frac{V}{N_{BC}} = \frac{5 \text{ volts}}{1.2 \times 10^{16}/\text{cm}^3} = 4.2 \times 10^{-16} \text{ volt cm}^3 \qquad (7\text{-}9)$$

At a junction depth of 2.7 microns we obtain, therefore, a collector-base capacitance of approximately 10^4 pf/cm^2. For the double-base-stripe geometry shown in Fig. 7-4, the junction area (assuming a rectangular collector volume) is approximately 11.3 mil^2.

$$C_{TC} = 10^4 \text{ pf/cm}^2 \times 11.3 \text{ mil}^2 \times 6.45 \times 10^{-6} \text{ cm}^2/\text{mil}^2 = 0.7 \text{ pf} \qquad (7\text{-}10)$$

As a matter of interest, the collector-base capacitance would be approximately 25 per cent less if we designed for the single-base-stripe geometry (Fig. 7-5), as a result in the reduction in the area of the collector-base junction. Thus, C_{TC} for the single-base-stripe transistor would equal 0.5 pf.

The collector-base capacitance for the 0.1-ohm-cm transistor is calculated as follows:

$$\frac{N_{BC}}{N_o} = \frac{8.6 \times 10^{16}/\text{cm}^3}{5 \times 10^{18}/\text{cm}^3} = 1.7 \times 10^{-2} \qquad (7\text{-}11)$$

$$\frac{V}{N_{BC}} = \frac{5 \text{ volts}}{8.6 \times 10^{16}/\text{cm}^3} = 5.8 \times 10^{-17} \text{ volt cm}^3 \qquad (7\text{-}12)$$

At a junction depth of 2.7 microns, we obtain a capacitance per unit area of 2×10^4 pf/cm^2, which yields

$$C_{TC} = 2 \times 10^4 \text{ pf/cm}^2 \times 11.3 \text{ mil}^2 \times 6.45 \times 10^{-6} \text{ cm}^2/\text{mil}^2 = 1.5 \text{ pf} \qquad (7\text{-}13)$$

Once again, for the single-base-stripe geometry the capacitance would be 25 per cent less, or approximately 1.1 pf.

The collector-substrate isolation junction contributes a third capacitance that must be considered. This is the prime parasitic capacitance that differentiates the integrated circuit device from its discrete counterpart. This parasitic isolation capacitance also has two components of differing characteristics: the bottom component associated with the p-type substrate region which is fundamentally a step junction, and the sidewall component associated with the p-type isolation diffusion which has a low gradient at the junction. For the bottom component it is reasonable to assume that the junction is abrupt and that the depletion layer spreads completely to the substrate side of the junction. This is illustrated in Fig. 7-8 for typical reverse-bias conditions. Therefore, at 5 volts total, we find that for 10-ohm-cm p type or $1.4 \times 10^{15}/cm^3$, the capacitance is about 5×10^3 pf/cm^2. For the sidewall, the junction has a graded profile resulting from the deep p-type isolation diffusion. Using the Lawrence and Warner curves for a boron surface concentration of $N_o = 5 \times 10^{20}/cm^3$, diffused to a junction depth of $x_j = 25 \times 10^{-4}$ cm into a background of $N_{BC} = 1.2 \times 10^{16}/cm^3$, we obtain a capacitance per unit area at 5 volts of approximately 7×10^3 pf/cm^2. It should be pointed out that this calculation is based on a one-dimensional solution of the diffusion equation, which gives only an approximate result for the cylindrical sidewall junction in question. The two-dimensional problem remains to be solved.

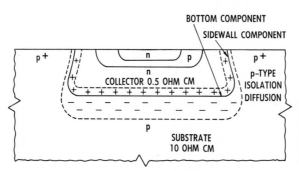

Fig. 7-8 Cross section of a monolithic integrated circuit transistor, showing spreading of depletion layer into the substrate side of the collector-substrate junction.

If the isolation diffusion had a depth precisely equal to the depth of the substrate-epitaxial junction, then it would be appropriate to use for the double-base transistor the outer rectangle in Fig. 7-4 (10 by 8.5 mils) for calculating the bottom component. On the same basis we could treat the sidewall component in terms of a quarter-cylinder geometry which intersects the surface along the dashed rectangle (8 by 6.5 mils). However, any tendency to overshoot in isolation diffusion will diminish both bottom and sidewall areas and will diminish sidewall capacitance per unit area through progressive grading of the junction. (Diffusion at the epitaxial-substrate junction during the lengthy isolation diffusion causes the capacitance per unit area for the bottom component to be less than was calculated above.) In the light of all these factors, another engineering approximation is appropriate: Let us treat the isolated island as a rectangular volume having the dimensions 8 by 6.5 by 1 mil, and having a step-junction bottom component and a graded-junction sidewall component with the properties already computed.

Expressed in customary engineering units, the bottom isolation capacitance is 0.032 pf/mil^2, and the sidewall isolation capacitance is 0.044 pf/mil^2. These values will increase if the resistivities are lowered, and it must be borne in mind that these values are voltage-dependent. In a monolithic integrated circuit, the substrate is usually returned to the most negative potential of the circuit. Therefore, if the collector potential varies, the parasitic isolation capacitance will change accordingly.

The total respective capacitances at 5 volts reverse bias are computed as follows for the non-gold-doped transistors having the geometries of Figs. 7-4 and 7-5:

$$C_{TS} = 0.032 \text{ pf/mil}^2 \times (6.5 \times 8) \text{ mil}^2 + 0.044 \text{ pf/mil}^2 \times (29 \times 1) \text{ mil}^2$$
$$= 1.66 \text{ pf} + 1.28 \text{ pf} \approx 2.9 \text{ pf} \quad \text{(double base stripe)} \tag{7-14}$$

$$C_{TS} = 0.032 \text{ pf/mil}^2 \times (6.5 \times 7) \text{ mil}^2 + 0.044 \text{ pf/mil}^2 \times (27 \times 1) \text{ mil}^2$$
$$= 1.46 \text{ pf} + 1.19 \text{ pf} \approx 2.7 \text{ pf} \quad \text{(single base stripe)} \tag{7-15}$$

Repeating the method of calculation of C_{TS} for 0.1 ohm cm, we may still use the same value for the bottom component of 0.035 pf/mil². Again using a graded-junction approximation for the sidewall component, we find that for an impurity level of $8.6 \times 10^{16}/\text{cm}^3$, we obtain a capacitance of about 0.1 pf/mil². Thus, the total substrate capacitance for the gold-doped transistor is

$$C_{TS} = 1.66 \text{ pf} + 0.1 \text{ pf/mil}^2 \times (29 \times 1) \text{ mil}^2$$
$$= 1.66 \text{ pf} + 2.9 \text{ pf} = 4.6 \text{ pf} \quad \text{(double base stripe)} \tag{7-16}$$

$$C_{TS} = 1.46 \text{ pf} + 0.1 \text{ pf/mil}^2 \times (27 \times 1) \text{ mil}^2$$
$$= 1.46 \text{ pf} + 2.7 \text{ pf} = 4.2 \text{ pf} \quad \text{(single base stripe)} \tag{7-17}$$

It is interesting to note that in the non-gold-doped transistors the sidewall component is an important term, and in the gold-doped transistors it is the dominant term. The collector resistivity is of course the major consideration here. The other processes which utilize opposing diffusions as a method of isolation have higher substrate capacitances because the bottom components have the same capacitances per unit per area as the sidewall component. In any event, the high parasitic capacitance associated with the junction isolation of monolithic integrated circuit transistors is one of the serious limitations on the frequency response of such circuits.

7-5   Current Gain

In Sec. 4-2 a current-dependent expression was developed [Eq. (4-23)] for the reciprocal of the common emitter current gain of a transistor. For present purposes we will add a term I_{RE}/I_E to that expression to take account of increases in $1/\beta$ at very low currents. I_{RE} is emitter recombination current. This added term is particularly important in gold-doped transistors. The complete expression is thus

$$\frac{1}{\beta} \approx \frac{\rho_E X_B}{\rho_B L_{pE}} \left(1 + \frac{I_E X_B}{2q D_{nB} A_E N_B'}\right) + \frac{X_B^2}{4 L_{nB}^2} + \frac{s A_s X_B}{2 A_E D_{nB}} + \frac{I_{RE}}{I_E} \tag{7-18}$$

To review, the first term gives the basic expression for $1/\beta$, and the factor in parentheses describes its increase at high currents. The second term is related to base transport and is close to zero for most designs. The third term accounts for surface recombination effects.

By inserting the appropriate values into Eq. (7-18) we obtain values of β in the neighborhood of 50 for either the 0.5- or 0.1-ohm-cm transistor structures. It is difficult to measure the exact value of s, the surface recombination velocity, and therefore, of necessity, the calculated value is approximate. Nevertheless, it is of interest to determine at what current the β starts to fall off because of high-level injection effects, since this determines the maximum current that a given geometry is capable of handling. This current rating or capability is determined as the value of I_E when the second term in parentheses in Eq. (7-18) reaches a value of 0.1, or

$$\frac{I_E X_B}{2q D_{nB} A_E N_B'} = 0.1 \tag{7-19}$$

This current, at which the β begins to fall off, is calculated by substituting the appropriate values into Eq. (7-19) and solving for I_E.

Solving Eq. (7-19) for I_E, and using (1×1.5) mils^2 for the emitter area, A_E, and $N'_B = 1.8 \times 10^{17}/\text{cm}^3$ yields for the 0.5-ohm-cm collector transistor

$$I_E = \frac{0.2 \times 1.6 \times 10^{-19} \text{ coul} \times (1 \times 1.5) \text{ mil}^2 \times 6.45 \times 10^{-6} \text{ cm}^2/\text{mil}^2 \times 12 \text{ cm}^2/\text{sec} \times 1.8 \times 10^{17}/\text{cm}^3}{0.7 \times 10^{-4} \text{ cm}}$$

$$= 9.6 \text{ mA} \qquad (7\text{-}20)$$

The diffusion constant of 12 cm^2/sec is calculated from the minority-carrier mobility of 450 cm^2/volt sec, or the electron mobility on the base side of the emitter junction. We see that the β will begin to fall off in the vicinity of 10 mA.

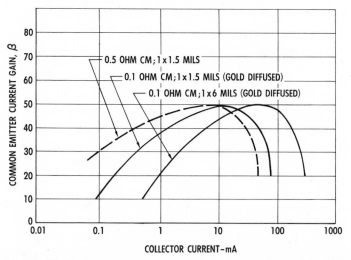

Fig. 7-9 Typical β-versus-current characteristics for several monolithic integrated circuit transistor structures.

Going to a 0.1-ohm-cm gold-doped structure, we obtain the maximum current simply by correcting the values of D_{nB} and N'_B. These new values are 9 cm^2/sec and $5 \times 10^{17}/\text{cm}^3$, respectively. Thus, the maximum current for the 0.1-ohm-cm device is 2.1 times that of the 0.5-ohm-cm device, or approximately 20 mA. These two calculations are best summarized by referring to the curves shown in Fig. 7-9 where β is plotted as a function of collector current. It can be seen that for both 1- by 1.5-mil geometries the β is reasonably flat in the range from 1 to 10 mA. For the 0.1-ohm-cm structure, the β tends to hold up a little bit better at higher currents. At the low-current end in the vicinity of 0.1 mA, the β for the 0.1-ohm-cm transistor is lower than that of the 0.5-ohm-cm transistor. The falloff in low-current β is associated with the gold diffusion.

From a design point of view, the maximum current that can be handled by a particular geometry is proportional to the length of the emitter. Therefore, higher current operation can be obtained simply by modifying the design to make the emitter stripe longer. For example, if we take the 0.1-ohm-cm transistor structure and increase the length of the emitter from 1.5 to 6 mils, we obtain a β-versus-current curve in which the current performance is improved by a factor of approximately 4. In other words, whereas the β of the 1- by 1.5-mil transistor begins to fall off at 20 mA, that of the 1- by 6-mil transistor would begin to fall off at 80 mA. Thus emitter stripe length is a very important design factor in determining the current-handling capability of a particular geometry.

The *effective* emitter length is dependent upon whether we have a single- or double-base-stripe geometry. Generally speaking, only those edges of an emitter that are bounded by a closely spaced base contact are effective in determining the length of the emitter. Therefore, using our 0.1-ohm-cm-collector model as an example, a transistor with a single base stripe of 1 by 1.5 mils would have a β peak at 5 mA; a double-base-stripe version of the same transistor would peak at 10 mA. In a similar manner, a 1- by 6-mil geometry would peak at 20 mA for a single-base-stripe transistor, and at 40 mA for a double-base-stripe device. In the respective cases, the effective emitter lengths are 1.5, 3.0, 6.0, and 12.0 mils.

7-6 Saturation Characteristics

In addition to parasitic capacitance, the characteristics of a monolithic transistor in saturation differ markedly from those of the discrete planar epitaxial device, primarily because the connection to the collector region is made at the top side rather than at the bottom. This manifests itself in a larger value for r_{SC}, as will be described in the paragraphs to follow. The theoretical expression for $V_{CE(SAT)}$ for an n-p-n device is[1]

$$V_{CE(SAT)} \approx \frac{-kT}{q} \ln \frac{\alpha_i(1 - I_C/\beta I_B)}{1 + (I_C/I_B)(1 - \alpha_i)} + I_C r_{SC} \qquad (7\text{-}21)$$

Here, α_i is the inverse alpha of the transistor. For a transistor with a 0.5-ohm-cm collector, α_i is approximately equal to 0.1. The first term of Eq. (7-21) represents the magnitude of the junction voltage in saturation, and the second term is the voltage drop across r_{SC}, the series resistance in the collector. For a p-n-p device, the sign before the kT/q term will be positive, and the $I_C r_{SC}$ term will be negative.

For a typical case where $\alpha_i = 0.1$, $I_C = 5$ mA, $I_B = 0.5$ mA, and $\beta = 50$, we get for the first term in the $V_{CE(SAT)}$ expression

$$V_{CE} \approx -0.026 \ln \frac{0.1(1 - 0.2)}{1 + 10(1 - 0.1)} = -0.026 \ln 0.008 = 0.1 \text{ volt} \qquad (7\text{-}22)$$

It now remains to calculate the magnitude of r_{SC} on the basis of the specified geometry and resistivity. Referring to Fig. 7-4, it can be seen that we are concerned with the resistance of the collector region that is bounded by the active edge of the emitter and the inside edge of the collector contact. Obviously current flows to all portions of the collector contact rectangle from the active edge or edges of the emitter. But to obtain a very rough estimate of r_{SC} we can divide the collector into trapezoidal regions, as shown by the dotted lines in Fig. 7-4, and then consider current to flow only in the upper and lower trapezoids. Thus, for a double-base-stripe geometry there are two trapezoidal regions in parallel. If the resistance of each trapezoid is approximated by $\rho_C d/\bar{l}X_C$, the collector series resistance is approximately

$$r_{SC} = \frac{\rho_C d}{2\bar{l}X_C} \tag{7-23}$$

where ρ_C is the resistivity of the collector region, d is the distance between the emitter edge and the collector contact edge, X_C is the thickness of the collector region, and $\bar{l}$ is given by

$$\bar{l} = \frac{1}{2}(l_E + l_C) \tag{7-24}$$

From Fig. 7-4, we see that

$$\bar{l} = \frac{1}{2}(1.5 + 4.5) = 3.0 \text{ mils} \tag{7-25}$$

Therefore $\rho_C = 0.5$ ohm cm, $d = 2$ mils, $X_C = 22$ microns, and we have

$$r_{SC} \approx \frac{0.5 \text{ ohm cm} \times 2 \text{ mils}}{2 \times 3 \text{ mils} \times 22 \times 10^{-4} \text{ cm}} = 75 \text{ ohms} \tag{7-26}$$

This is a rough figure for the series resistance for the non-gold-doped transistor, where the resistivity is equal to 0.5 ohm cm. For a gold-doped transistor, where $V_{CE(SAT)}$ is intended to be as small as possible, r_{SC} is reduced simply by lowering the resistivity. Therefore, by going to 0.1 ohm cm, we see that the collector series resistance is reduced by a factor of 5 or $r_{SC} \approx 15$ ohms. One important fact that should be noted is that there is no difference in series resistance between the double-base-stripe geometry and the single-base-stripe geometry. This should become apparent upon inspection of Figs. 7-4 and 7-5. In Fig. 7-5 the distance from the active emitter edge to either collector contact is the same as in Fig. 7-4.

We can now determine the magnitude of $V_{CE(SAT)}$ for each of the monolithic transistor structures. For a collector current of 5 mA, we have a series voltage drop through the 75 ohms equal to about 0.4 volt. This value, in addition to the junction potential given by Eq. (7-22), yields a total saturation voltage of 0.5 volt for an I_C/I_B ratio of 10.

For the gold-doped 0.1-ohm-cm device the series voltage drop is considerably lower. For 15 ohms and 5 mA collector current, this drop is equal to 0.075 volt. The junction potential must be recalculated to obtain the correct value because the effective α_i for the gold-doped structure is much lower than that of the non-gold-doped device. Letting $\alpha_i = 0.01$, we have

$$V_{CE} = -0.026 \ln \frac{0.01(1 - 0.2)}{1 + 10(1 - 0.01)} = -0.026 \ln 0.00073 = 0.19 \text{ volt} \tag{7-27}$$

Therefore, the sum of the series drop and the junction potential yields a total $V_{CE(SAT)}$ of approximately 0.26 volt. This value is approximately a factor of 2 less than that calculated for the non-gold-doped 0.5-ohm-cm transistor.

When I_C is equal to zero, there is an offset voltage which, from Eq. (7-21), is $V_{CE} \approx (-kT/q) \ln \alpha_i$. This gives a calculated offset voltage for the non-gold-doped transistor of 0.06 volt. Since the gold-doped transistor has a smaller α_i, its offset voltage is higher and is 0.12 volt.

If a higher level of current operation is required, then by scaling up the geometry to a 1- by 6-mil structure, for example, the series resistance can be reduced even further. For an emitter length of 6 mils,

$$\bar{l} = \tfrac{1}{2}(l_E + l_C) = \tfrac{1}{2}(6 + 9) = 7.5 \text{ mils} \tag{7-28}$$

and
$$r_{sc} \approx \frac{0.1 \text{ ohm cm} \times 2 \text{ mils}}{2 \times 7.5 \text{ mils} \times 22 \times 10^{-4} \text{ cm}} = 6 \text{ ohms} \tag{7-29}$$

Thus, the scaling up of the geometry reduces the series resistance from about 15 to 6 ohms.

If we saturate the gold-doped transistor at a collector current level of 20 mA and an I_C/I_B ratio of 10, then we obtain the same junction potential V_{CE} as given by Eq. (7-27). The series voltage drop at 20 mA through 6 ohms would equal 0.12 volt. Therefore, the total $V_{CE(SAT)}$ for the 1- by 6-mil gold-doped monolithic transistor at 20 mA is 0.31 volt.

One useful method of reducing the collector series resistance of a monolithic transistor is illustrated in Fig. 7-10. This is the so-called "buried" layer process by

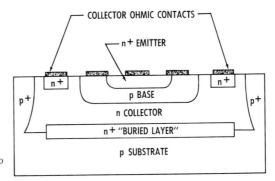

Fig. 7-10 Use of a "buried" n^+ layer to reduce collector series resistance.

which a heavily doped n^+-type region is sandwiched between the n-type epitaxial collector and the p-type substrate. This buried n^+ region has the effect of shunting the high-resistivity collector region, thereby reducing the series resistance considerably. There are two basic methods of achieving this particular structure, namely, (1) by diffusing the n^+ layer into the p-type substrate before the growth of the n-type epitaxial collector, and (2) by selectively growing the n^+ regions, using masked epitaxial techniques, and then continuing on by growing the n-type collectors epitaxially. This technique results in nearly an order of magnitude reduction in r_{sc}. The striking advantage of the buried layer structure is that for saturated switching transistors we can now design on the basis of higher resistivities for the collector region, in order to reduce capacitance and still obtain very low r_{sc}.

7-7 Frequency Response of Monolithic Transistors

The frequency response of a monolithic transistor is best characterized by the parameter f_T, which is that frequency at which the magnitude of β is equal to unity in a grounded-emitter circuit. Equation (4-58) can be used to estimate f_T. If we use 0.4 rad (23°) as a typical value of excess phase, Eq. (4-58) becomes

$$\frac{1}{f_T} \approx 2\pi \times 1.4 \left(r_e C_{TE} + \frac{X_B{}^2}{5D_{nB}} + \frac{X_m}{v_{sc}} + r_{sc} C_{TC} \right) \qquad (7\text{-}30)$$

We will now evaluate the time constants and the delays, in order to determine the relative importance of each and to estimate f_T. The calculations are for a total reverse voltage of 5 volts and a current of 5 mA.

The emitter time constant is

$$\frac{1}{\omega_E} = r_e C_{TE} = \frac{kT}{qI_E} C_{TE} \qquad (7\text{-}31)$$

At 5 mA, r_e is equal to 5.2 ohms. From the previous discussion on capacitance, we saw that the forward-biased C_{TE} for the 0.5-ohm-cm transistor was roughly 6 pf, and for the 0.1-ohm-cm case 10 pf. Therefore, for the non-gold-doped case,

$$\frac{1}{\omega_E} = 5.2 \text{ ohms} \times 6 \times 10^{-12} \text{ farad} = 0.3 \times 10^{-10} \text{ sec} \qquad (0.5 \text{ ohm cm}) \quad (7\text{-}32)$$

and for the gold-doped case,

$$\frac{1}{\omega_E} = 5.2 \text{ ohms} \times 10 \times 10^{-12} \text{ farad} = 0.5 \times 10^{-10} \text{ sec} \qquad (0.1 \text{ ohm cm}) \quad (7\text{-}33)$$

The second term, which is related to the base transit time, is

$$\frac{1}{\omega_B} = \frac{X_B{}^2}{5D_{nB}} \qquad (7\text{-}34)$$

where X_B is the base thickness, and D_{nB} is again the diffusion constant corresponding to the mobility just at the base side of the emitter junction. The diffusion constant for electrons entering the base of the 0.5-ohm-cm model is, as noted before, equal to 12 cm²/sec, and for the 0.1-ohm-cm model, the diffusion constant has a value of 9 cm²/sec. Substituting these values into Eq. (7-34), we obtain

$$\frac{1}{\omega_B} = \frac{(0.7 \times 10^{-4} \text{ cm})^2}{5 \times 12 \text{ cm}^2/\text{sec}} = 0.8 \times 10^{-10} \text{ sec} \qquad (0.5 \text{ ohm cm}) \quad (7\text{-}35)$$

$$\frac{1}{\omega_B} = \frac{(0.7 \times 10^{-4} \text{ cm})^2}{5 \times 9 \text{ cm}^2/\text{sec}} = 1.1 \times 10^{-10} \text{ sec} \qquad (0.1 \text{ ohm cm}) \quad (7\text{-}36)$$

The third term in Eq. (7-30) is related to the finite time that it takes carriers to travel through the collector depletion layer. Assuming that the carriers are traveling at their scattering-limited velocity, $v_{sc} = 8.5 \times 10^6$ cm/sec, the transit time is

$$t_d = \frac{X_m}{v_{sc}} = \frac{1 \times 10^{-4} \text{ cm}}{8.5 \times 10^6 \text{ cm/sec}} = 0.1 \times 10^{-10} \text{ sec} \qquad (0.5 \text{ ohm cm}) \quad (7\text{-}37)$$

$$t_d = \frac{X_m}{v_{sc}} = \frac{0.5 \times 10^{-4} \text{ cm}}{8.5 \times 10^6 \text{ cm/sec}} = 0.06 \times 10^{-10} \text{ sec} \qquad (0.1 \text{ ohm cm}) \quad (7\text{-}38)$$

The fourth and last term is a function of the charging of the collector capacitance through the collector series resistance. However, we must also take into consideration the charging of the substrate capacitance. The overall time constant is approximately

$$\frac{1}{\omega_C} = r_{sc}C_{TC} + \frac{r'_{sc}C_{TS}}{2} \tag{7-39}$$

In the second term of Eq. (7-39), r'_{sc} is a very rough estimate of the series resistance of the entire collector region over the area of the substrate capacitance; it is treated as the paralleled resistance of two equal rectangles. Replacing the distributed $r'_{sc}C_{TS}$ with an approximate lumped equivalent gives rise to the factor of 2. For a substrate junction of 8 by 6.5 mils,

$$r'_{sc} \approx \frac{\rho_c d}{2lX_C} = \frac{0.5 \text{ ohm cm} \times 4 \text{ mils}}{2 \times 6.5 \text{ mils} \times 1 \text{ mil} \times 2.54 \times 10^{-3} \text{ cm/mil}} = 60 \text{ ohms}$$
$$\text{(0.5 ohm cm)} \qquad (7\text{-}40)$$

$$r'_{sc} \approx \frac{\rho_c d}{2lX_C} = \frac{0.1 \text{ ohm cm} \times 4 \text{ mils}}{2 \times 6.5 \text{ mils} \times 1 \text{ mil} \times 2.54 \times 10^{-3} \text{ cm/mil}} = 15 \text{ ohms}$$
$$\text{(0.1 ohm cm)} \qquad (7\text{-}41)$$

The calculations given above are of course for the double-base-stripe geometry, and it is assumed that the collector is 1 mil or 25 microns thick. If we now substitute the previously determined r_{sc} and capacitance values into Eq. (7-39), we obtain for the respective collector time constants

$$\frac{1}{\omega_C} = 75 \text{ ohms} \times 0.65 \text{ pf} + \frac{60 \text{ ohms} \times 2.9 \text{ pf}}{2} = 1.4 \times 10^{-10} \text{ sec}$$
$$\text{(0.5 ohm cm)} \qquad (7\text{-}42)$$

$$\frac{1}{\omega_C} = 15 \text{ ohms} \times 1.3 \text{ pf} + \frac{15 \text{ ohms} \times 4.6 \text{ pf}}{2} = 0.5 \times 10^{-10} \text{ sec}$$
$$\text{(0.1 ohm cm)} \qquad (7\text{-}43)$$

Here we see the harmful effect that the parasitic capacitance has on the magnitude of this time constant. In discrete passivated epitaxial transistors, where there are no parasitic capacitances, the second term of the above equations would equal zero, and the time constants would be considerably smaller. This clearly points out how the parasitic capacitance degrades the frequency response of the monolithic transistor.

We can now add up all the terms that were calculated, substitute them into Eq. (7-30), and obtain final values for f_T. For the non-gold-doped case,

$$\frac{1}{f_T} \approx 2\pi \times 1.4 \times 2.6 \times 10^{-10}$$
$$\text{(0.5 ohm cm)} \qquad (7\text{-}44)$$

$$f_T \approx 4.4 \times 10^8 \text{ cps}$$

and for the gold-doped case,

$$\frac{1}{f_T} \approx 2\pi \times 1.4 \times 2.2 \times 10^{-10}$$
$$\text{(0.1 ohm cm)} \qquad (7\text{-}45)$$

$$f_T \approx 5.2 \times 10^8 \text{ cps}$$

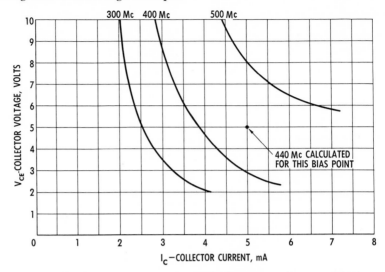

Fig. 7-11 Contours of constant gain-bandwidth frequency f_T for a monolithic integrated circuit transistor with a 1- by 1.5-mil emitter and a 0.5-ohm-cm collector.

Thus we see that for the described models of the monolithic transistor we obtain an f_T at 5 volts and 5 mA of approximately 440 and 520 Mc, respectively. It is interesting to note that even though the resistivity was reduced for the gold-doped transistor design, the f_T comes out to be about 100 Mc higher. This is attributed only to the fact that the collector time constant $1/\omega_C$ is considerably lower because r_{SC} has been reduced. Actual f_T data for a 0.5-ohm-cm, 1- by 1.5-mil monolithic transistor are given in Fig. 7-11.

For simplicity in these engineering calculations, we have made no distinction between the *physical* or junction-to-junction base thickness and the effective base thickness. The latter takes account of the finite spreading of the collector junction depletion layer into the base region. We have employed the 0.7-micron figure for both and have obtained good approximations.

7-8 Summary of Characteristics and Circuit Applications of Monolithic Transistors

The properties of the monolithic transistor that were calculated in the previous sections are presented in Table 7-1, along with some observed values for both the non-gold-doped design and the gold-doped design. A comparison of the values for each characteristic reveals how significant the resistivity of the epitaxial collector is in determining breakdown voltages, capacitances, series resistance, and frequency response.

The non-gold-doped design with the 0.5-ohm-cm collector is very similar to the 2N918 passivated epitaxial transistor, which is its closest discrete counterpart. The f_T for the 2N918, however, is about twice as high, or 900 Mc, since the 2N918 has less parasitic capacitance and resistance.

The frequency $f_{\max}$ is defined as that frequency at which the matched grounded-emitter power gain is equal to unity, or 0 db, and is given by Eq. (4-60), which is repeated here for convenience.

$$f_{\max} \approx \sqrt{\frac{f_T}{8\pi r_B' C_{TC}}} \qquad (4\text{-}60)$$

For the 0.5-ohm-cm monolithic transistor, we have

$$f_{\max} \approx \sqrt{\frac{440 \times 10^6}{8\pi \times 20 \text{ ohms} \times 0.65 \times 10^{-12} \text{ farad}}} = 1.1 \text{ gigacycles} \qquad (7\text{-}46)$$

For the 2N918, $f_{\max}$ is considerably higher because of the higher f_T. Also, by using a lower base sheet resistance, 50 ohms per square instead of 200 ohms per square, r_B' is reduced by a factor of 4. The combination of both effects makes the $f_{\max}$ for the 2N918 well over 2 gc. Since power gain decreases approximately as the square of frequency, or 6 db/octave, then for an $f_{\max}$ of 1.1 gc, we would expect a matched power gain of 6 db at 550 Mc, 12 db at 275 Mc, and 18 db at 138 Mc. Monolithic integrated amplifier circuits incorporating the 1- by 1.5-mil geometry for the transistor have demonstrated power gains over 20 db at 130 Mc (i.e., $f_{\max} \approx 1.1$ gc).

The gold-doped switching transistor described in Table 7-1 closely resembles the 2N709 passivated epitaxial discrete transistor. These devices are gold-doped to kill lifetime, and thereby reduce the amount of stored charge when switched into saturation. Since the lifetime is in the order of 10 nsec, we would expect a storage time constant of roughly 10 nsec. The f_T for the monolithic transistor is about 500 Mc, compared to about 800 Mc for the 2N709. Also, $V_{CE(SAT)}$ for the mono-

Table 7-1 Summary of Calculated and Observed Characteristics for 1 Mil × 1.5 Mil Double-base-stripe Monolithic Transistors

Transistor characteristic	Non-gold-doped 0.5-ohm-cm collector	Gold-doped 0.1-ohm-cm collector
BV_{CBO}*	55 volts	25 volts
BV_{EBO}*	7 volts	5 volts
BV_{CEO}	23 volts	14 volts
BV_{CS}*	75 volts	25 volts
C_{TE} (forward bias) ..	6 pf	10 pf
C_{TE} at 0.5 volt	1.5 pf	2.5 pf
C_{TC} at 5 volts	0.7 pf	1.5 pf
C_{TS} at 5 volts	2.9 pf	4.6 pf
β at 10 mA*	50	50
β at 0.1 mA*	30	10
r_{SC}	75 ohms	15 ohms
$V_{CE(SAT)}$ at 5 mA ...	0.5 volt	0.26 volt
V_{BE} at 10 mA*	0.85 volt	0.85 volt
f_T at 5 volts, 5 mA ..	440 Mc	520 Mc
$f_{\max}$	1.1 gc	
τ_S		10 nsec

*Observed values.

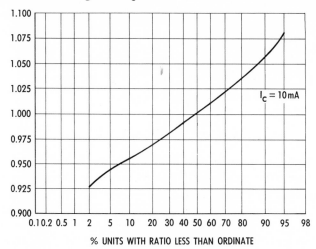

Fig. 7-12 Distribution of V_{BE} ratios for a monolithic transistor pair.

lithic transistor is 0.26 volt, compared to 0.18 volt for the 2N709. For both of these, we again see the effect of parasitics on the device characteristics. The substrate capacitance, in particular, is most deleterious to the switching speed of logic circuits because of the fact that C_{TS} must be charged through the load resistor R_L. This becomes the most significant time constant in a diode transistor logic (DTL) circuit.

Another circuit application of the monolithic transistor is the analogue-type differential amplifier. This is a basic linear amplifier circuit often used either as an operational amplifier for servo controls or as a sense amplifier for computer memories. For the differential amplifier circuit, the matching and tracking characteristics of β and V_{BE} are important design requirements.

Since both these characteristics are a function of sheet resistance and/or surface effects, we would expect excellent matching characteristics for a pair of transistors fabricated simultaneously within the same monolithic chip of silicon. Figure 7-12 is a plot of the distribution of the V_{BE} ratio for such a monolithic pair. Here we

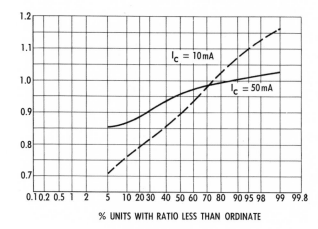

Fig. 7-13 Distribution of β ratios for a monolithic transistor pair.

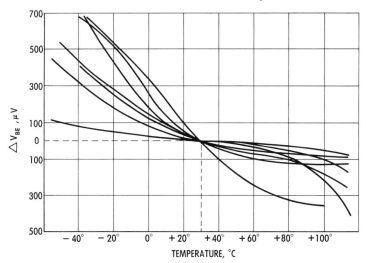

Fig. 7-14 Differential V_{BE} versus temperature relative to 30°C.

see that the V_{BE} ratio is maintained within ± 7.5 per cent for 90 per cent of the units, with more than 80 per cent of the pairs within a ± 4 per cent ratio. Figure 7-13 is a similar plot for the β ratio at two different current levels. At the higher current, where the effect of surfaces on β is negligible, the β ratio for 75 per cent of the units is maintained within 10 per cent. At the lower currents, the betas are within 20 per cent for 80 per cent of the units. The temperature drift of several differential amplifiers was measured, and the results showing the V_{BE} offset voltage relative to 30°C are plotted in Fig. 7-14. It can be seen that over the temperature range from -50 to $+120$°C, the V_{BE} drift averaged less than 10 μv/deg C.

7-9   The Five Basic Diode Connections of the Integrated Circuit Transistor

Diodes find widespread use in integrated circuits that are used for digital applications. This is particularly evident from the large number of diodes utilized in DTL circuits. Of course, diodes are used in integrated circuits in many other applications as well. In view of this, we will now proceed to consider how the integrated circuit transistor can be used as a diode in a monolithic integrated circuit. It is common practice to use transistor structures in this way because transistors must be formed anyway, and they can thus be obtained more "cheaply" than specialized diode structures. We will give numerical examples only for the non-gold-doped structure, since this will illustrate the principles adequately; a number of the properties which are to be treated have already been considered in the first half of this chapter as they pertain to both types of transistors.

Figure 7-15 shows five different ways[2] in which the monolithic transistor structure can be utilized as a diode and presents each connection arrangement schematically as well as structurally. Also included in Fig. 7-15 are diagrams of the minority-carrier distributions in the various regions of the structure under conditions of forward bias, with the distributions produced by each junction shown independently.

The carrier diagram for each of these configurations will be particularly helpful in understanding the mechanism of storage time and diode recovery. This, of course, is a critical quantity for diodes used in switching applications. The reader will recall from the fundamentals of p-n junction theory given in Chap. 2 that the carrier currents that flow are proportional to the slopes of the carrier distributions. Also, the magnitude of the slope is determined both by the injected minority-carrier level

$$n = n_p \, e^{qV/kT} \tag{7-47}$$

$$p = p_n \, e^{qV/kT} \tag{7-48}$$

and by the minority-carrier diffusion length or the thickness of the region, whichever is smaller. These five configurations will be referred to in the sections to follow and will be compared.

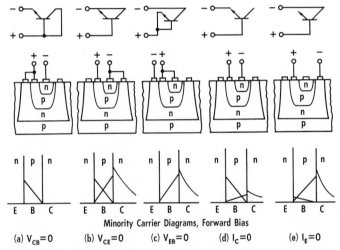

Minority Carrier Diagrams, Forward Bias

(a) $V_{CB}=0$ (b) $V_{CE}=0$ (c) $V_{EB}=0$ (d) $I_C=0$ (e) $I_E=0$

Fig. 7-15 The five basic diode connections of the integrated circuit transistor, including diagrams of the minority-carrier distributions in the various regions of the structure under forward bias.

Quantities such as breakdown voltage, leakage current, capacitance, diode recovery time, and forward voltage drop differ among these various connections and constitute the basis for choice.

The first arrangement (Fig. 7-15a) is the case where the emitter-base diode is used and the collector-base junction is shorted ($V_{CB} = 0$). Under forward-bias conditions the current that flows will consist mainly of minority carriers (electrons) injected into the p-type base layer since the emitter is heavily doped. If we assume a thin enough base with respect to the lifetime of the p-type layer, then we can further assume that no recombination takes place in the base region. This would establish in the base a linear minority-carrier distribution, as shown in Fig. 7-15a. At the collector-base junction, the minority-carrier level is reduced approximately to its equilibrium value.

The second diode arrangement, in which the emitter is shorted to the collector ($V_{CE} = 0$), is shown in Fig. 7-15b. This is a case where both the emitter-base and collector-base junctions are forward-biased. Here current is injected into the base from both junctions. The total minority-carrier distribution in the base is simply the sum of the two distributions which, for clarity, have been shown independently. Since the collector region is relatively lightly doped, there is a significant injection of holes into that region from the base. In the base region the injected level at the collector is higher than the injected level at the emitter, because the diffused impurity concentration of the base decreases with distance. Thus the equilibrium minority-carrier concentrations are higher at the collector junction boundaries than at the emitter junction boundaries.

The third configuration, shown in Fig. 7-15c, is the case where the emitter is shorted to the base ($V_{EB} = 0$) and the diode consists of the base-collector junction. The minority-carrier diagram for this case is similar to the collector portion of the diagram for the previous arrangement.

The fourth diode arrangement, shown in Fig. 7-15d, consists of an emitter-base diode where the collector is open-circuited (floating) so that $I_C = 0$. Because minority carriers are injected into the base region under forward-bias conditions, the floating collector junction assumes a slight forward-bias potential. This forward bias causes a diffusion current into the base which is equal and opposite to the minority-carrier drift current that crosses the collector depletion layer. Thus, the forward-bias potential is an equilibrium condition, resulting from the fact that the net collector current is zero.

The fifth connection, shown in Fig. 7-15e, is the case where $I_E = 0$ and the diode consists of the forward-biased collector-base junction. Here the emitter junction assumes an equilibrium forward-bias potential, and the carrier diagram is as shown in the figure.

For an integrated circuit transistor the base side of the collector-base junction is more heavily doped than the collector side. Thus, when the collector-base junction is forward-biased, more minority carriers are injected into the collector than into the base. This is shown in Fig. 7-15b to e. It is assumed here that minority-carrier storage in the substrate has been avoided through biasing techniques.

7-10 Diode Reverse Breakdown Voltages

Since the emitter-base, collector-base, and collector-substrate junctions approach step junctions for large reverse bias, we can assume step-junction behavior for reverse breakdown voltage considerations. There is sufficient difference between impurity levels on the two sides of each of these junctions so that, at higher voltage levels, the depletion layer will spread mostly into one side. Therefore, for the breakdown calculations we can use the curve shown in Fig. 2-20, which gives the avalanche breakdown voltage for silicon as a function of impurity concentration.

Referring to Fig. 7-15, we can see that of the five diode arrangements, a, b, and d are each limited by the avalanche breakdown of the emitter-base junction. Actual measurements of integrated circuit structures employing these connections yield a breakdown in the 5- to 7-volt range, as noted earlier.

For the diode connections given by Fig. 7-15c and e, the breakdown voltage of the collector-base diode must be considered. In this particular case, the breakdown is limited by the impurity level in the epitaxial-collector region. For the 0.5-ohm-cm collector, as also noted earlier, this avalanche breakdown voltage is about 55 volts. Actually, the collector-base breakdown voltage may not be reached in a device if the base is extremely thin so that breakdown is limited by punch-through to the emitter junction. This is particularly prevalent in thin-base structures that have relatively high base sheet resistances. If the transistor is punch-through-limited, then we would observe a breakdown for condition e which is higher than that of condition c by BV_{EBO}, as described in Sec. 4-6. In other words, by shorting the emitter to the base we could measure the true punch-through voltage. Repeating the pertinent equation for convenience, we have, under open-circuit conditions for case e,

$$BV_{CBO} = V_{PT} + BV_{EBO} \qquad (4\text{-}28)$$

where V_{PT} is, of course, the punch-through voltage. In summary, the collector-base diode arrangements offer a higher breakdown voltage than the emitter-base diode arrangements, although for low-level switching circuits, the magnitude of BV_{EBO} is more than adequate.

The breakdown voltage of the collector-to-substrate junction is another important consideration. As pointed out in Sec. 7-2, this is limited by the graded junction between the p-type diffused isolation region and the epitaxial collector. BV_{CS} is on the order of 75 volts.

7-11   Diode Leakage Currents

As noted in Sec. 7-3, the leakage current that flows in a reverse-biased silicon junction is a function of the number of recombination centers existing in the depletion layer of the junction. Gold atoms are excellent recombination centers, and hence the gold diffusion process used to kill lifetime has an important effect on leakage current. Bakanowski and Forster[3] showed that the reverse current in silicon high-speed switching diodes will increase as the temperature of gold diffusion increases, as shown in Fig. 7-16, where the bars indicate the maximum and minimum values. The reverse current caused by charge generation I_g is given by Eq. (7-4).

Generation rate g will range in value from $10^{15}/cm^3$ sec for a non-gold-doped structure to as much as $10^{17}/cm^3$ sec for a heavily gold-doped junction. Regardless of the generation rate, the connections for $V_{CB} = 0$ or $I_C = 0$ should yield the smallest values of reverse current. This is true because the emitter-base junction is dominant in these connections, and this junction has the smallest area and the thinnest depletion layer. The collector-to-base configuration given by $V_{EB} = 0$, or $I_E = 0$, will yield a higher reverse current. Finally, the configuration illustrated in Fig. 7-15b, where $V_{CE} = 0$, yields the highest reverse current since both junctions are connected in parallel. It is difficult to calculate accurately the magnitude of these various reverse currents because, in the fabrication of monolithic structures, there is also a certain amount of surface leakage superimposed. In any event, the observed currents would measure from 0.1 to 100 nA. These leakage levels are low enough for most circuit applications.

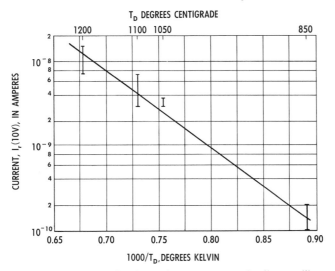

Fig. 7-16 Experimentally observed reverse current in discrete silicon diodes as a function of gold diffusion temperature. (*After Bakanowski and Forster.*[3])

The charge generation reverse current is proportional to the intrinsic carrier concentration n_i, which increases approximately an order of magnitude for every $30°C$. In other words, at $85°C$, the charge generation current would be approximately 100 times the room-temperature value.

7-12 Diode Capacitances

In the five diode connection arrangements, there are the three distinctly different junctions whose capacitances have already been discussed in Sec. 7-4. These are the emitter-base junction, the collector-base junction, and the collector-substrate junction.

Once again we will use the step-junction (n^+-p) approximation for the emitter-base junction. From Eq. (2-78) we obtain for this situation

$$C_{TE} = A_E \sqrt{\frac{q\kappa\epsilon_o N_B'}{2V}} \qquad (7\text{-}49)$$

For the sake of a specific calculation, let us assume a reverse bias of 5 volts. Using the same area and impurity concentration values as in Sec. 7-4, we can evaluate the radical once more with the aid of Fig. 2-18. The result is 4×10^4 pf/cm². Hence, the total emitter-base capacitance at 5 volts reverse bias is

$$C_{TE} = 1.9 \text{ mil}^2 \times 6.45 \times 10^{-6} \text{ cm}^2/\text{mil}^2 \times 4 \times 10^4 \text{ pf/cm}^2 = 0.5 \text{ pf} \quad (7\text{-}50)$$

The capacitance C_{TC} of the collector-base junction for this structure at a bias of 5 volts has been calculated previously [Eq. (7-10)], yielding 0.7 pf. For a single-base-stripe geometry often used for diodes, the area is reduced to 2.5 by 3 mils, and this leads to the result that $C_{TC} = 0.5$ pf.

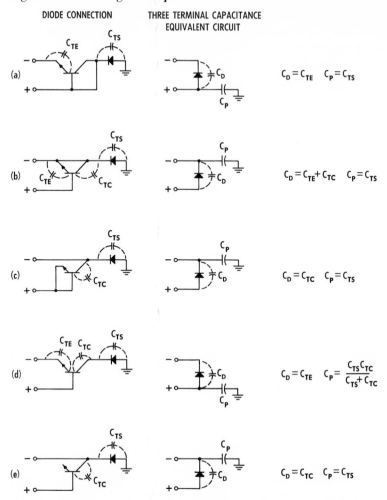

DIODE CONNECTION   THREE TERMINAL CAPACITANCE
                            EQUIVALENT CIRCUIT

(a) $C_D = C_{TE}$ $C_P = C_{TS}$

(b) $C_D = C_{TE} + C_{TC}$ $C_P = C_{TS}$

(c) $C_D = C_{TC}$ $C_P = C_{TS}$

(d) $C_D = C_{TE}$ $C_P = \dfrac{C_{TS} C_{TC}}{C_{TS} + C_{TC}}$

(e) $C_D = C_{TC}$ $C_P = C_{TS}$

Fig. 7-17   Effective capacitances of the five diode configurations. C_D denotes the capacitance across the diode, and C_P is the parasitic capacitance.

The collector-substrate or isolation junction contributes the third capacitance that must be considered. We saw in Sec. 7-4 that the substrate capacitance was approximately 2.9 pf at 5 volts reverse bias. This is the case for a transistor having a 0.5-ohm-cm collector, a 10-ohm-cm p-type substrate, and a double-base-stripe geometry. For a single-base-stripe geometry, we saw that the substrate capacitance is equal to approximately 2.7 pf. The small difference between the two arises from the small difference in relative areas required in the isolation islands for the two transistor structures.

In calculating the effective capacitance of each of the five diode configurations, we must consider both the capacitance across the diode and the capacitance of the collector-substrate junction C_{TS}. Since the substrate is normally connected to the most negative potential (for a p substrate), the substrate terminal of C_{TS} is at signal ground. The resultant capacitance network becomes a three-terminal structure with the collector-substrate capacitance appearing as a parasitic element.

The capacitances of the five configurations are given in Fig. 7-17, where the capacitance across the diode is denoted as C_D, and the parasitic capacitance as C_P. Note that connection d has the smallest parasitic capacitance.

7-13 Diode Storage Time (Diode Recovery)

In digital applications, the ability of a diode to respond to the applied pulse becomes a very important consideration for logic circuit design. A p-n junction which is conducting a steady-state forward current will not turn off immediately when the applied voltage is reversed. This is the phenomenon of minority-carrier storage, which is a function of the carrier lifetime of the region into which injection occurs. The lower the lifetime, the more rapidly the injected carriers will recombine, and the quicker the diode returns to the equilibrium OFF state. The most convenient way of measuring carrier storage is to measure the diode recovery time t_{dr}, which is related to lifetime τ as follows:[3, 4]

$$t_{dr} \approx 0.9\tau \qquad \text{(step junction)} \qquad (7\text{-}51)$$

$$t_{dr} \approx 0.5\tau \qquad \text{(graded junction)} \qquad (7\text{-}52)$$

Equations (7-51) and (7-52) apply for conventional diodes when the ratio of initial reverse current to forward current is unity. Recovery time for integrated circuit diodes will, of course, also be a function of the lifetime and geometry of the various regions where charge is stored.

For a non-gold-doped integrated circuit transistor, the minority-carrier lifetime would ordinarily be in the vicinity of 10 μsec. When lower storage times are required, as discussed in Sec. 3-5, the use of gold diffusion as a last step will reduce the lifetime to the order of about 10 nsec or less. Figure 7-18 shows a curve of typical recovery time for discrete diodes as a function of the temperature of gold diffusion, as

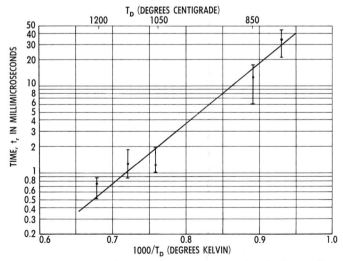

Fig. 7-18 Experimentally observed reverse recovery time in discrete silicon diodes as a function of gold diffusion temperature. (*After Bakanowski and Forster.*[3])

observed experimentally by Bakanowski and Forster.[3] It is seen that at the higher temperatures much higher concentration of gold is achieved, resulting in a greater concentration of impurity recombination centers.

The minority-carrier diagrams for all the five diode connections have been redrawn in Fig. 7-19, where the shaded areas denote the amount of stored charge under forward-bias conditions. The values of t_{dr} quoted in this figure are typical values when the forward current equals the initial reverse current. In each case it is assumed that the forward current is the same. In Fig. 7-19a, when the collector-base junction is shorted, we have the smallest t_{dr} because this is the only condition in which no additional charge is stored in the collector. In Fig. 7-19d, when the collector is floating, a forward-bias equilibrium potential exists, and charge is stored in the collector as well as additional charge in the base. Therefore, this results in a considerably higher t_{dr} than in Fig. 7-19a. When the emitter-base junction is shorted, as in Fig. 7-19c, we have a case comparable to Fig. 7-19d, because the forward-biased collector-base junction injects charge into both the base and collector. When the emitter junction floats, as in Fig. 7-19e, the stored charge is still greater. The longest diode recovery time is observed for Fig. 7-19b, where both junctions are heavily forward-biased and there exists the largest amount of stored charge. It should be apparent that if the integrated circuit device were gold-doped, the recovery time relationship of the five diode connections would still apply; however, the absolute level for t_{dr} would be proportionately lower in each case.

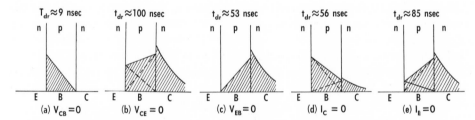

Fig. 7-19 Minority-carrier diagrams for the five diode connections. The shaded portions denote the amount of stored charge in each area under forward-bias conditions. The diode recovery times given are typical values for non-gold-doped structures.

7-14   Forward Characteristics

Let us now turn our attention to the forward characteristics of the five different connections in order to get a comparison of the forward voltage drops when the diodes are conducting the same current.

It is possible to solve for these voltages through use of the nonlinear transistor model.[1, 5-7] In this model the effects of all device junctions (including the collector-substrate junction) may be accounted for in detail. This treatment will be presented in "Analysis and Design of Integrated Circuits." However, without going into these details, some conclusions can still be reached on the basis of the bulk resistances of the various regions of the device. Let us determine the magnitude of these bulk resistances for a typical integrated circuit diode. This step is more difficult than we might initially suppose, since the effective volumes for determining bulk resistance vary with the diode connection, and are not necessarily the same as for the integrated circuit transistor. For example, in the collector-base diode with the emitter open-circuited (diode e), we would expect that the bulk of the current would flow across the four vertical sides of the collector junction, rather than under and near the emitter, for two reasons. The first is that the sides are, of course, closer to the contacts. In addition, the built-in base field associated with the impurity gradient is in a direction such that it opposes the forward current flow of this diode, and this field is strongest under the emitter.

With this in mind, we note that one approach for calculating the approximate r_{SC} (the bulk resistance of the collector) for the case where the emitter is open-circuited would be to use four trapezoids and to determine their parallel resistance. On the basis of Fig. 7-4 and Eq. (7-23) we have for the resistance of each of the smaller trapezoids,

$$R \approx \frac{\rho_C d}{X_C(l_b + l_c)/2} = \frac{0.5 \text{ ohm cm} \times 0.5 \text{ mil}}{22 \times 10^{-4} \text{ cm} \times 3 \text{ mils}} = 38 \text{ ohms} \qquad (7\text{-}53)$$

and for the larger,

$$R = \frac{0.5 \times 0.5 \text{ mil}}{22 \times 10^{-4} \text{ cm} \times 4.5 \text{ mils}} = 25 \text{ ohms} \qquad (7\text{-}54)$$

Adding these resistances in parallel yields an effective r_{SC} of approximately 7 ohms. We must emphasize again that care must be taken to select the proper regions for computing bulk resistance and that calculated results are usually only approximate in nature.

Experimental results are given in Table 7-2 for forward voltage V_F for the five diode connections at a current of 10 mA. Each datum is an average of readings taken for transistors having the double-base-stripe geometry of Fig. 7-4 with the substrate floating.

Table 7-2   Forward Voltage for the Five Diode Connections

Diode connection	V_F at 10 mA
(a) $V_{CB} = 0$	0.85
(b) $V_{CE} = 0$	0.92
(c) $V_{EB} = 0$	0.94
(d) $I_C = 0$	0.96
(e) $I_E = 0$	0.95

The fact that diode connection d has the largest forward voltage can be justified by use of the nonlinear model approach. On the other hand, in connnection a (collector-base shorted) the device is still operating as a transistor, and thus the base current is considerably less than the collector current. Consequently, the voltage drop across the base resistance is considerably smaller than in the other diode connections. For forward currents greater than a milliampere this amounts to an appreciable reduction, with the result that at these currents, connection a exhibits the smallest forward voltage.

From a device design point of view, the diode series resistances can be lowered, simply by lowering the sheet resistances of either the base diffusion or the collector region. For example, lowering the sheet resistance of the base region lowers r'_B. However, this would be achieved at the expense of certain desirable transistor and resistor properties. Similarly, r_{SC} could be lowered by decreasing the resistivity and increasing the thickness of the epitaxial collector. However, this will increase the capacitance per unit area of both the collector junction and the sidewall component of the substrate parasitic capacitance. Making the collector thicker would necessitate a considerably longer isolation diffusion time, since the latter varies as the square of the required diffusion depth.

7-15   p-n-p Parasitic Transistor Action

When the integrated circuit appears within a monolithic block along with other components, the substrate must be returned to the most negative point of the circuit. This is essential from the standpoint of preventing any forward conduction of the collector-substrate junction, and to keep its parasitic capacitance at an absolute minimum. When the structure is connected as a diode, particularly in those cases where the collector-base junction is forward-biased, we encounter a p-n-p parasitic transistor. In this p-n-p transistor the reverse-biased substrate serves as the collector, the n-type epitaxial layer is the base, and the diffused p-type base is the emitter. In other words, the p-n-p transistor consists of the base, collector, and substrate of the integrated circuit n-p-n transistor. The equivalent circuit of this four-layer device illustrating the p-n-p action is shown in Fig. 7-20. In this particular illustration, the emitter is shown floating, the base is forward-biased with respect to the collector, and the substrate is reverse-biased with respect to the collector. Thus, we have an effective p-n-p transistor which will shunt current from the diode down into the substrate. This current-shunting action will definitely be affected by the common emitter current gain, or β, of the p-n-p transistor.

The common base current gain α is the product of the emitter efficiency and base transport factor. Assuming that our model is non-gold-doped, we could expect minority-carrier lifetimes on the order of 10 μsec. If we compute the X_B/L_p ratio for this structure for a base thickness of approximately 20 microns, we arrive at a base transport factor very close to unity. Emitter efficiency may be calculated by considering the ratio of the base sheet resistance to the collector sheet resistance. Again for the high-lifetime case, we would obtain emitter efficiency on the order of 0.5 to 0.7. This corresponds to a β range of about 1 to 2.3. Although the gain of the p-n-p transistor is extremely low, it nevertheless can bypass a significant amount of current. In the case where the monolithic transistor is gold-doped, the parasitic p-n-p action is virtually eliminated, since

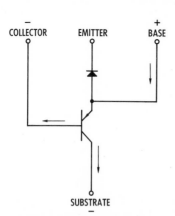

Fig. 7-20 Equivalent circuit of an integrated circuit transistor, illustrating p-n-p parasitic transistor action.

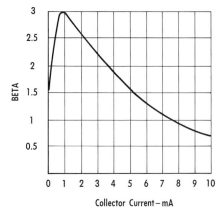

Fig. 7-21 Typical β-versus-current curves for a p-n-p parasitic transistor.

the lifetime in the collector region is so low that "base" transport is essentially zero. Measurements of the p-n-p parasitic action of actual integrated circuit devices reveal betas in the range of 1 to 3 for high-lifetime structures, and betas as low as 0.01 for gold-doped structures.

Let us now apply this consideration to each of the five diode connections. In *a* because the collector-base junction is shorted, there can be no p-n-p transistor action. In all the other configurations a significant amount of current is bypassed into the substrate. This is illustrated in Table 7-3, where the entry entitled p-n-p β is interpreted as the ratio of substrate current to the current flowing out of the n terminal of the diode.

It should be noted that the p-n-p structure for condition *c* will yield a lower β than that of *e*. This is associated with the level of minority carriers at the emitter-base junction. This carrier level will vary, depending on whether the emitter-base junction is shorted or not. In the shorted condition, given by *c*, the efficiency of injection by the *emitter* of the parasitic p-n-p transistor is lower, since a larger amount of current is injected into the diffused p region (the base of our standard integrated circuit transistor). Actual measurements of such structures indicate that for condition *c* we will obtain a β of approximately 2, whereas, by letting the emitter float, the β increases to approximately 3.

In diode connection *d*, the base of the p-n-p transistor (which corresponds to the collector of our integrated circuit structure) is floating. Thus when the diffused p region is made positive and the substrate is made negative, we have a p-n-p transistor in an active condition, since the collector-base junction of the n-p-n transistor is forward-biased because of the forward bias of the diode. Figure 7-21 is a plot of β versus current for a typical p-n-p parasitic transistor for a non-gold-doped structure. It will be noted that the β peaks to a value of 3 at 1 mA and falls off rapidly to about 0.8 at 10 mA.

The p-n-p transistor action can be quite harmful if it is not taken into account in the design of integrated circuits. This is especially true of DTL circuits where we use a diode in series with the base of the transistor to be driven. When the transistor is to be turned on through the diode with a positive pulse, it is essential that all the applied current feed into the base of the driven transistor. However, if the β

of the p-n-p device associated with the driving diode is at all significant, then the source current would be bypassed by the shunting action of the parasitic transistor. In some cases, however, this characteristic may be utilized as an antisaturation feature.

7-16 Summary of Integrated Circuit Diode Considerations

We can now summarize all the preceding sections of this chapter by comparing results with the various diode connections. The typical values previously discussed are all summarized in Table 7-3.

Diode a, in which the collector-base junction is shorted, is perhaps the most useful configuration from the standpoint of the requirements for high-speed diodes that are to be used in digital integrated circuits. Here we have the lowest forward voltage drop and no p-n-p action to the substrate. Furthermore, the storage time is quite low since charge is stored only in the base. The storage time for this diode configuration is reduced considerably when the structure is gold-doped. For switching applications, a 7-volt breakdown rating is usually adequate.

The configuration given by d, in which the collector is floating, is also useful for switching circuits. Because of the additional stored charge in the floating collector, this configuration could be used as a storage diode to be placed in series with the base of the transistor in DTL integrated circuitry. The stored charge feature can be used for obtaining a high-speed turn-off of the transistor as it comes out of saturation. The fact that this particular structure has the highest forward voltage drop makes it useful from the standpoint of noise immunity in DTL circuits. Finally, as illustrated in Fig. 7-17, this diode connection has the smallest parasitic capacitance. The reader will note that the configuration in b could also be used as a stored charge device.

The collector-base configurations of c and e have the highest reverse voltage ratings. Both of these suffer from the standpoint of having relatively high p-n-p betas; nevertheless, in a gold-doped integrated circuit structure the p-n-p β would be virtually zero, and hence in such structures diodes c and e are useful as general-purpose diodes.

Table 7-3   Summary of Typical Values for Various Diode Connections

Characteristic	(a) $V_{CB} = 0$	(b) $V_{CE} = 0$	(c) $V_{EB} = 0$	(d) $I_C = 0$	(e) $I_E = 0$
Breakdown voltage, volts	7	7	55	7	55
Storage time, nsec	9	100	53	56	85
Forward voltage, volts	0.85	0.92	0.94	0.96	0.95
p-n-p β	0	3	2	3	3
C_D, pf (5 volts reverse bias)	0.5	1.2	0.7	0.5	0.7
C_P, pf (substrate at 5 volts negative with respect to collector)	2.9	2.9	2.9	1.2*	2.9

* Collector-base junction will assume slight forward-bias potential so that capacitance will increase to approximately 2 pf. This appears in series with substrate capacitance of 2.9 pf, resulting in the net value of 1.2 pf.

Finally, it should be noted that it is possible to fabricate an integrated circuit diode by using the collector-base junction without diffusing an emitter. This connection has the advantage that the collector-base junction area may be reduced, yielding a smaller C_{TC}.[8]

REFERENCES

1. Ebers, J. J., and J. L. Moll: Large-signal Behavior of Junction Transistors, *Proc. IRE,* vol. 42, pp. 1761–1772, December, 1954.
2. Lin, H. C.: Diode Operation of a Transistor in Functional Blocks, *IEEE Trans. Electron Devices,* vol. ED-10, no. 3, pp. 189–194, May, 1963.
3. Bakanowski, A. E., and J. H. Forster: Electrical Properties of Gold-doped Diffused Silicon Computer Diodes, *Bell System Tech. J.,* vol. 39, pp. 87–104, January, 1960. Figures 7-16 and 7-18 reprinted by permission of the copyright owner, American Telephone & Telegraph Company, and the authors.
4. Kingston, R. H.: Switching Time in Junction Diodes and Junction Transistors, *Proc. IRE,* vol. 42, pp. 829–834, May, 1954.
5. Hamilton, D. J., F. A. Lindholm, and J. A. Narud: Large-signal Models for Junction Transistors, Digest of Technical Papers, 1963 International Solid-state Circuits Conference; also, Comparison of Large Signal Models for Junction Transistors, *Proc. IEEE,* vol. 52, pp. 239–248, March, 1964.
6. Meyer, C. S., J. A. Narud, and D. J. Hamilton: Nonlinear Transistor Model, Motorola Integrated Circuits Design Course, July, 1963; also, Meyer, C. S., D. J. Hamilton, and D. K. Lynn (eds.): "Analysis and Design of Integrated Circuits," Chap. 5, McGraw-Hill Book Company, New York, 1965.
7. Narud, J. A., and M. J. Callahan: Network Theory for Integrated Circuits, *IEEE Trans. Circuit Theory,* vol. CT-11, pp. 312–313, June, 1964.
8. Seelbach, W. C.: Diode-transistor Logic, Motorola Integrated Circuits Design Course, July, 1963; also, Meyer, C. S., D. J. Hamilton, and D. K. Lynn (eds.): "Analysis and Design of Integrated Circuits," McGraw-Hill Book Company, New York, 1965.

8

FIELD-EFFECT DEVICES FOR
INTEGRATED CIRCUITS

The field-effect transistor[1] is a semiconductor device with electrical characteristics which strongly resemble those of a vacuum-tube pentode. It existed as a laboratory curiosity for approximately its first decade, or from 1952 until 1962. In the fast-moving semiconductor device world this was indeed a long gestation period. Fundamentally this occurred because the field-effect transistor requires a distribution of impurities with values and tolerances that are far more difficult to achieve than those of conventional junction transistors. Basically it requires a thin, lightly doped layer between two thicker, more heavily doped layers of opposite type. With most of the fabricational approaches which have been used, the problem has been one of controlling a small difference between two relatively large quantities in order to generate the critical center layer. For example, when just diffusion is used, the difference between two diffused distributions must be accurately controlled. Only recently has the semiconductor device technology reached a degree of refinement which permits us to achieve the desired structure reproducibly. Not surprisingly, there are now several practical ways of making the device, each with attendant pros and cons.

The development of the field-effect transistor can be traced in terms of these fabricational methods, with special emphasis on junction-forming methods. Interesting field-effect devices have been made by the alloy technique,[2, 3] by the growth-from-the-melt technique,[4] by cutting and etching,[5, 6] by diffusion,[7-9] by epitaxy,[10] and by various combinations of these.[11-16] Now that the field-effect transistor has matured as a practical device, the scene is dominated primarily by the double-diffused[8] and epitaxial-diffused[16] varieties. Both varieties have found use in integrated circuits.

The field-effect transistor (frequently abbreviated FET) differs distinctly from the conventional junction transistor because its operation depends upon the flow of majority carriers. Therefore it falls in the class of *unipolar* transistors, or those in which only one type of carrier predominates.[1, 17] Conventional transistors are *bipolar* in this sense. Because the FET is the only member of the unipolar class which has been realized to date, the labels "field effect" and "unipolar" are sometimes used interchangeably.

The FET enjoys several clear advantages over the conventional transistor: It is remarkably free of noise. It is more resistant to the degrading effects of nuclear radiation because carrier lifetime effects are comparatively unimportant to its operation. It is more readily integrated in monolithic fashion in certain important configurations than is the junction transistor; this is true because currents in the FET flow primarily in the plane of the wafer or die, whereas those in the conventional transistor flow primarily normal to it. The FET is inherently more burnout-resistant than the conventional transistor.

There are additional distinguishing attributes of the FET which are sometimes advantageous. It exhibits a high input impedance—typically many megohms. In this respect it resembles a vacuum tube. Because it is voltage-controlled, it can readily be "self-biased," and this fact frequently makes for a simpler circuit than the conventional transistor equivalent. The FET exhibits a kind of nonlinearity which can be exploited in automatic-gain-control applications.

The chief shortcoming of the FET is its relatively small gain-bandwidth product. For a given state of the art (in terms of achievable dimensions, achievable doping tolerances, etc.) a larger value of this product can be obtained by making a conventional transistor.[18] Although the FET is free from carrier-transit-time limitations, its parasitic junction capacitances place it at a relative disadvantage. We now have a related device, however, which exhibits a substantially larger gain-bandwidth product than the junction-type FET discussed above; the isolated-gate (or insulated-gate) field-effect transistor,[19-21] sometimes abbreviated IGFET, has appreciably smaller parasitic capacitances. This device is treated in Sec. 8-4. The IGFET is not yet as well understood as the older FET. Translated into practical terms, this means that its stability and reliability suffer by comparison with those of the older device.

Although Shockley's description and detailed analysis of the FET[1] is the primary landmark in the development pattern of the junction-type devices, there were interesting early examples of the related concept of a thin sheet of polycrystalline semiconductor material whose conductivity could be controlled by an adjacent element.[22, 23] The spirit of these proposals has found realization in the recent thin-film devices,[24] which employ polycrystalline evaporated layers of materials such as cadmium sulfide. The great attraction of this approach lies in its similarity to thin-film techniques for making passive components. But important problems relating to stability must be solved for this device also if it is to compete with the junction-type FET.

The advantages of field-effect devices in integrated circuits have been noted,[25, 26] and these devices have already arrived in hybrid applications.[27] They will be able to perform many useful functions in monolithic circuits also, as double-diffused and epitaxial-diffused procedures for such circuits are further refined. The IGFET also shows great promise for monolithic circuits, especially in view of its structural simplicity, and should find wide application as soon as factors affecting its reliability are better understood.

8-1 Field-effect Transistor Operation and Design Principles

Figure 8-1 shows schematically a junction-type field-effect transistor. It is a p-n-p structure which superficially resembles a conventional transistor. But as Fig. 8-1 shows, the current flow is parallel to the junctions rather than normal to them.

At the heart of the field-effect transistor is the depletion layer inevitably associated with a p-n junction, as described in Sec. 2-3, and the dependence of its properties upon applied voltage. Suppose that voltages are applied to the FET as shown in Fig. 8-1a. Because p$^+$-n junctions have been assumed here, as pointed out in Sec. 2-3 it is valid to consider only the portion of the depletion layer on the lightly doped side. Thus for the bias values shown, significant depletion layers exist only in the n regions labeled "channel" and "drain." We are making the convenient assumption that the equilibrium or zero-bias depletion layer is negligible, and that the entire n region is uniformly doped.

The portions of the structure labeled "gate" are treated as equipotential regions. The gates have appreciable conductivity and in normal operation, carry vanish

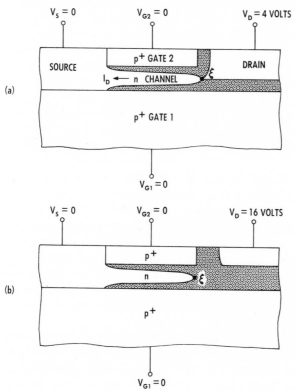

Fig. 8-1 Schematic cross section of a field-effect transistor with gates and source grounded: (a) With a drain voltage V_D equal to the pinch-off voltage V_P; (b) with a drain voltage equal to four times the pinch-off voltage.

ingly small currents; so this is an excellent assumption. In most present devices the gates are common. This can be arranged readily within the silicon, through metallizing, or through wire bonding. For purposes of the present discussion, then, we will let both gates as well as the "source" be at ground potential.

The Effects of Drain Bias. When a positive voltage is applied to the drain terminal (4 volts in this example, Fig. 8-1*a*), this full voltage appears across the junctions bounding the drain region, since the gates are at ground potential. The junctions bounding the source region have no voltage across them. Thus there is a transition from no voltage to full voltage occurring along the junctions bounding the channel region. This voltage variation with distance is of course a consequence of the *IR* drop associated with the current I_D flowing in the channel. At this point we may note that majority carriers—electrons in this case—are streaming from source to drain. This accounts partially for these strange-sounding terminal designations. The remaining justification rests with the nonambiguous initial letters so provided for subscript purposes.

Figure 8-1*a* depicts the condition where the two depletion layers have just met at the median plane of the channel at the point ξ. This is termed the *pinch-off* condition. Now it is interesting to inquire what happens when drain voltage V_D is further increased. To a first approximation, the depletion layers bounding the channel and source regions remain unchanged, while those bounding the drain region grow thicker. This situation is shown in Fig. 8-1*b* where drain voltage has been increased by a factor of 4, so that depletion layer thickness increases by a factor of 2 in this step-junction example. Although the drain voltage V_D has been increased by a factor of 4, the drain current I_D is changed only slightly, for reasons given below. Still further increases in V_D will ultimately lead to avalanche breakdown somewhere in the drain-region junction, and current through the device will increase sharply.

Let us examine now the current-voltage characteristics of this device in the normal operating range, or at voltages below breakdown. With gates and source common as before, and with a very small voltage applied to the drain, the FET exhibits a resistance given simply by $\rho l/A$, where ρ is the resistivity of the channel, l is its length, and A is the cross-sectional area of the channel normal to the current path. These dimensions are indicated in Fig. 8-2. Clearly A is equal to $2a_c z$, where $2a_c$ is channel thickness and z is the lateral extent of the channel so that the low-voltage resistance of the device may be written as

$$R_o = \frac{\rho l}{2a_c z} \tag{8-1}$$

As drain voltage is increased, depletion layers begin to grow in the channel region (as well as in the drain region), reducing its cross-sectional area; consequently channel resistance begins to increase. This is because the growing depletion layer with its near-zero carrier concentration acts as an insulator in so far as conduction parallel to the junction is concerned. The *pinching* effect of this thickening insulator produces the nonlinearity apparent in the initial portion of the *I-V* character-

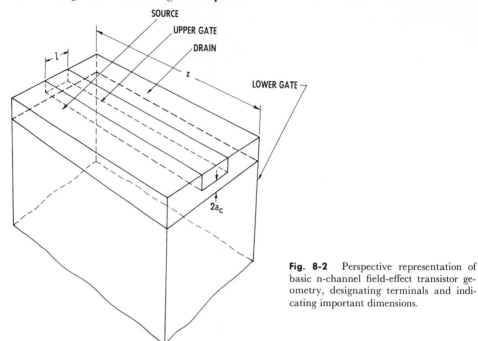

Fig. 8-2 Perspective representation of basic n-channel field-effect transistor geometry, designating terminals and indicating important dimensions.

istic in Fig. 8-3*a*. This process culminates in the pinch-off condition depicted in Fig. 8-1*a*. On the *I-V* characteristic (Fig. 8-3*a*) this corresponds to the point with coordinates I_P and V_P.

For further increases in V_D, the drain current remains very nearly constant until the breakdown voltage is reached. A first-order explanation for this constancy of drain current follows from the cross-sectional pictures sketched in Fig. 8-1. We have shown there that channel shape (as defined by the depletion layers in the channel region) does not change appreciably with increases in drain voltage above V_P. It is also true that the end-to-end voltage drop in the channel, the *IR* drop in the undepleted portion of the channel from the point ξ at which pinch-off first occurred to the source end of the channel, remains at V_P with increases in V_D above V_P. The constancy of this voltage drop is enforced by the one-to-one relationship existing between depletion layer voltage (that from the equipotential gate to the point ξ) and depletion layer thickness a_c. Thus it follows that channel current will be constant over the same voltage range for which channel resistance and channel voltage are constant.

According to this picture the electrons arriving at the point ξ are then swept to the drain through the intervening depletion layer. Their density in transit may not be negligible, but it seems likely that it is less than in the channel itself. As a hydrodynamic analogy we can think of a stream which flows in a channel growing progressively narrower and steeper, and which finally escapes in a waterfall, or at least in a very steep chute.

The Effects of Gate Bias. Thus we have accounted qualitatively for all features of the *I-V* characteristic in Fig. 8-3*a*. Let us now bias the gates with respect to the source and observe the effect, leaving the drain unbiased for the moment. Normal

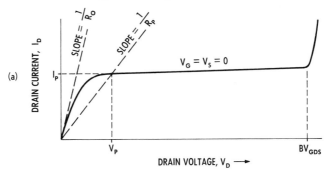

Fig. 8-3 (*a*) Drain current versus drain voltage for the field-effect transistor with gates and source grounded. Current is nearly constant from the pinch-off voltage to the breakdown voltage. (*b*) Family of output characteristics for a typical field-effect transistor for 1-volt input steps.

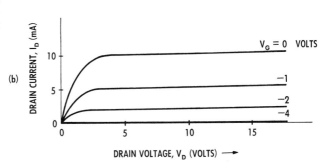

(b)

gate bias is in the reverse direction, or negative with respect to the source in the present n-channel case. Let this bias be 1 volt, or one-fourth of the voltage required to produce the pinch-off condition. In accordance with the parabolic relationship between depletion layer thickness and voltage, this will reduce the conducting channel thickness by a factor of 2. Applying drain voltage will now induce a sequence of events much like those described above for unbiased gates, but the pinch-off condition will now be reached at a lower drain voltage. The resulting *I-V* characteristic is shown in Fig. 8-3*b* for $V_G = -1$ volt. Further increments in gate voltage will further reduce drain current, but with diminishing effectiveness again because of the nonlinear law relating depletion layer thickness and voltage. Thus we have generated a family of characteristics similar to those of a pentode tube.

Device Analysis. A complete analysis of the FET was given by Shockley[1] in the paper which originally announced the concept. That analysis will not be repeated here, though some of its results will be given. His analysis is based on the *gradual approximation*. This simply assumed that *l* is large compared to channel half-thickness a_c (see Fig. 8-2). Therefore the depletion layer thickness changes slowly with position along the channel. As a result, over most of the channel's length it is valid to use the one-dimensional form of Poisson's equation, as was done in Sec. 2-3. Then we have a simplified picture wherein the field in the depletion layer is everywhere normal to the junction, and the field in the conducting channel is parallel to the junctions. This distortion of the true situation makes the necessary equations very simple. But the distortion becomes severe at the drain end of the channel as the pinch-off condition is approached. The simplifying assumptions lead, for example, to a prediction of infinite field at the point ξ at pinch-off. But this problem has not prevented the gradual approximation from giving excellent predictions of device properties, and for analytical purposes it has been helpful to use ξ (which Shockley termed the *extrapolated pinch-off point*) as a point of reference. Additional detailed attention was given to this critical region in an early paper.[28]

Although the fundamental equations based on the gradual approximation have been rederived many times, no significant and tractable refinement of that basic approximation has been made, nor has it apparently been needed. But integrated circuit and device technology has now progressed to a point where it is quite feasible to make a field-effect device with $l \approx a_c$ with both dimensions being very small, a trend which maximizes gain-bandwidth. Hence a modified theory may be necessary in the future.

Dacey and Ross[2,3] reported the first experimental confirmation of the existing theory. They also gave consideration to certain complicating factors such as parasitic resistance, carrier injection effects, temperature effects, and the field dependence of carrier mobility (see Sec. 1-6).

More recently there have been efforts toward generating models of the device which take account of the junction capacitance in more precise and detailed fashion than at first.[29] Some field-effect device properties have been recalculated for junction impurity profiles other than the p$^+$-n or n$^+$-p varieties,[6,13,30] and for device geometries other than rectangular. However, all these calculations employ the gradual approximation.

The Current-Voltage Equation. From Shockley's gradual-case analysis of the device of Figs. 8-1 and 8-2 comes the following equation for the drain current I_D in terms of terminal voltages V_S, V_D, and V_G:

$$I_D = G_o(V_D - V_G)\left[1 - \frac{2}{3}\left(\frac{V_D - V_G}{V_P}\right)^{1/2}\right] - G_o(V_S - V_G)\left[1 - \frac{2}{3}\left(\frac{V_S - V_G}{V_P}\right)^{1/2}\right]$$

$$(8\text{-}2)$$

Here G_o, the initial or low-voltage conductance of the channel, is of course $1/R_o$ and is thus given by

$$G_o = \frac{2a_c z}{\rho l} = 2q\mu N_c a_c \frac{z}{l} \tag{8-3}$$

where the second form follows from Sec. 1-6; N_c is the net impurity concentration in the channel and μ is the appropriate carrier mobility. The quantity V_P was described as the voltage which must be applied to the drain with source and gates tied to ground to cause the depletion layers to merge (in the extrapolated sense) at the drain end of the channel. It is given by

$$V_P = \frac{q N_c a_c^2}{2\kappa\epsilon_o} \tag{8-4}$$

It is convenient to let this quantity take on a positive or negative sign depending on whether an n-channel or a p-channel device, respectively, is under discussion. That is, let the charge q take on the sign appropriate to the ions remaining in the depleted region in the channel. Subject to this interpretation, Eq. (8-2) is equally valid for p-channel and n-channel devices. It is merely necessary to substitute appropriate algebraic signs along with terminal voltages. It follows that a negative drain current, or conventional current out of the drain terminal will be obtained with a p-channel unit.

This kind of analysis yields an equation which describes only the curved portions of the *I-V* characteristics depicted in Fig. 8-3*b*. The constant-current portions were originally inferred from physical considerations and have been verified experimentally.

Pinch-off Current and Transconductance. Letting $V_S = V_G = 0$ and $V_D = V_P$ in Eq. (8-2), and substituting the results from Eqs. (8-3) and (8-4), we arrive at the expression for pinch-off current:

$$I_P = \frac{G_o V_P}{3} = \frac{q^2 \mu N_c^2 a_c^3}{3\kappa\epsilon_o} \frac{z}{l} \tag{8-5}$$

Through similar analyses it is possible to arrive in a straightforward way at expressions for the pinch-off voltage and current for a number of other geometrical situations and impurity distributions. These are summarized in Table 8-1, together with expressions for the low-voltage conductance G_o.

Transconductance for the device of Figs. 8-1 and 8-2 is found by differentiating Eq. (8-2) with respect to V_G:

$$g_m = \frac{\partial I_D}{\partial V_G}\bigg|_{V_D = \text{constant}} = \frac{G_o}{V_P^{1/2}}[(V_D - V_G)^{1/2} - (V_S - V_G)^{1/2}] \tag{8-6}$$

Of particular interest is the initial transconductance g_{mo}, which occurs when $V_S = V_G = 0$ and at some drain voltage in excess of V_P. This is also the maximum transconductance. Basically this is true because a depletion layer grows rapidly with voltage at first, and then slows. The condition that pinch-off has just been reached can be conveniently placed into Eq. (8-6) by specifying that $V_D - V_G = V_P$. Note from Fig. 8-3*b* that this will lead to the desired result since the constant-current portions of the characteristics are tangent to the curved portions [which are indeed the only portions to which Eqs. (8-2) and (8-6) apply] at precisely the points where pinch-off is reached. This substitution gives the interesting result that

$$g_{mo} = G_o = 2q\mu N_c a_c \frac{z}{l} \tag{8-7}$$

for that step-junction device.

For small input signal voltages this maximum value of transconductance can be realized by simply letting the gate float. The built-in junction bias of a few tenths of a volt enables one to let the gate swing slightly into forward bias without drawing appreciable current; this possibility obviously simplifies certain types of circuits.

Qualitative Design Considerations. Table 8-1 emphasizes a number of important points. The first is that pinch-off voltage depends upon only one dimensional factor—channel thickness (or its analogue). In most cases V_P varies as the square of this dimension and as the first power of the channel doping. Hence a thin heavily doped channel can be *pinched off* with the lowest voltage, sheet conductance being

Table 8-1 Low-voltage Conductance, Pinch-off Voltage, and Pinch-off Current for Various Field-effect Structures

An n-type channel is assumed in every case; μ_n is the electron mobility in the channel and N_D is the donor concentration in the channel.

Refs.	Impurity profile	Geometry	Low-voltage conductance G_o	Pinch-off voltage V_P	Pinch-off current I_P
1	p+-n step junction	Rectangular channel, two junctions, channel thickness = $2a_c$	$2q\mu_n N_D a_c \dfrac{z}{l}$	$\dfrac{qN_D a_c^2}{2\kappa\epsilon_0}$	$\dfrac{q^2\mu_n N_D^2 a_c^3}{3\kappa\epsilon_0}\dfrac{z}{l}$
1	p+-n step junction	Rectangular channel, one junction, channel thickness = a_c	$q\mu_n N_D a_c \dfrac{z}{l}$	$\dfrac{qN_D a_c^2}{2\kappa\epsilon_0}$	$\dfrac{q^2\mu_n N_D^2 a_c^3}{6\kappa\epsilon_0}\dfrac{z}{l}$
13	p+-n step junction	Annular channel, source radius = r_S, drain radius = r_D, two junctions, channel thickness = $2a_c$	$\dfrac{4\pi q\mu_n N_D a_c}{\ln(r_S/r_D)}$	$\dfrac{qN_D a_c^2}{2\kappa\epsilon_0}$	$\dfrac{2\pi q^2\mu_n N_D^2 a_c^3}{3\kappa\epsilon_0 \ln(r_S/r_D)}$
13	p+-n step junction	Annular channel, source radius = r_S, drain radius = r_D, one junction, channel thickness = a_c	$\dfrac{2\pi q\mu_n N_D a_c}{\ln(r_S/r_D)}$	$\dfrac{qN_D a_c^2}{2\kappa\epsilon_0}$	$\dfrac{\pi q^2\mu_n N_D^2 a_c^3}{3\kappa\epsilon_0 \ln(r_S/r_D)}$
6, 13	p+-n step junction	Filamentary channel of radius r_o and of length l	$\dfrac{\pi r_o^2 q\mu_n N_D}{l}$	$\dfrac{qN_D r_o^2}{4\kappa\epsilon_0}$	$\dfrac{\pi q^2\mu_n N_D^2 r_o^4}{16\kappa\epsilon_0 l}$
	Symmetrical step junction	Rectangular channel, two junctions, channel thickness = $2a_c$	$2q\mu_n N_D a_c \dfrac{z}{l}$	$\dfrac{qN_D a_c^2}{\sqrt{2}\,\kappa\epsilon_0}$	
	Symmetrical step junction	Rectangular channel, one junction, channel thickness = a_c	$q\mu_n N_D a_c \dfrac{z}{l}$	$\dfrac{qN_D a_c^2}{\sqrt{2}\,\kappa\epsilon_0}$	
13	Linearly graded junction	Rectangular channel, one junction, channel thickness = a_c, impurity gradient = a	$\dfrac{q\mu_n a a_c^2 z}{2l}$	$\dfrac{2qa a_c^3}{3\kappa\epsilon_0}$	$\dfrac{2q^2\mu_n a^2 a_c^5}{15\kappa\epsilon_0}\dfrac{z}{l}$
13	Linearly graded junction	Annular channel, one junction, channel thickness = a_c, impurity gradient = a	$\dfrac{\pi q\mu_n a a_c^2}{\ln(r_S/r_D)}$	$\dfrac{2qa a_c^3}{3\kappa\epsilon_0}$	$\dfrac{4\pi q^2\mu_n a^2 a_c^5}{15\kappa\epsilon_0 \ln(r_S/r_D)}$
30	Parabolic	Rectangular channel, two junctions, channel thickness = $2a_c$, maximum net donor concentration in channel = N_M		$\dfrac{3qN_M a_c^2}{4\kappa\epsilon_0}$	

held constant. Clearly this is the direction to go to maximize transconductance (the amount of conductance that can be controlled by a given applied voltage).

An interesting benefit accompanying a low pinch-off voltage is a tendency toward a temperature-independent pinch-off current.[31] ($V_P = 0.92$ volt was reported as optimum in a specific family of diffused devices.) In thick-channel devices, I_P declines with increasing temperature because it is directly proportional to carrier mobility in every case, and mobility decreases with increasing temperature in the room-temperature range (Sec. 1-6). But in a device with a pinch-off voltage less than one volt, the built-in voltage and its accompanying depletion layer can no longer be regarded as negligible. Since built-in voltage ψ_o declines with increasing temperature as the Fermi levels on both sides of the junction progress toward the middle of the gap (Sec. 1-5), the channel in such a device tends to open up, and this can compensate the declining carrier mobility.

Since typical pinch-off voltages are larger than one volt, most devices exhibit a negative temperature coefficient of drain current I_D. This is a factor in the inherent burnout resistance of the FET. A second factor is of course its natural current-limiting tendency.

Gate voltage is used most "efficiently" when the accompanying depletion layer extends mainly into the channel. Depletion layer spread on the gate side of the junction performs no useful function. The p^+-n-p^+ structure depicted in Fig. 8-1 is thus a good one from this point of view. But as noted above, a heavily doped channel is also advantageous. In today's practical structures the design compromise thus entailed frequently involves approximately equal doping in the gate and channel regions. This gives reasonable efficiency, and at the same time gives acceptably low parasitic capacitance per unit area. It also makes the critical dimensions less subject to change through solid-phase diffusion during heat treatment procedures.

It is apparent in Table 8-1 that pinch-off current I_P is an extremely sensitive function of channel thickness. This emphasizes the difficulty of controlling I_P. Drain current also varies directly with carrier mobility μ while V_P is independent of μ. Thus transconductance is favored by a high value of μ. For this reason n-type channels are preferred. Further, certain intermetallic materials are very promising for the FET and will certainly be used when their technology permits. Some of these materials have very high majority-carrier mobilities, and their comparatively low minority-carrier mobilities are not a handicap in the FET.

Pinch-off current is also directly proportional to the aspect ratio of the channel z/l (as is transconductance), while pinch-off voltage is independent of this quantity. Increasing z/l simply puts more squares of channel in parallel, in the sheet-resistance sense. A device with $z/l = 1$ would, for typical profiles, have an I_P of perhaps 100 μA with g_{mo} less than 100 μmhos, which is too small to be useful in most applications. Typical values of z/l range from 5 to 100.

A gain-bandwidth limitation is encountered as z/l is increased to increase transconductance; ultimately the overall size of the device and its parasitic capacitances must increase. An additional gain-bandwidth interplay can be seen in the variation of transconductance and parasitic capacitance with gate bias. Moving toward zero gate bias enhances the former and worsens the latter.

Noise.   The subject of noise in field-effect transistors has received recent serious attention.[32-34]   As in the conventional transistor, there is a $1/f$ noise component which is associated with surface effects.   In a well-made FET this can be reduced to very low levels indeed.   Noise behavior in the FET is best characterized by an equivalent noise resistance, and as van der Ziel[33] noted for certain samples he had investigated, it is ". . . about a factor of four better [lower] than the shot noise resistance of a vacuum tube with comparable transconductance and considerably better than the noise resistance of transistor circuits at high input impedance levels." Findings are that the dominant noise component in the FET is the thermal noise of the conducting channel; the channel current does not have shot noise associated with it, although the gate junctions can contribute significant shot noise if the gate currents are excessive.

8-2   Other Junction-type Field-effect Devices

Numerous variations on the field-effect transistor are possible.   Common to all of these is a junction with a laterally varying bias produced by a current flowing parallel to the junction.   Some of these embodiments, as we will see, may be regarded as integrated forms of multi-FET circuits.

Current Limiter.   By making the gates and source common in an FET, we obtain a two-terminal device.   Figure 8-3a shows the resulting current-regulating characteristic.   This diode has come to be known as a *current limiter*.[11, 13]   Obviously, all the formulas in Table 8-1 are applicable to this device.   The current limiter is quite analogous to the Zener diode; the former does for current what the latter does for voltage.

The attractiveness of current limiters in integrated circuits stems from several factors. Large-value conventional resistors pose a problem, while the large dynamic resistance of the current limiter is relatively easy to achieve.   Even given the large-value conventional resistor, a much larger voltage is required to drive a specified current through it than is required to achieve the same current in a current limiter. Given, in turn, the high voltage (which should not be a foregone conclusion), we must then consider the dissipation difference between the two cases.   The difference can easily exceed a factor of 10.   To the systems designer constantly facing the problem of cooling his integrated circuitry, this is a key consideration.   On the debit side is the difficulty of combining conventional transistors and field-effect devices in a monolithic circuit.

The current limiter may be used for straightforward regulation, or as a protective device (a true "limiter").   It may be used as a load; in this sense it is analogous to an inductor, exhibiting a large ratio of ac to dc resistance.   It may be used for waveshaping or clipping.   In charging a capacitor it generates a useful voltage ramp.   An example of how it may replace a resistor and do the job better is provided in digital-to-analogue converters.[13, 35]

Remote Cutoff Transistor.   Standard field-effect transistors that are designed for high transconductance at low pinch-off voltages have *sharp cutoff* (or perhaps *sharp pinch-off*) characteristics.   In certain applications such as AGC circuits it is desirable to have *remote cutoff* or variable-μ characteristics.   This remote cutoff characteristic also gives more gradual control and reduces crosstalk effects.[36]

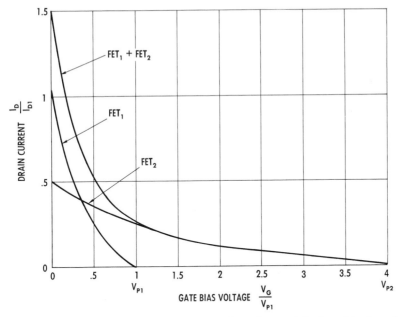

Fig. 8-4 Normalized drain-current-versus-gate-voltage characteristics for a thin-channel device (FET$_1$), a thick-channel device (FET$_2$), and the parallel combination constituting a remote cutoff FET configuration.

The remote cutoff transistor gives the desired characteristics without sacrifice in initial transconductance as is the case with high-pinch-off voltage low-pinch-off current FETs. The desired characteristics may be obtained from two standard FETs of different pinch-off characteristics connected in parallel. The normalized transfer characteristic of each device is shown in Fig. 8-4. One device has a high initial transconductance at a low pinch-off voltage. The other device has a somewhat lower transconductance but a high pinch-off voltage. The result of the parallel combination is also shown in Fig. 8-4. A variety of cutoff characteristics is obtainable by placing more than two transistors in parallel and by selecting individual characteristics.

Although the desired cutoff characteristics are obtainable from the parallel combination of discrete FETs, it is better to design these characteristics into the remote cutoff transistor. In this device, channel regions of differing thickness are placed in parallel. The thicker channel portion will determine the voltage at which the device will cut off. The thinner channel portion with its associated geometry will primarily determine the initial transconductance.

For the characteristics shown in Fig. 8-4, with V_{P2} four times higher than V_{P1}, one portion of the channel is twice as thick as the other portion. Suppose a device with an initial transconductance higher than 6,000 μmhos and a cutoff voltage of 20 volts is desired. Suppose further that the pinch-off current contribution of the thin-channel portion is to be twice as large as that of the thick-channel portion, as was the case in Fig. 8-4. Also, let the two channel regions differ again by a factor of 2 in thickness. With a 1-ohm-cm epitaxial channel layer, the thickness of a double-gate device for 20 volts pinch-off is 4.2 microns. For one-fourth this voltage, or 5 volts, the thinner portion must be 2.1 microns thick. If I_{P1} is to be twice I_{P2}, then z_1/l_1 is 16 times greater than z_2/l_2. Taking z_1/l_1 equal to 32 and z_2/l_2 equal to 2, then $I_{P1} = 10.4$ mA and $I_{P2} = 5.2$ mA, $g_{mo1} = 6,720$ μmhos and $g_{mo2} = 840$ μmhos. It can be seen from these values that the initial transconductance is primarily determined by the low pinch-off section while the high cutoff voltage is determined by the high pinch-off section. Figure 8-5 represents in a simplified manner a remote cutoff FET. The thin-channel region has a large aspect ratio for high transconductance, while the thick-channel region has a small ratio for lower pinch-off current.

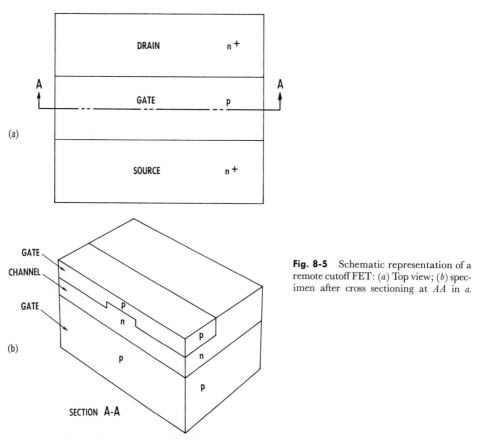

Fig. 8-5 Schematic representation of a remote cutoff FET: (*a*) Top view; (*b*) specimen after cross sectioning at *AA* in *a*.

Remote cutoff transistors may be made from a double-epitaxial p-n-p structure similar to that of an epitaxial-diffused FET (Sec. 8-3) but with a thicker n-channel layer. This epitaxial layer will be the thickest portion of the channel. The thinner portion of the channel is formed by selectively diffusing boron through the top p layer and into the n layer to reduce the channel to the desired thickness. Figure 8-6 shows a pattern which has been used to produce a remote cutoff FET. The curved ends are the thicker channel region while the legs are the diffused thinner channel region.

Field-effect Tetrode. By placing two field-effect channels back to back with a single junction between, one generates a four-terminal device with interesting

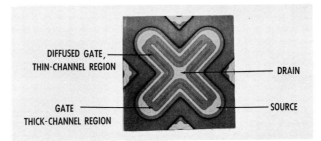

Fig. 8-6 Top view of an experimental remote cutoff FET.

DIFFUSED GATE, THIN-CHANNEL REGION

DRAIN

GATE THICK-CHANNEL REGION

SOURCE

properties. The field-effect tetrode[14, 15] does not have gate terminals as such, since each channel is in a sense a gate for the other. The device is shown schematically in Fig. 8-7a. An analogous but not identical complementary FET configuration is shown in Fig. 8-7b. The supplementary gates are left out of Fig. 8-7 in order to simplify the diagrams. In the tetrode case these gates must be very lightly doped in comparison to the channels, in order to keep the accompanying depletion layers mainly in the supplementary gates; it is intended that the channel be modulated only by the depletion layer of the central junction.

An analysis of the field-effect tetrode was made,[15] subject to the assumptions that a step junction exists with uniform (but not necessarily equal) doping in the

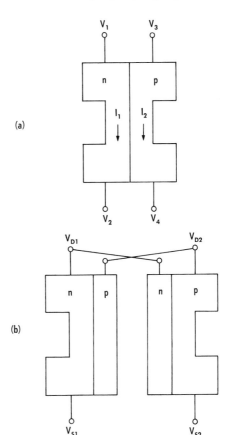

Fig. 8-7 (a) Schematic representation of the field-effect tetrode; (b) discrete-FET configuration with properties qualitatively similar to those of the tetrode in some applications.

two channels, that the gradual approximation is once more valid, and that the junction is never forward-biased. Further, this analysis assumed a structure in which the two channels exhibit the same pinch-off voltage, V_P. The analysis yielded two equations, one for the current in each channel. Each current is a function of all four of the terminal voltages.

$$I_1 = G_1(V_1 - V_2)\left[1 - \frac{2}{3V_P^{1/2}} \frac{(V_1 - V_3)^{3/2} - (V_2 - V_4)^{3/2}}{(V_1 - V_3) - (V_2 - V_4)}\right] \tag{8-9}$$

$$I_2 = G_2(V_3 - V_4)\left[1 - \frac{2}{3V_P^{1/2}} \frac{(V_1 - V_3)^{3/2} - (V_2 - V_4)^{3/2}}{(V_1 - V_3) - (V_2 - V_4)}\right] \tag{8-10}$$

Here G_1 and G_2 are the low-voltage conductances of the respective channels. These equations apply only to a structure which is symmetric with respect to pinch-off voltage, the case which is the most interesting one from the applications point of view.

The field-effect tetrode has several interesting properties which can be simulated by the FET arrangement shown in Fig. 8-7b. Among these are a two-terminal voltage-controlled negative resistance when terminals 2 and 3 are connected together, and nonreciprocal behavior when the FET is used as a two-port device.

What is probably the most interesting application of the tetrode, however, cannot be simulated with field-effect transistors. This is its use as an electronically variable resistor which is completely linear in the sense that its resistance is not modulated by the signal voltage. For comparison, it is instructive to consider the FET as an electronically variable resistor. In Fig. 8-3b it is apparent that the initial or low-voltage resistance of the device from drain to source can be adjusted through gate bias. But it is also apparent that the FET is not a linear resistive element. Furthermore, with heavier bias, pinch-off occurs at an even lower drain voltage: i.e., the nonlinearity grows more severe.

Now consider the tetrode as a variable resistor. Figure 8-8 shows a circuit configuration which illustrates the principle. The bias voltage V_b establishes a depletion layer of uniform thickness everywhere; the only direct current in the cir-

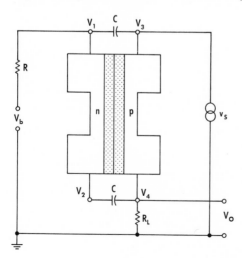

Fig. 8-8 Circuit for using the field-effect tetrode as an electronically variable resistor. (*After Stone and Warner.*[15])

cuit is junction leakage current. A capacitor C, whose reactance is small compared to channel resistance at the frequency of the signal voltage v_s, ensures that the signal voltage will not appear to any significant degree across the junction. Therefore, signal voltage can exceed bias voltage, pinch-off voltage, and even junction breakdown voltage. Limits on signal voltage are set by dissipation considerations. To an excellent approximation the full signal voltage is applied from end to end on the two channels in parallel, and signal currents flow in inverse ratio to the channel resistances. Because signal modulation of the depletion layer is thus eliminated, the tetrode can be used as a variable resistor for high-frequency signals.

The circuit in Fig. 8-8 includes a load resistance R_L. The resistor R has a value that is small compared with the resistance of the junction, with which it is in series, but large enough for isolation purposes. In this circuit, V_b can be a dc bias, as before, or it can be a low-frequency ac voltage which modulates the signal from v_s.

The tuning ratio for this variable resistor can be very large indeed. The high-resistance limit is in the megohm range for symmetrical pinch-off conditions.

8-3 Field-effect Device Technologies

During the years in which field-effect devices existed only as laboratory items, the main difficulty encountered was connected with generating and controlling the high-sheet-resistance region required for the channel. Today, the arrival of new techniques such as epitaxy and photo-resist masking, and the refinement of older techniques, such as diffusion and alloying, have overcome this obstacle and have made field-effect devices commercially feasible. Of the methods outlined below, the double-diffused approach is probably more compatible than any of the others with the more or less standard monolithic integrated circuit procedures.

Double-diffused Devices. Basically there are two methods of forming high-sheet-resistance channels by diffusion alone. The first[9] involves diffusion of the same impurity type from both sides of the wafer, either simultaneously or in two steps. This process requires precise control of wafer thickness uniformity as well as of diffusion depth. Figure 8-9 shows the finished structure.

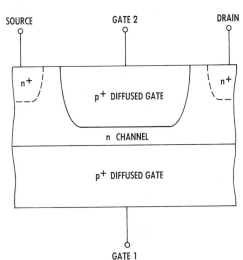

Fig. 8-9 Schematic cross section of an FET formed by diffusion from both sides of wafer.

The second all-diffused approach to field-effect device fabrication employs the double-diffusion technique.[7, 8] This process is more compatible with integrated circuit technology—especially the monolithic case—than are the two-side-diffused procedures, basically because the structure is formed from one side of the wafer. The first diffusion is usually done with boron to form the lower gate junction and the source and drain regions. Obviously this can be carried out in the usual n-type island of a monolithic circuit. The second diffusion employs phosphorus to form the upper gate.

It is evident that a double-diffused field-effect transistor is qualitatively similar to a double-diffused conventional transistor, but there are important distinctions in detail:

1. The channel layer (p type as described here) is at least an order of magnitude higher in sheet resistance than is the base of the corresponding n-p-n conventional transistor.

2. Current must not be permitted to flow from source to drain *around* the upper gate. Thus the upper gate must be closed on itself, as in Fig. 8-14, or else must extend clear across the area of p diffusion.

3. For a standard FET, the channel must not have thick regions which would have a shunting effect. On the other hand, *spikes* (see Chap. 12) or other diffusion defects connecting the gates together are not necessarily a fatal flaw. (The analogous defect in a conventional transistor is of course fatal, but the thick-region defect is not.) This is fortunate because the double-diffused FET with its thin p-type layer is particularly subject to spikes.

4. The gate-source or gate-drain breakdown voltage is analogous to BV_{EBO} in the conventional transistor. To raise this voltage to interesting levels it is necessary to reduce the boron surface concentration to a low level. Hence a deeply diffused gaussian distribution is usually used (see Sec. 3-1). In principle, either type can be made, and as explained in Sec. 8-1, the n-type channel device has a superior figure of merit because gain varies with carrier mobility.

Let us outline the fabrication steps very briefly. Typically, the starting material may be 5-ohm-cm n-type silicon. First, a uniform layer of silicon dioxide is grown over the top surface. By photo-resist techniques the oxide is selectively removed to define the first diffusion. Boron is predeposited (Chap. 12) and driven in to a depth of several microns. The oxide is permitted to regrow to provide a mask for the gate diffusion. The gate pattern is defined by photo-resist techniques. Phosphorus is then diffused to produce the gate. A *diffuse-and-try* procedure may be used to obtain the desired sheet resistance. That is, after diffusion the wafer may be checked electrically and then subjected to further diffusion if the channel is too conductive.

The profile resulting with the double-diffusion approach is shown in Fig. 8-10, and the cross section of the resulting structure is shown in Fig. 8-11. (The isolating junction for monolithic devices has been omitted to simplify the diagram.) Finally, source, drain, and gates are metallized. The gates may be intentionally

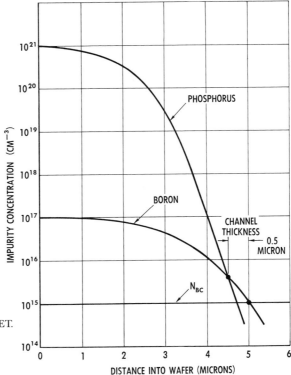

Fig. 8-10 Profile of double-diffused FET.

made common through diffusion mask design or metallizing, or they may be left separate for some special application.

Epitaxial-diffused Devices. Some of the shortcomings of the double-diffused structure may be overcome by the use of epitaxy. An excellent approach for making field-effect devices combines the advantages of diffusion and epitaxy. Epitaxy is best suited for sheet-resistance control, whereas diffusion is best suited for lateral-geometry control. Two methods are available utilizing epitaxy and diffusion. One process is similar to the double-diffused approach. It provides a uniformly doped, relatively high resistivity layer in place of the first-diffusion layer. Either n-channel or p-channel devices may be made this way. With this process either the epitaxial layer or the substrate will determine breakdown voltage. For example, a 1-ohm-cm n-layer grown on a 0.5-ohm-cm p-type substrate will give a mini-

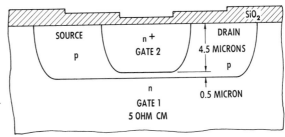

Fig. 8-11 Schematic cross section of double-diffused FET before aperture cutting for metallization.

mum of 25 volts breakdown. In this example the channel doping is made lower than the substrate doping to force most of the depletion layer spread into the channel.

Figure 8-12 indicates some of the process steps. The starting epitaxial n layer is about 4 microns thick. Figure 8-12a shows a deep oxide-masked p-type diffusion which is performed to isolate adjacent devices. Figure 8-12b shows the top-gate diffusion which not only defines the gate geometry but also, by means of its depth, determines the channel thickness. A 1-ohm-cm 2-micron channel will give a pinch-off voltage of about 4 volts. The final step before metallizing as shown in Fig. 8-12c is the source and drain diffusion, which provides a high concentration for a low-resistance contact and prevents the depletion layer in the drain region from spreading to the surface at high drain voltages. This diffusion is confined

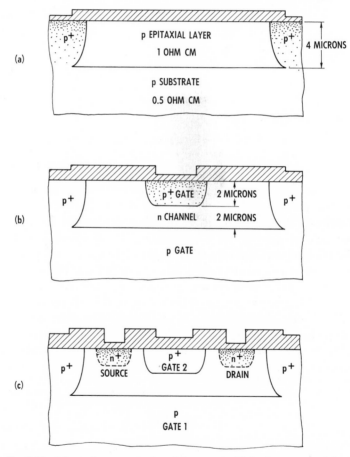

Fig. 8-12 Schematic representation of the steps in fabricating an epitaxial-diffused FET in a one-epitaxial-layer wafer: (*a*) Wafer cross section after p-type diffusion to form isolated islands for individual devices; (*b*) cross section after gate diffusion; (*c*) cross section after source and drain enhancement diffusion and before aperture cutting for metallization.

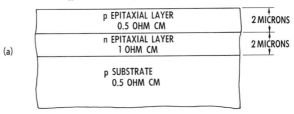

(a)

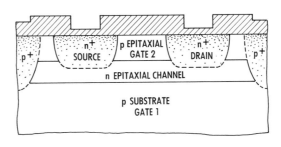

(b)

Fig. 8-13 Representation of two stages in the fabrication of an epitaxial-diffused FET in a two-epitaxial-layer wafer: (*a*) Cross section of starting wafer; (*b*) cross section after two diffusion steps and before aperture cutting for metallization.

to the high-resistivity regions to preserve a high gate-drain and gate-source breakdown voltage.

The second epitaxial-diffused process is that which uses epitaxy only to control channel sheet resistance, and diffusion only to control lateral geometry.[16] It starts with a p-n-p or an n-p-n wafer embodying two epitaxial layers. Since epitaxy is basically a *growing-on* process, precise values of sheet resistance can be produced. After the desired layer is grown, the doping impurity is changed and the opposite conductivity type is grown. This results in a high-sheet-resistance layer enclosed by regions of opposite conductivity. In this structure, pinch-off voltage has already been determined by the epitaxial process. It is only necessary to define the channel lateral dimensions and simultaneously to provide low-resistance source and drain contacts to the ends of the channel.

The procedure is straightforward. A 1-ohm-cm n-type layer 2 microns thick is grown epitaxially on a 0.5-ohm-cm p-type substrate. After the 2-micron n layer has been grown, the impurity doping is switched to p type, and an additional 2-micron-thick 0.5-ohm-cm layer is grown. The resultant p-n-p structure is shown in Fig. 8-13a. (We will consider only an n-channel example.) Next a deep p-type isolation diffusion is performed to terminate the n-type channel. Then the oxide is selectively removed from the source and drain regions, and phosphorus is diffused through the top p layer and into the n layer. This diffusion not only ties the eventual source and drain terminals to the ends of the channel but also defines the top gate and channel lateral geometry. Diffusion depth here is very noncritical since channel sheet resistance has already been determined by epitaxy. The only requirements for this diffusion is that it must go through the top p layer. Overshooting into the bottom p substrate will have a trifling effect on capacitance and on lateral dimensions.

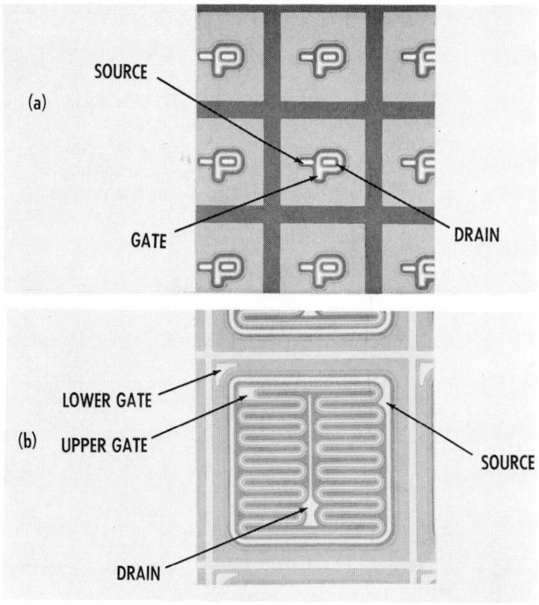

(a)

SOURCE

GATE   DRAIN

(b)

LOWER GATE

UPPER GATE

SOURCE

DRAIN

Fig. 8-14 Top-view patterns of two epitaxial-diffused FETs formed on two-epitaxial-layer wafers. Wafer specifications for the two devices are identical. (*a*) A high-frequency device on a 25-mil die; (*b*) a power device on a 50-mil die.

Figure 8-13*b* shows a cross section of the device prior to metallizing. Figure 8-14 shows top views of two transistors that have been made by the two-epitaxial-layer epitaxial-diffused method. The smaller is a high-frequency device with a typical I_P of 1 mA and a g_{mo} of 700 μmhos. For the larger or power device, I_P is typically 40 mA with a g_{mo} of 20,000 μmhos. For both, typical voltages are $V_P = 3.5$ volts and $BV_{GDS} = 35$ volts.

Epitaxial-alloyed Devices. The epitaxial-alloyed process is similar to the single-epitaxial-layer diffused process. But in the present case the top gate is formed by alloying instead of diffusion. Starting with the 1-ohm-cm n-type epitaxial layer on a 0.5-ohm-cm p-type substrate (but with a 2-micron layer instead of the 4-micron layer), a masked p-type diffusion is performed. Again, the purpose is to isolate each device from its neighbors on the wafer by interrupting the n layer. The source and drain regions are then given an n-type diffusion to enhance conductivity. After all the diffusion steps are performed, patterns are etched in the oxide for the top gate, source, and drain. Aluminum is evaporated onto the wafer and selectively removed from all areas where oxide has not been removed. The aluminum is then alloyed to form a p-n junction for the gate in the high-resistivity n region and at the same time produce the metallized ohmic contact to the source and drain. The final structure is shown in Fig. 8-15.

The depth of alloying is very small—approximately 0.1 micron—and so the final channel thickness does not change significantly. Thus channel thickness is controlled only by epitaxy. Although good low-leakage junctions can be made by the alloy process, more consistent junctions can be formed by other methods.

8-4 Isolated-gate FET

The isolated-gate field-effect transistor,[19-21] or IGFET, is a recent addition to the family of field-effect devices. Although, its electrical characteristics are very similar to those of the junction-type FET, it differs in a fundamental way from that device (and indeed, it likewise differs from all members of the field-effect family discussed above). In the junction-type devices, the channel is bounded by metallurgical p-n junctions. In the IGFET, the channel and lower gate (or substrate) are homogeneous metallurgically (that is, they are identical in impurity doping). The induced channel of the IGFET is distinguished from the lower gate in that it has a majority-carrier type opposite that of the lower gate.

The structure is shown schematically in Fig. 8-16a. Junction-FET terminology has been adopted for this device. For operation the lower p region is usually connected to the source to eliminate that capacitance from the input circuit. The channel is produced by an *inversion* of conductivity type resulting from the interaction of the silicon surface, the silicon oxide layer, and the metal deposited on top of the silicon oxide. Both the chemistry and physics of this interaction are only partly understood at this point. Indeed the IGFET seeks to exploit surface effects which have plagued the transistor since its inception and which, for the most part, have been "solved" by circumvention. The stimulus of the IGFET coupled with the new, simple, and quantitative experiments it makes possible is serving to advance the understanding of remaining integrated circuit and discrete semiconductor device surface problems. At present, stability of IGFET devices is adequate for many applications, particularly in digital integrated circuits where circuit simplifications may often be achieved by using enhancement-mode IGFETs.

One may speculate that a surface-normal field produced by positive ions in or near the oxide layer induces the n-type channel in this device. This field can be modulated by bias applied to the metal gate electrode applied over the oxide. This electrode is the *isolated gate.* Making it negative with respect to the source causes channel conductivity to decrease, as in the junction-type n-channel FET.

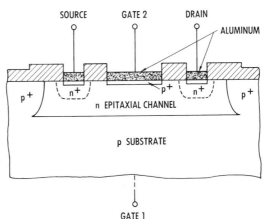

Fig. 8-15 Schematic cross section of an FET made by the epitaxial-alloyed process.

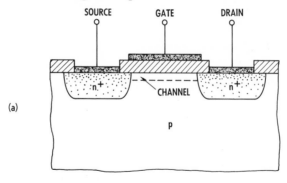

(a)

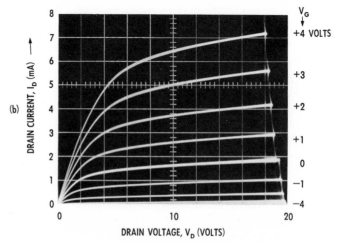

(b)

Fig. 8-16 (*a*) Cross-sectional view of an isolated-gate field-effect transistor (IGFET); (*b*) output characteristics of an IGFET.

However, positive bias may also be applied safely to the isolated gate, and this enhances channel conductivity. This dual possibility for gate bias polarity is a distinction and advantage of the IGFET. The two modes of operation are termed the *depletion* and *enhancement* modes, respectively. Figure 8-16*b* shows static output characteristics illustrating both modes of operation for an n-channel device. It is quite possible to make a p-channel IGFET for enhancement-mode operation. Obtaining a suitable initial p-type channel for depletion-mode operation is much more difficult, however. Hence most IGFET work is done with n-channel devices.

The most significant advantage of the IGFET aside from its structural simplicity lies in the fact that the parasitic capacitance between the isolated gate and other regions or terminals can be made smaller for a given top-view geometry than the corresponding capacitance in a junction-type device. This is true because at low gate bias the isolating oxide is frequently thicker than the corresponding junction-

FET depletion layer, and its relative dielectric permittivity κ is smaller than that of silicon (1.5 versus 12). Of particular importance is the reduction in drain-gate feedback capacitance (Miller capacitance) with the added advantage that it is voltage-independent. As an overall result, bandwidth is enhanced by at least a factor of 10 over that of the comparable junction FET.

REFERENCES

1. Shockley, W.: A Unipolar "Field-effect" Transistor, *Proc. IRE,* vol. 40, pp. 1365–1376, November, 1952.
2. Dacey, G. C., and I. M. Ross: Unipolar "Field-effect" Transistor, *Proc. IRE,* vol. 41, pp. 970–979, August, 1953.
3. Dacey, G. C., and I. M. Ross: The Field Effect Transistor, *Bell System Tech. J.,* vol. 34, pp. 1149–1189, November, 1955.
4. Wallace, R. L., L. G. Schimpf, and E. Dickten: A Junction Transistor Tetrode for High-frequency Use, *Proc. IRE,* vol. 40, pp. 1395–1400, November, 1952. Early models of this device (which has two opposed base leads) were kindly supplied to the first author by E. Dickten in 1957. Those with abnormally thin bases functioned as efficient field-effect transistors when the emitter and collector were used as gates.
5. Haring, H. E., and W. A. Sunder: private communication, 1956.
6. Tezner, S.: A New High Frequency Amplifier (in French), *Compt. rend.,* vol. 246, p. 72, Jan. 6, 1958.
7. D'Asaro, L. A.: private communication, 1959.
8. Bosenberg, W. A., J. A. Olmstead, and K. Wybrands: Design and Application of Silicon Unipolar Transistors Made by Diffusion Techniques, Annual Meeting of the IRE Professional Group on Electron Devices, Washington, D.C., October, 1961.
9. Lawrence, H.: A Diffused Field Effect Current Limiter, *IRE Trans. Electron Devices,* vol. ED-9, pp. 82–87, January, 1962.
10. Klink, H., and G. C. Onodera: Localized Epitaxial Growth for Field Effect Transistor Fabrication, Meeting of the Electrochemical Society, Pittsburgh, Pa., April, 1963.
11. Warner, R. M., Jr.: A New Passive Semiconductor Component, *IRE Natl. Conv. Record,* vol. 6, part 3, pp. 43–48, 1958.
12. Nelson, H.: The Preparation of Semiconductor Devices by Lapping and Diffusion Techniques, *Proc. IRE,* vol. 46, pp. 1062–1067, June, 1958.
13. Warner, R. M., Jr., W. H. Jackson, I. E. Doucette, and H. A. Stone, Jr.: A Semiconductor Current Limiter, *Proc. IRE,* vol. 47, pp. 44–56, January, 1959.
14. Stone, H. A., Jr.: Theory and Use of Field-effect Tetrodes, *Electronics,* vol. 32, pp. 66–68, May 15, 1959.
15. Stone, H. A., Jr., and R. M. Warner, Jr.: The Field-effect Tetrode, *Proc. IRE,* vol. 49, pp. 1170–1183, July, 1961.
16. Onodera, G. C., W. J. Corrigan, and R. M. Warner, Jr.: Silicon Field-effect Transistor with Internal Epitaxial Channel, *Proc. IRE,* vol. 50, p. 1824, August, 1962.
17. Shockley, W.: Transistor Electronics: Imperfections, Unipolar and Analog Transistors, *Proc. IRE,* vol. 40, pp. 1289–1301, November, 1952.
18. Early, J. M.: Structure-determined Gain-band Product of Junction Triode Transistor, *Proc. IRE,* vol. 46, pp. 1924–1927, December, 1958.

19. Kahng, D., and M. M. Atalla: Silicon–Silicon Dioxide Field Induced Surface Devices, presented at IRE–AIEE Solid-state Device Research Conference, Carnegie Institute of Technology, Pittsburgh, Pa., June 13–15, 1960.
20. Wanlass, F. M., and C. T. Sah: Nanowatt Logic Using Field-effect Metal-oxide Semiconductor Triodes, presented at the International Solid-state Circuits Conference, Philadelphia, Feb. 20, 1963.
21. Hofstein, S. R., and F. P. Heiman: The Silicon Insulated-gate Field-effect Transistor, *Proc. IEEE,* vol. 51, pp. 1190–1202, September, 1963.
22. Lilienfeld, J. E.: Device for Controlling Electric Current, U.S. Patent 1,900,018, Mar. 7, 1933.
23. Heil, O.: Improvements in or Relating to Electrical Amplifiers, and Other Control Arrangements and Devices, British Patent 439,457, Sept. 26, 1939.
24. Weimer, P. K.: The TFT—A New Thin-film Transistor, *Proc. IRE,* vol. 50, pp. 1462–1469, June, 1962.
25. Wallmark, J. T., and S. M. Marcus: Integrated Devices Using Direct-coupled Unipolar Transistor Logic, *IRE Trans. Electron. Computers,* vol. EC-8, no. 2, pp. 98–107, June, 1959.
26. Csanky, G., and R. M. Warner, Jr.: Two New Compatible Logic Elements, Digest of Technical Papers, International Solid-state Circuits Conference, pp. 30–31, Philadelphia, February, 1963.
27. Bailey, D. C.: High Input Impedance Amplifier; MC1515, MC1516 Integrated Circuits, Preliminary Specification, Motorola Semiconductor Products Division.
28. Prim, R. C., and W. Shockley: Joining Solutions at the "Pinch-off Point" in the Field-effect Transistor, *IRE Trans. Electron Devices,* vol. PGED-4, pp. 1–14, December, 1953.
29. Lindholm, F. A., and D. C. Latham: Junction Capacitance of Field Effect Transistors, *Proc. IEEE,* vol. 51, pp. 404–405, February, 1963.
30. Warner, R. M., Jr.: Epitaxial FET Cutoff Voltage, *Proc. IEEE,* vol. 51, pp. 939–940, June, 1963.
31. Hoerni, J. A., and B. Weir: Conditions for a Temperature Compensated Silicon Field Effect Transistor, *Proc. IEEE,* vol. 51, pp. 1058–1059, July, 1963.
32. Lauritzen, P. O.: Field Effect Transistors as Low-noise Amplifiers, Digest of Technical Papers, International Solid-state Circuits Conference, pp. 62–63, Philadelphia, February, 1962.
33. van der Ziel, A.: Thermal Noise in Field-effect Transistors, *Proc. IRE,* vol. 50, pp. 1808–1812, August, 1962.
34. Bruncke, W. C.: Noise Measurements in Field-effect Transistors, *Proc. IEEE,* vol. 51, pp. 378–379, February, 1963.
35. Grubbs, W. J., and E. I. Doucette: private communication, 1958.
36. Terman, F. E.: "Electronic and Radio Engineering," 4th ed., McGraw-Hill Book Company, New York, 1955.

9

OTHER ACTIVE DEVICES FOR
INTEGRATED CIRCUITS

In addition to the transistors and diodes discussed in the preceding chapters, many other active p-n junction devices are used to varying degrees in specialized integrated circuits applications. When used in hybrid integrated circuits, these devices may have characteristics identical to those they would exhibit mounted in separate packages and used as discrete components. But when they are used in monolithic integrated circuits, modifications must often be made in their design in order for these devices to exhibit comparable characteristics and still be compatible with monolithic integrated circuit processing.

Three basic problem areas are encountered when adapting devices to monolithic integrated circuits. These are:

1. Process incompatibility: The processes required to form the desired element may be incompatible with the other processes used in forming a monolithic integrated circuit, or vice versa.

2. Top contact requirement: All contacts to a monolithic integrated circuit must be made to its top surface. With many devices this introduces undesirable parasitic series resistances and lateral biasing of component p-n junctions.

3. Isolation parasitic effects: Operating modes of the device may be changed because the additional p-n junctions which are present for isolation purposes have parasitic properties (chiefly capacitance) associated with them.

Table 9-1 lists several active devices which may be used in integrated circuits and indicates whether or not changes in the devices are necessary.

9-1 Tunnel Diode (and Backward Diode)

The tunnel diode[1] consists of a p-n junction made with the following two metallurgical properties:

233

1. Impurity contents on both sides of the p-n junction are very high, of the order of $10^{19}/cm^3$, making the material degenerate. This is sometimes designated as a p^+-n^+ junction.

2. The chemical impurity transition from p type to n type is very sharp, resulting in an abrupt junction.

Table 9-1   Using Other Active Devices in Integrated Circuits

Device	Hybrid		Monolithic	
	U	C	U	C
Tunnel diode	×			
Variable-capacitance diodes. . .	×	×		×
Unijunction transistor		×		×
p-n-p-n switches.	×	×		×

U = use in unchanged form.
C = change necessary or desirable.

The electrical characteristics of a tunnel diode are shown in Fig. 9-1a. Its two positive-resistance regions, separated by a well-defined negative-resistance region, give rise to both logic and low-noise continuous-wave applications, and its very nonlinear regions can be used for mixing. If the impurity content on one side of the abrupt p-n junction is not quite degenerate, the negative-resistance region is absent (or very small), but the device still conducts very efficiently in the opposite direction. This is called a *backward diode* because it rectifies better (at low currents)

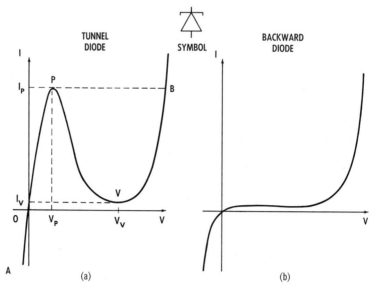

Fig. 9-1 Current-versus-voltage characteristics of (*a*) the tunnel diode and (*b*) the backward diode. V_p, I_p, V_v, and I_v refer to peak voltage, peak current, valley voltage, and valley current, respectively, for the tunnel diode. Note that the backward diode shows greater conductivity in the reverse direction than in the forward direction.

ın the normally forward direction than in the normally reverse direction (Fig. 9-1*b*).

The "bump" in the tunnel diode *V-I* curve (*OPV* in Fig. 9-1*a*), and its high conduction in the inverse direction (*OA*) differentiate its characteristic from that of a normal diode. (In the backward diode, only the inverse conduction characteristic is different.) Both the abnormal forward and reverse characteristics are caused by quantum-mechanical tunneling of electrons through the p-n junction barrier, producing current effectively in parallel to that carried by the more common minority-carrier effects. This tunnel current is an exceedingly sensitive function of the junction barrier thickness, dropping off in an exponential manner with junction grading. Also, if the impurity content on both sides of the junction is not sufficiently high, even with an abrupt junction, the tunnel (or backward) diode cannot be made, because there is no usable source or sink for tunneling electrons. Since the tunneling process is exceedingly fast, high-frequency performance of the tunnel diode is determined primarily by its parasitic junction capacitance and series resistance.

Tunnel diodes are made by an alloying process, because it is the most convenient method of producing an abrupt junction. Major characteristics such as peak current I_p are extremely sensitive to junction abruptness. It is usual to reduce the junction area by etching until the desired value of I_p is obtained. The structure then looks as illustrated schematically in Fig. 9-2. High-frequency low-current (mA range) units in which the junction diameter is less than 1 mil are very fragile.

Peak currents are generally in the 1- to 100-mA range, with junction capacitances, for "fast" devices such that the capacitance in pf is less than the peak current I_p, in mA. The peak-to-valley current ratio I_p/I_v for good germanium and gallium arsenide tunnel diodes should be greater than 10. V_p, the voltage at the peak P, is in the range of 50 to 100 mv. The voltage at point B depends on the semiconductor band gap (or energy gap), being approximately 0.5 volt for germanium, and approximately 1 volt for gallium arsenide. The series resistance is a parasitic entity that limits frequency response. For good units, the series resistance should be less than $10/I_p$, where I_p is in mA.

The use of tunnel diodes in monolithic integrated circuits is exceedingly difficult

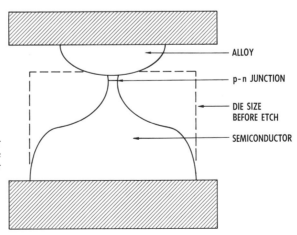

Fig. 9-2 Tunnel diode structure after etching to produce the desired I_p. Note the size of the die before and after etching.

ALLOY

p-n JUNCTION

DIE SIZE
BEFORE ETCH

SEMICONDUCTOR

because of the need for etching of the tunnel diode die to obtain the desired value of I_p, the necessity of providing a uniform degenerate region into which to alloy, and finally, because of the fragility of the finished device. Also, silicon, which forms the substrate for almost all integrated circuits, because of its band structure does not yield tunnel diodes with characteristics nearly as useful as those made from germanium or gallium arsenide. Hence, the use of tunnel diodes in integrated circuits for the foreseeable future will be limited to the small, encapsulated[2] devices such as the one shown in Fig. 9-3, for use in hybrid structures.

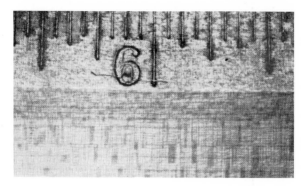

Fig. 9-3 Micro tunnel diode shown in the loop of the 6 on a standard ruler.

9-2 Variable-capacitance Diodes

The term *variable-capacitance diode* connotes a p-n junction diode in which the variation of junction capacitance with voltage is exploited.[3] Three specific types are the varactor, parametric, and tuning diodes.

For an abrupt junction under large negative-bias conditions,

$$C \propto V_t^{-1/2} \tag{9-1}$$

where V_t is the total voltage across the junction, consisting of the built-in contact potential added to the externally applied voltage. (With respect to algebraic sign, the contact potential is a *reverse* voltage; its magnitude is approximately 0.6 volt.) If the device becomes forward-biased, C increases rapidly, and minority-carrier storage effects can alter the form of Eq. (9-1). However, varactor diodes are not operated in this forward-bias region; so we shall not be concerned with it here. It should be noted, however, that the operation of a varactor diode into a slight forward bias at high frequencies does not necessarily result in a lossy unit, since by proper design, the minority carriers injected during the forward pulse can be extracted by the junction as it swings into reverse bias.

For a graded junction, in which case the impurity concentration changes in a nearly linear fashion for an appreciable distance on either side of the p-n boundary,

$$C \propto V_t^{-1/3} \tag{9-2}$$

In many cases, the impurity distribution is neither abrupt nor linear, and so the capacitance varies with voltage somewhere between the square root and cube root curves. In the p-i-n diode (a diode with a high resistivity or nearly intrinsic layer of either n or p type between low-resistivity p-type and n-type regions), the space-charge region punches through the center layer at a low voltage and grows only slightly thicker for higher voltages. Thus the capacitance is almost independent of voltage, and the device acts very much like a fixed parallel-plate capacitor.

The equivalent circuit for a variable-capacitance diode is shown in Fig. 9-4. $C(V)$ depends on the impurity distribution, as discussed above. $G(V)$ is determined by the junction leakage current, which is usually less than 1 μA, and often less than 1 nA. R_s is the series resistance of the semiconductor regions (and contacts). For small-area devices, R_s is a spreading resistance, determined by the junction diameter d and resistivity ρ, on the side whose resistance is being considered according to the relationship

$$R_s = \frac{\rho}{2d} \qquad \text{(for an abrupt junction)} \qquad (9\text{-}3)$$

Note that because of the spreading of the space charge, R_s is also a function of voltage. For very high frequency operation, the inductance and capacitance of the package become important.

The figure of merit of a variable-capacitance diode (including package) is given by

$$Q = \frac{1}{G/\omega C + \omega R_s C} \qquad (9\text{-}4)$$

At low frequencies,

$$Q \approx \frac{\omega C}{G} \qquad (9\text{-}5)$$

At high frequencies,

$$Q \approx \frac{1}{\omega R_s C} \qquad (9\text{-}6)$$

Hence, Q goes through a maximum at

$$f_p = \frac{1}{2\pi C} \sqrt{\frac{G}{R_s}} \qquad (9\text{-}7)$$

For voltage-variable tuning capacitors (those where the capacitance change of the p-n junction is used to tune a circuit), the frequency range covered may

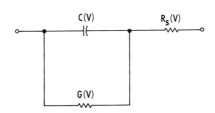

Fig. 9-4 Equivalent circuit and quality equations for variable-capacitance diodes.

$$Q = \frac{1}{G/\omega C + \omega R_s C} \qquad\qquad f_c = \frac{1}{2\pi R_s C}$$

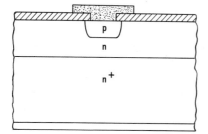

Fig. 9-5 Conventional epitaxial passivated variable-capacitance diode.

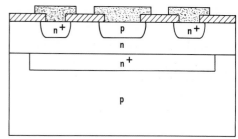

Fig. 9-6 Variable-capacitance diode with top contacts and buried layer compatible with monolithic integrated circuits.

be such that both the low- and high-frequency limitations are important, and therefore the diode should be designed to operate near f_p. For varactor diodes (where the nonlinear capacitance is used to generate harmonics) and parametric diodes (where the nonlinear capacitance is used to produce gain when driven by a pump signal), operation is mainly at high frequencies.

A cutoff frequency, where $Q = 1$, can be derived from Eq. (9-6):

$$f_C = \frac{1}{2\pi R_s C} \tag{9-8}$$

where f_C is voltage-dependent. However, since R_s is (approximately) inversely

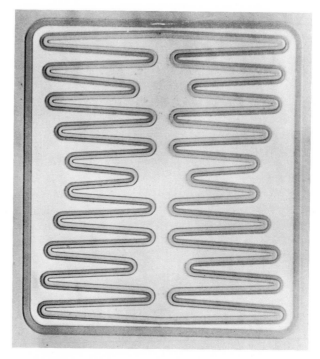

Fig. 9-7 Photomicrograph of a varactor diode suitable for use in monolithic integrated circuits.

proportional to junction area, and C is proportional to it, the value of f_C is (to a first approximation) a constant for a given impurity distribution. For example, we might have $R_s = 1$ ohm at $C = 1$ pf for $f_C \approx 200$ gc. The size of the junction is then chosen to give the desired capacitance by considerations such as impedance or power output. Silicon makes excellent variable-capacitance diodes, although gallium arsenide is, in some respects, superior.

The main determining factor in the performance of a variable-capacitance diode is generally the term R_s; structure design and processing are chosen to minimize it. Figure 9-5 shows the use of epitaxy to minimize R_s for a conventional variable-capacitance diode. The series resistance also adds noise in amplifier applications, and reduces efficiency when used for multiplication. When considered for application to a monolithic integrated circuit, the top contact requirement is the main limitation, and variable-capacitance diodes of large area (i.e., varactors and tuners) must employ buried layers to lower R_s, as shown in Fig. 9-6. For the small-area (parametric) diodes, this is not such an important consideration since most of R_s appears as the junction spreading resistance.

It is possible to make variable-capacitance diodes in monolithic integrated circuits having f_C within a factor of about 2 of that for discrete varactor diodes. A buried n^+ layer with a sheet resistance of about 10 ohms per square is utilized. A narrow, interdigitated structure (like a power transistor) is required to reduce the effective number of squares to less than 0.1, and at the same time keep the junction area small. A photograph of such a compatible varactor diode is shown in Fig. 9-7. A group of four top-contact diodes of more conventional configuration, having an appreciably lower f_C, is shown in Fig. 9-8.

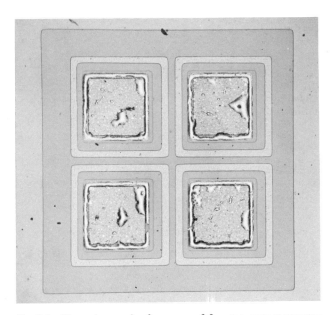

Fig. 9-8 Photomicrograph of a group of four top-contact varactor diodes for use in monolithic integrated circuits.

9-3 Unijunction Transistor

The unijunction transistor [4,5] has a single p-n junction with two (ohmic) base contacts, as shown in Fig. 9-9a. It is used as a switch or relaxation oscillator; its operation depends upon resistivity modulation (lowering) caused by copious minority-carrier injection. With base 2 open (or shorted to base 1), the junction-base-1 characteristic looks like a p-n junction diode, which, because of the geometry, has a rather poor forward characteristic, as shown in Fig. 9-9b.

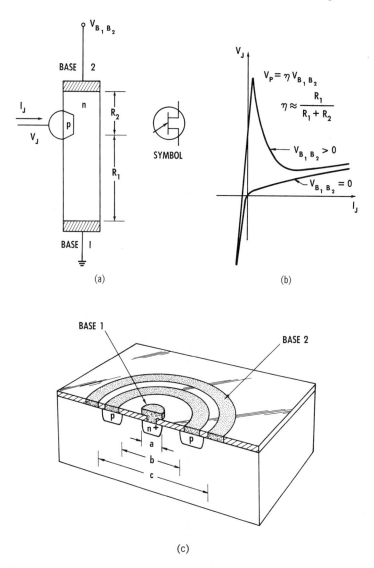

(a)

(b)

(c)

Fig. 9-9 The unijunction transistor: (*a*) A schematic representation; (*b*) its operating characteristics; (*c*) a modified unijunction transistor geometry for use in monolithic integrated circuits.

When a positive bias $V_{B_1B_2}$ is applied to base 2 with respect to base 1, the silicon bar acts as a potential divider for the p-n junction, and it floats at a positive bias less than $V_{B_1B_2}$. The potential at the junction edge closest to base 1 is

$$V_{J_1} = \frac{R_1}{R_1 + R_2} V_{B_1B_2} \tag{9-9}$$

where R_1 is the resistance of the silicon bar between the lower junction edge and base 1, and $(R_1 + R_2)$ is the resistance of the bar between base contacts.

For positive potentials less than V_{J_1} applied to the junction, it is still reverse-biased because of the voltage induced by $V_{B_1B_2}$. When $V_P \approx V_{J_1} + 0.5$ volt, the junction begins to inject an appreciable number of holes into the n-type bar. These are swept toward base 1, modulating (lowering) the resistivity of the silicon in that region. This requires the potential distribution in the bar to shift, lowering V_{J_1}. Since V_{J_1} drops as I_J increases, there results a negative-resistance region (Fig. 9-9b). As I_J increases further, the modulation saturates, and the negative resistance terminates in a low positive-resistance region.

The standoff ratio η is given by

$$\eta = \frac{V_P}{V_{B_1B_2}} \approx \frac{V_{J_1}}{V_{B_1B_2}} = \frac{R_1}{R_1 + R_2} \tag{9-10}$$

Typical standoff ratios run from 0.5 to 0.8. Interbase resistance $(R_1 + R_2)$ is generally in the range 1 to 10 kilohms. The peak point V_P, which can occur at a low positive or negative current at room temperature, moves toward negative I_J as temperature is increased. The unijunction transistor is used as a switch having an electrically variable peak point. Also, since the value of η is determined primarily by a simple potential division, it is very temperature-stable.

The unijunction transistor as depicted in Fig. 9-9a cannot be used in monolithic integrated circuits because the requirements for a shaped bar, alloy junction, and specific atmosphere are undesirable from a compatibility standpoint. A modified, compatible structure is shown in Fig. 9-9c. Here, the spreading resistance of the small n^+ region is utilized to obtain high values of η and interbase resistance. With $V_{B_1B_2}$ applied, most of the potential drop is close to the n^+ contact because of its small size. The potential appearing at the inner edge of the p-n junction is V_{J_1}, so that

$$\eta \approx \frac{V_{J_1}}{V_{B_1B_2}} = 1 - \frac{a}{b} \tag{9-11}$$

Also,

$$R_{B_1B_2} \approx \frac{\rho}{\pi}\left(\frac{1}{a} - \frac{1}{c}\right) \tag{9-12}$$

Unijunction transistor properties attainable with the structures shown in Fig. 9-9a and c are quite similar. A photograph of a compatible unijunction transistor is shown in Fig. 9-10.

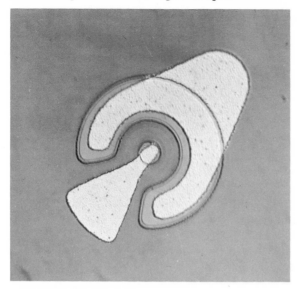

Fig. 9-10 Photomicrograph of a unijunction transistor for use in monolithic integrated circuits.

9-4 p-n-p-n Switches

The p-n-p-n diode[6] (four-layer diode) and triode[7-9] (controlled rectifier) are bistable devices having efficient high- and low-resistance regions. Device geometries are shown in Fig. 9-11, and device characteristics in Fig. 9-12. With bias applied as indicated, the center junction is reverse-biased, and limits current until a breakover voltage V_{BO} (which may be the avalanche voltage of the central junction) is reached.

The four-layer diode (Fig. 9-11) may be analyzed as being composed of two transistor sections: a p-n-p section having current gain α_n, and an n-p-n section with α_p, sharing a common collector junction. The total current gain is the sum of α_p and α_n, which are assumed to vary with current, but not with voltage. That is, α_p and α_n are measured at low voltages. At appreciable reverse voltages on the center junction, avalanche multiplication increases current gain. The value of the multiplication factor is given by Eq. (2-83), repeated here:

$$M(V) = \frac{1}{1 - (V/V_B)^n} \qquad (2\text{-}83)$$

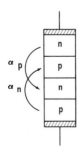

The exponent n is in the range 1 to 5, depending on the semiconductor material and impurity profile. The value of n is low for holes; high for electrons. The total current gain of the four-layer diode is then

$$\alpha = M(\alpha_p + \alpha_n) \qquad (9\text{-}13)$$

Fig. 9-11 Schematic representation of a four-layer diode.

In the region 0 to V_{BO} (Fig. 9-12), the current flowing is

$$I = \frac{I_{CO}}{1 - M(\alpha_p + \alpha_n)} \qquad (9\text{-}14)$$

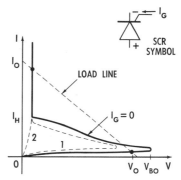

Fig. 9-12 Current-versus-voltage characteristics for the four-layer diode and triode.

where I_{CO} is the reverse leakage current of the central junction. At V_{BO}, $M(\alpha_p + \alpha_n) \rightarrow 1$, and so the current can increase greatly. The curve from this point on is the locus of points where $M(\alpha_p + \alpha_n) = 1$. As current increases, α_p and α_n increase, primarily because of field-aided diffusion in one or both regions. Hence, M must decrease, and by Eq. (2-83), V decreases. This gives a negative-resistance region which terminates at I_H (hold current), where $\alpha_p + \alpha_n = 1$ (independent of any avalanche multiplication), and all three p-n junctions are forward-biased. The four-layer diode can be switched from V_o to I_o by supplying a voltage pulse of sufficient magnitude to exceed V_{BO}. To turn the device off, I must be reduced below I_H. Voltage across the device in the ON region is approximately 1 volt.

The controlled rectifier (Fig. 9-13) behaves similarly, except that a base (gate) current may be supplied to the n-p-n transistor section. The base current causes current to flow in the n-p-n structure, increasing I, and hence increasing $(\alpha_p + \alpha_n)$. This reduces the blocking characteristic to curve 1. If the load line is as shown in Fig. 9-12, then this amount of gate current will turn the controlled rectifier on by lowering its breakdown voltage to the condition where the only stable point left is I_o. If a larger gate current is applied, then curve 2 results, the *blocking* characteristics having been completely removed.

The current-gain conditions whereby a p-n-p-n structure can act as an efficient four-layer diode or a controlled rectifier are then:

1. $\alpha_p + \alpha_n < 1$ at low currents.
2. $(\alpha_p + \alpha_n)$ increases beyond unity at some (usefully low) current.

The p-n-p-n switch is a regenerative device, remaining on or off until switched to the other condition. There is no lateral base biasing, as in the case of a transistor, since, in the ON position, no gate current flows. Hence, the entire area of the structure is utilized, and a simple circular geometry (rather than the interdigitated structure required for high-current-diffused silicon transistors) works well. The hold current ranges from micro-amperes to milliamperes, even for very high current (i.e., 50 amp) units. Turn-off gain is more difficult to achieve, being of the order of 10 for a current of 5 amp. This means that a gate current of 500 mA will raise I_H until it exceeds 5 amp.

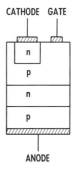

Fig. 9-13 Schematic representation of a silicon controlled rectifier (SCR) or four-layer triode.

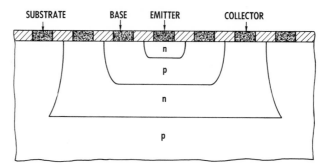

Fig. 9-14 Schematic representation of an n-p-n transistor in monolithic integrated circuits, showing the p-n-p-n structure.

The current gains α_p and α_n can both be low, since only their sum has to be greater than unity to cause switching. Hence, many multijunction structures in monolithic integrated circuits can inadvertently switch. For example, because of p-n junction isolation, an n-p-n transistor made in a monolithic integrated circuit (Fig. 9-14) has an n-p-n-p structure from the emitter to the substrate. This can be prevented from switching by controlling geometry and impurity contents to keep $\alpha_p + \alpha_n < 1$, which is difficult, or by purposely keeping the collector-substrate junction reverse (or zero) biased.

Problems involved in designing p-n-p-n switches for monolithic integrated circuits are the need for top contacts (which require a buried layer for efficient operation) and isolating a four-region structure. This latter requirement will generally limit the value of V_{BO} to <20 volts for many practical cases, since processing from one side will require that the center p-n junction be formed by the intersection of two diffused profiles. A compatible geometry is shown in Fig. 9-15, utilizing a combination of epitaxial and diffusion techniques.

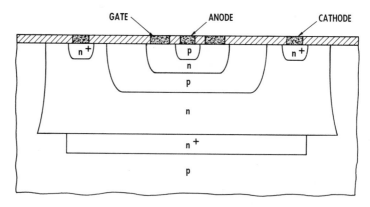

Fig. 9-15 Schematic representation of a p-n-p-n switch for use in monolithic integrated circuits.

REFERENCES

1. (*a*) Gentile, S. P.: "Basic Theory and Application of Tunnel Diodes," D. Van Nostrand Co., Inc., Princeton, N.J., 1962.
   (*b*) Lesk, I. A., N. Holonyak, Jr., U. S. Davidsohn, and M. W. Aarons: Germanium and Silicon Tunnel Diodes: Design, Operation and Application, 1959.
2. Blank, J. M., I. A. Lesk, and J. J. Suran: Practical Considerations in Thin Circuit Micro-electronics, *Proc. NEC,* p. 438, 1960.
3. Blackwell, L. A., and K. L. Kotzebue: "Semiconductor-diode Parametric Amplifiers," Prentice-Hall, Inc., Englewood Cliffs, N.J., 1961.
4. Brown, S. R., and T. P. Sylvan: Silicon Unijunction Transistor, *Electron. Design,* Jan. 8 and 22, 1958.
5. Lesk, I. A., and V. P. Mathis: The Double-base Diode: A New Semiconducting Device, *IRE Natl. Conv. Record,* part 6, p. 2, 1953.
6. Moll, J. L., M. Tanenbaum, J. M. Goldey, and N. Holonyak, Jr.: P-N-P-N Transistor Switches, *Proc. IRE,* vol. 44, pp. 1174–1182, September, 1956.
7. Mackintosh, I. M.: The Electrical Characteristics of Silicon P-N-P-N Triodes, *Proc. IRE,* vol. 46, pp. 1229–1235, June, 1958.
8. Aldrich, R. W., and N. Holonyak, Jr.: Multiterminal P-N-P-N Switches, *Proc. IRE,* vol. 46, pp. 1236–1239, June, 1958.
9. "Silicon Controlled Rectifier Manual," General Electric Company.

10

PASSIVE COMPONENTS FOR INTEGRATED CIRCUITS

In discussing passive components for integrated circuits, we must differentiate between components designed for monolithic circuits (where all resistance and capacitance functions are obtained by utilizing the basic properties of the silicon crystal and of the junctions formed within this material) and the other types of integrated circuits such as hybrid circuits. In monolithic circuits, capacitors are formed by utilizing the inherent capacitance of a diffused p-n junction within the silicon material, and resistors are made by utilizing the bulk resistivity of the silicon itself. Since in monolithic circuits all parts are fabricated on or within a common substrate, they must be electrically isolated from one another. A common technique for accomplishing this isolation is the separate *isolation diffusion* treated at length in Chaps. 5, 7, and 12, which creates a pair of p-n junctions between all parts. On the substrate these isolating junctions are, in effect, back-to-back diodes so that regardless of the voltage polarity between any two parts, those parts are always separated by the high resistance of a back-biased diode. The isolation diffusion, of course, has associated with it an inherent capacitance between all parts and the common substrate, and this must be taken into account.

Hybrid circuits, as defined in this book, also include components made principally by masked diffusion processes. But, whereas monolithic circuits have all their component parts fabricated simultaneously on or within a single semiconductor crystal, the parts of a hybrid circuit are made separately, and are then interconnected individually on a ceramic substrate by means of wire bonds or metallization patterns. Thus, the components for hybrid circuits are inherently insulated and, although these components may be made by the same processes as monolithic components, the circuits do not require the additional isolation diffusion. They are relatively free, therefore, from many of the parasitics associated with monolithic devices.

Compatible integrated circuits are those utilizing a combination of semiconductor and thin-film processes. The range of passive component values in such circuits is greater than for the exclusively semiconductor devices, and component tolerances and temperature coefficients are, in some instances, more suitable for circuit design. These advantages are counterbalanced by the increased number of processes required and the associated higher costs. The following discussion considers the design and fabrication of passive integrated circuit components from all three integrated circuit standpoints.

10-1 Junction Capacitors

A p-n junction possesses capacitance because of the double layer of ionic charge associated with it. Chapter 2 developed this double-layer picture in a quantitative way for a simplified junction model, and Sec. 2-5 specifically addressed the subject of junction capacitance. In brief, increasing reverse bias on a junction uncovers an increasing amount of ionic charge on the two sides by retracting the mobile-carrier clouds which normally balance the ionic charge. The boundaries of these space-charge regions are the "plates" of the capacitor. One lies on either side of the junction, and the spacing between them is typically of the order of a micron. In silicon the relative dielectric permittivity is about 12, the leakage conductance shunting the capacitor is low, and the breakdown voltage can be made very high (by trading off capacitance per unit area), so that a junction constitutes a useful capacitor. It may be used as a voltage-variable capacitor,[1,2] or as a fixed-value device.

Junction Capacitors for Monolithic Circuits. Let us review briefly the steps in fabricating a junction capacitor in a monolithic circuit. The "boundary condition" existing here is that the capacitor must be formed simultaneously with other circuit elements.

Basically fabrication of the entire circuit, after the proper sequence of masks has been designed, begins with a 5- to 10-ohm-cm p-type silicon wafer on which a 25-micron-thick layer of 0.5-ohm-cm n-type silicon has been grown epitaxially. The epitaxial layer is covered with a thin layer of silicon dioxide. The wafer is then masked and etched, and subjected to a deep p-type diffusion which completely penetrates the n-type epitaxial layer to join the p-type substrate beneath, leaving oxide-covered n-type "islands" completely surrounded by p-type material. An oxide layer is then regrown over the diffused portions of the wafer, and the resulting structure is illustrated in Fig. 10-1.

Each n-type island provides the basis for the remaining diffusions which form the various integrated circuit elements, and each is separated from all others by p-n–n-p junctions, or back-to-back diodes, whose reverse leakage currents normally are less than 0.1 μA, thus providing adequate dc electrical isolation. The n-type epitaxial islands on the substrate have the proper resistivity for the collector regions of transistors, for the anodes of diodes, *and for one plate of a junction capacitor.*

In a second masked etching and diffusion process, the bases of transistors, the required resistors, and the second elements of diodes and junction capacitors are formed. This diffusion is also p type, but is much shallower than the previous

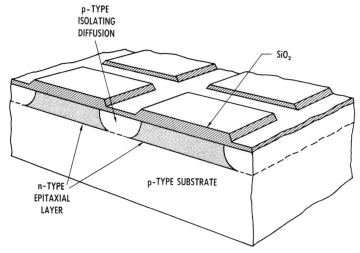

Fig. 10-1   Electrical isolation of n-type areas by p-type isolating diffusion.

isolation diffusion and does not penetrate the epitaxial layer; thus it forms the required p-n junctions directly within the epitaxial film.   Again, the newly diffused areas are covered with an oxide layer and, except for the formation of ohmic contacts to the two capacitor plates, the fabrication of the junction capacitor is complete.   The ohmic contacts to the shallow p-type diffused regions and the epitaxial n regions representing the capacitor plates are formed in an aluminum metallization process to be discussed later.   Figure 10-2 is a photomicrograph of a typical junction-type capacitor for monolithic integrated circuits.

The cross-sectional view (Fig. 10-3) of a typical junction capacitor clearly shows the two junctions associated with any diffused capacitor in a monolithic circuit. Each of these junctions has an associated capacitance—the desired capacitance of junction J_2 and the parasitic capacitance of J_1.   Since the capacitance of J_1 appears between any element of a monolithic circuit and the substrate, there exists

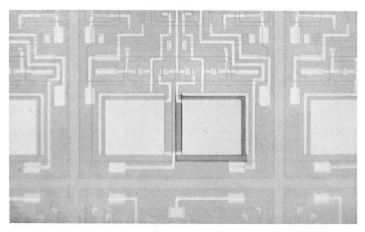

Fig. 10-2   Junction-type capacitor for monolithic integrated circuits.

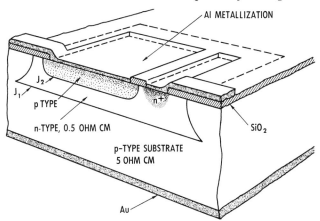

Fig. 10-3 Cross-sectional view of typical junction capacitor showing the two junctions associated with a diffused capacitor in a monolithic circuit.

a parasitic capacitance coupling (consisting of the series connection of the J_1 capacitances) between any two elements on a common substrate. In addition, every junction capacitor has an associated series parasitic resistance. This resistance is the result of the bulk resistance of the n region.

The parasitic elements in a typical monolithic junction capacitor are shown in its equivalent circuit (Fig. 10-4a). Here C_2 is the desired capacitance, C_1 is the parasitic capacitance, and R is the series resistance. The two diodes are the "idealized" diodes of the two junctions. From the equivalent circuit it is evident that a high ratio of C_2 to C_1 is desirable in order to obtain maximum signal transfer from point A to point B.

The actual capacitance value of a semiconductor junction is a function of the area of the junction, of the impurity concentration in the highest-resistivity material forming the junction (in this case the n-type epitaxial layer), and of the

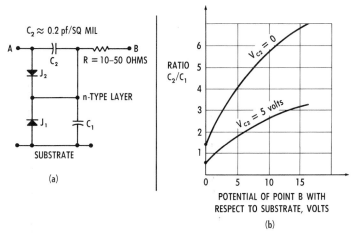

Fig. 10-4 (*a*) Equivalent circuit and (*b*) transfer ratio C_2/C_1 for typical monolithic junction capacitor.

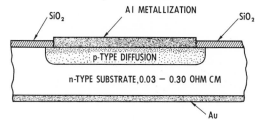

Fig. 10-5   Cross-sectional view of typical junction-type capacitor for hybrid integrated circuits.

voltage across the junction (see Sec. 2-5).   It is possible, therefore, to change the C_2/C_1 ratio by means of an applied bias voltage between point B and the substrate. The graph in Fig. 10-4b shows the variation of the C_2/C_1 ratio as a function of this bias, for two different values of voltage across capacitor C_2.   The maximum *transfer ratio* obtainable with a structure of this type is approximately 7:1.   The actual capacitance values can be calculated with the aid of Eq. (2-78) and Fig. 2-18.   It is also evident that the substrate must be the most negative point in the circuit, not only to minimize C_1, but also to prevent conduction of diode J_1 and associated problems which arise in the case where J_1 becomes forward-biased.

Junction Capacitors in Hybrid Circuits.   In the hybrid type of construction, the components may be physically isolated from one another on a ceramic wafer. Such components, therefore, do not require the additional isolation diffusions associated with monolithic designs and are relatively free of the parasitic effects associated with this diffusion into the substrate material.

A cross-sectional view of a typical junction-type capacitor for hybrid circuits is shown in Fig. 10-5.   The structure consists of a low-resistivity n-type substrate, a heavily doped p-type (boron) diffused area which forms a p-n junction, a silicon dioxide passivating layer, and an aluminum contact area to the p region.   The n-type substrate has a resistivity of 0.03 to 0.30 ohm cm ($N_D = 8 \times 10^{17}$ to 2.5×10^{16}/cm^3) and serves as the bulk material for mechanical strength as well as for the second capacitor contact.

A common practice in junction capacitors for hybrid circuits is to make a *binary* structure with several junctions, as shown in Fig. 10-6.   In this, each junction has twice the area and hence twice the capacitance of the next smaller one.   In this

Fig. 10-6   Binary junction capacitor for hybrid integrated circuits.

way a single chip may be used to provide a wide range of capacitance by simply utilizing the proper connections.

Design Considerations for Junction Capacitors.   The circuit designer must consider several factors when using junction-type capacitors in monolithic integrated circuits:

First, since the capacitor is normally formed at the same time as the collector-base junctions of any transistors that may occupy the same substrate, its capacitance per unit area is essentially fixed by the transistor requirements. For example, in integrated circuits the resistivity of the epitaxial layer is optimized to provide the best compromise between collector series resistance on the one hand, and collector breakdown voltage and parasitic capacitance on the other. This fixes an upper limit on achievable capacitance for a monolithic capacitor of a given size.

Second, the monolithic capacitor and the substrate collectively constitute a p-n-p transistor. Hence, the capacitor junction must be maintained in a reverse-biased condition to keep this transistor turned off. (The substrate junction is always reverse-biased.)

Third, the total capacitance is a function of the voltage across the junction. Thus an undesired capacitance modulation would occur if the circuit were subject to capacitor-bias variations.

Fourth, the series contact resistance for the diffused capacitor is approximately the same as that of the transistor collector—approximately 10 to 50 ohms. Because of this factor, the figure of merit for such a capacitor is comparatively low.

The foregoing discussion has assumed the use of the collector-base junction diffusion in the fabrication of a junction capacitor. In principle, at least, two other junctions are produced during the fabrication of an integrated circuit transistor which are available to the integrated circuit designer for the formation of junction capacitors. These are the emitter-base junction and the collector-substrate junction. The former may be used as a low-voltage junction capacitor; the latter is seldom used as a circuit element. Table 10-1 lists typical capacitance

Table 10-1   Capacitance per Unit Area

External bias, volts	*Capacitance per unit area, pf/mil²*
Collector-to-substrate Junction: 5-ohm-cm Substrate ($2.6 \times 10^{15}/cm^3$)	
0	0.16
−5	0.05
−10	0.035
Collector-to-base Junction: 0.5-ohm-cm Collector ($1.2 \times 10^{16}/cm^3$)	
0	0.2
−5	0.09
−10	0.06
Emitter-to-base Junction: 200-ohm/sq Base-diffusion Sheet Resistance before Emitter Diffusion	
0	0.89
−2	0.63
−5	0.4

Table 10-2   Range of Values for Junction Capacitors

Characteristic	Hybrid	Monolithic
Maximum capacitance per unit area, pf/mil^2	1	0.2 (for collector-base junction)
Maximum area, mil^2	10^4	2×10^3
Maximum capacitance, pf	10^4	400
Breakdown voltage, volts	5–50	5 or 20
Q	10–50	1–10
Voltage coefficient	$C \approx kv^{-1/2}$	$C \approx kv^{-1/2}$
Tolerance, %	± 10	± 20

per unit area values for each of these junctions as a function of impurity concentrations and bias conditions typical of integrated circuit transistor operation.

Capacitors for hybrid circuits, because they are constructed separately from other circuit elements and may employ starting materials with a relatively wide range of impurity concentrations and diffusion gradients, have a wider range of values than those in monolithic circuits. Table 10-2 compares some of the practical capacitor characteristics that are available for circuit applications in both hybrid and monolithic form.

The maximum breakdown voltage of a junction-type capacitor is determined by the impurity concentration of the material of the more lightly doped side of the junction. This can be estimated from Fig. 2-20.

10-2 Thin-film Capacitors

Thin-film capacitors, like their discrete counterparts, actually consist of two conductors separated by an insulator (dielectric), whereas semiconductor material fulfills both roles in the junction capacitor. The *compatibility* of thin-film devices, i.e., their ability to become an integral part of a block of silicon which embodies the other components of the monolithic integrated circuit, depends upon the compatibility of the processes used in forming the dielectric film.[3] Silicon dioxide thin films, for example, can be used readily with monolithic circuits since they are formed as part of the monolithic integrated circuit process. Others require special processing steps by means of which thin-film components can be fabricated on top of the semiconductor circuit without disturbing the existing monolithic structure. Several commonly used types of thin-film capacitors are discussed below.

Silicon Dioxide Capacitors. An example of a commonly used thin-film capacitor is the silicon dioxide capacitor, in which a low-resistivity silicon substrate acts as

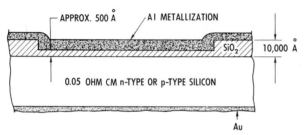

Fig. 10-7 Cross-sectional view of a silicon dioxide capacitor for hybrid integrated circuits.

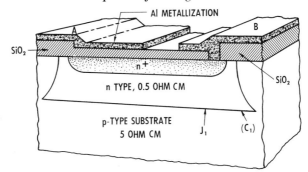

Fig. 10-8 Cross-sectional view of a silicon dioxide capacitor for monolithic integrated circuits.

one plate. A thin (500 Å) layer of silicon dioxide grown on the silicon substrate acts as the dielectric, and a film of aluminum metallization forms the top plate of the capacitor. Figure 10-7 shows a cross section of such a silicon dioxide capacitor for hybrid integrated circuit application.

The monolithic structure for this type of capacitor is shown in Fig. 10-8 where again, the structure is simply a dielectric between two conductors: the n^+ silicon and the aluminum metallization on the surface. Here, as for the junction capacitor, a p-n junction J_1 is used to provide isolation from the substrate. As shown in the equivalent circuit in Fig. 10-9a, the parasitic effects consist of a small series resistance R, a diode J_1, and its associated capacitance C_1 to the substrate. Figure 10-9b gives the transfer ratio C/C_1 of the structure as a function of voltage applied to junction J_1.

This type of capacitor has several advantages. First it is nonpolar; that is, it does not matter which of the two plates is positive or negative, thus giving more circuit flexibility. Second, the capacitance is constant; there is no voltage modulation to affect the circuit. Third, the Q is normally higher than for the junction type because the parasitic resistance R is lower than that in the junction capacitor, resulting again in greater flexibility in circuit applications.

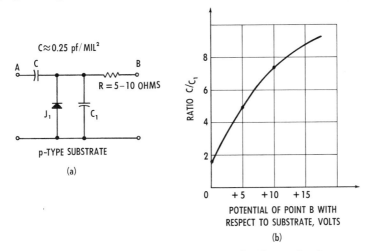

Fig. 10-9 (a) The equivalent circuit for a silicon dioxide capacitor for monolithic integrated circuits; (b) the transfer ratio C/C_1 of a typical monolithic silicon dioxide capacitor.

Typical measured capacitance values range from 0.25 to 0.30 pf/mil² for an oxide thickness of 800 to 1,000 Å. The practical lower limit on thickness is 500 Å because of the problems of obtaining a uniform oxide coating.

Tantalum Oxide (Ta_2O_5) Film Capacitors. Tantalum oxide capacitors[4] are produced by first sputtering a thin film of tantalum metal onto a suitable substrate. This serves as one plate of the capacitor. Sputtered tantalum metal films have excellent adherence properties because the substrate is, in effect, continuously cleaned during the sputtering process. The dielectric films for these capacitors are then prepared by anodizing the tantalum metal film to produce an oxide. The oxide formed has a high dielectric constant and a high breakdown strength. A disadvantage is that flaws which occasionally occur in the substrate are passed first into the metal and projected later as weak spots into the oxide layer. This can be corrected however, by an electrochemical back-etch procedure.

For the second capacitor plate, another film of tantalum metal is sputtered onto the tantalum oxide dielectric. Although it might seem practical to use aluminum as the second capacitor plate (in view of the fact that aluminum is utilized subsequently for forming the desired contacts), this is not feasible because aluminum would dissolve through the tantalum oxide at relatively low temperatures.

The compatible tantalum oxide capacitors are prepared by depositing the initial film of tantalum metal over the silicon dioxide covering the monolithic wafer. This introduces a small parasitic capacitance between the bottom plate of the capacitor and the silicon substrate. However, since the silicon dioxide layer under the capacitor can be made relatively thick, the parasitic capacitance to the substrate can be kept quite small.

Alumina (Al_2O_3) Capacitors. Compatible thin-film alumina capacitors (Fig. 10-10) are generally prepared as follows: First, a lower plate and contact of vacuum-evaporated aluminum is deposited over the silicon dioxide layer covering the

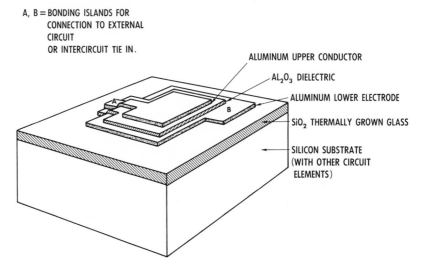

Fig. 10-10 Alumina thin-film coupling capacitor compatible with monolithic integrated circuits.

monolithic wafer. A thin film of nickel metal is then evaporated over the aluminum. The purpose of the nickel is to prevent migration of the aluminum metal into the alumina dielectric. Then the alumina dielectric is deposited over the nickel by the decomposition of an organo-aluminum compound. A nickel top plate is vacuum-evaporated over the alumina and, finally, an aluminum contact is vacuum-evaporated over the nickel top plate. Masked etching steps are employed to define the dimensions of the resulting capacitor. The comments concerning parasitics for tantalum oxide capacitors apply also to alumina capacitors.

Silicon Monoxide (SiO). Using low deposition rates, films with good dielectric properties can be made by evaporation of SiO. The dielectric constant of such deposits is less than that of the bulk material because of the lower density of the deposits. Because it is difficult to control the geometrical definition of SiO deposits, SiO films are used at present as large-area insulation only.

Table 10-3 lists some of the capacitor characteristics associated with each type of thin-film capacitor.

Table 10-3   Thin-film Capacitor Characteristics

Characteristic	Silicon dioxide	Alumina	Tantalum oxide
Maximum capacitance per unit area, pf/mil^2	0.25–0.4	0.3–0.5	2.5
Maximum value, pf	500	1,000	5,000
Maximum voltage, volts	50	20–50	20
Q (10 Mc).....................................	10–100	10–100	Good
Voltage coefficient	0	0	0
Dissipation factor (1 Mc)	0.7	0.5	5
Tolerance, %....................................	±20	±20	±20

Summary. From the foregoing discussion it is evident that many types of capacitors are available to the integrated circuit designer—with varying advantages and disadvantages. Diffused capacitors are relatively simple and inexpensive to produce, being fabricated simultaneously with other circuit elements within the monolithic circuit block. However, their maximum capacitance per unit area is relatively low, and they have inherently large parasitics. In addition, they are subject to capacitance modulation and must be properly polarized.

Compatible thin-film capacitors, on the other hand, can have relatively large capacitance values, and small parasitic effects. They are nonpolar and not subject to voltage modulation. However, they require additional process steps and are, therefore, more difficult to produce. And, even among the film capacitors there are variations in characteristics which may make one type or another the most desirable for a specific application.

10-3   Diffused Resistors

In integrated circuits, the resistor probably differs more from its discrete counterpart than any of the other components. Usually resistors can be incorporated in integrated circuits by either semiconductor or compatible thin-film techniques.

The basic technique for obtaining a diffused resistive element is the utilization of the bulk resistance of a defined volume of silicon. Consider, for example, a bar of silicon with a bulk resistivity of ρ. The end-to-end resistance of the bar is given by

$$R = \frac{\rho l}{A} \tag{10-1}$$

where l and A are the length and cross-sectional area, respectively, of the bar. Resistors of this nature may be formed in one of the isolated regions of the epitaxial layer on a typical substrate. However, it is much more common to employ a masked diffusion to establish a separate thin region to be used as a resistor during the diffusions which establish the base or emitter regions of associated transistors. The emitter diffusion makes available a low-resistivity region for resistor fabrication, while the base diffusion provides a medium-resistivity region. The latter is used most frequently because it strikes a reasonable compromise between a high value of resistivity which makes for a compact resistor and a low value of resistivity which provides a low temperature coefficient of resistance. The resistance of such a device is given by

$$R = \frac{\bar{\rho} l}{X_j w} \tag{10-2}$$

where $\bar{\rho}$ = average resistivity of diffused region
    l = length of diffused area
    w = width of diffused area
    X_j = depth of diffusion

The actual design of a diffused resistor is simplified by utilizing the concept of sheet resistance (discussed more fully in Sec. 3-3), defined by

$$R_S = \frac{\bar{\rho}}{X_j} \tag{10-3}$$

Substituting this into Eq. (10-2) gives

$$R = R_S \frac{l}{w} \tag{10-4}$$

Since R_S is determined by the requirements for the base or the emitter diffusions, the design of a monolithic resistor of a given value reduces to a simple problem in geometry. Thus for a given sheet resistance R_S, the value of a diffused resistor would be determined solely by l/w, the ratio of the length to the width.

As an example of this, let us determine the length-to-width ratio of a 4,000-ohm resistor fabricated during a base diffusion with a sheet resistance of 200 ohms per square:

$$\frac{l}{w} = \frac{R}{R_S} = \frac{4,000 \text{ ohms}}{200 \text{ ohms}} = \frac{20}{1} \tag{10-5}$$

Thus, for such a case, a 4,000-ohm resistor could be fabricated by employing a pattern 20 mils long by 1 mil wide or any pattern of the same proportions.

Figure 10-11 illustrates the mask layout of a typical diffused resistor with values given in the example. Here, the total resistance is determined by the 20- by 1-mil area of the 200-ohm-per-square p-type base diffusion. The ends of this bar are enlarged to provide for the ohmic contacts. Correction factors for these end effects will be discussed later. The edge of the n-type region must be approximately 2 mils away from the resistor area to allow for the spreading of the p-type isolation diffusion. Figure 10-12 shows a typical monolithic diffused resistor in cross section.

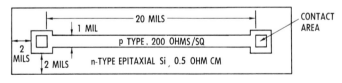

Fig. 10-11 Top view, showing dimension for mask layout purposes, of a 4,000-ohm diffused resistor.

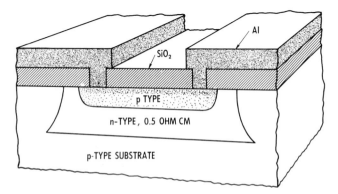

Fig. 10-12 Cross-sectional view of a typical monolithic diffused resistor.

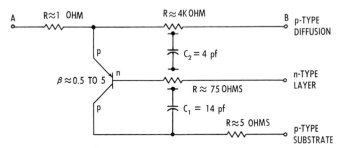

Fig. 10-13 Simplified equivalent circuit of a monolithic diffused resistor, showing the distributed parasitic capacitances and resistances in addition to the parasitic p-n-p transistors.

As shown in the equivalent circuit of Fig. 10-13, this method of fabricating a monolithic resistor produces both a distributed capacitance and a distributed transistor effect. Thus, the n-type layer now becomes the base of a low-β p-n-p transistor. This distributed transistor has a β in the 0.5 to 5 range. This low value of β results from the relatively thick (approximately 17 microns) base formed by the n-type epitaxial layer between the p-type substrate and the p-type

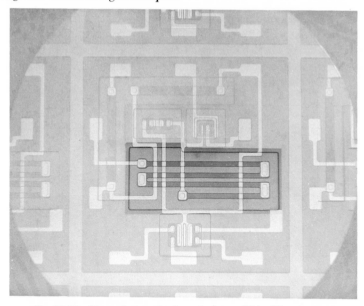

Fig. 10-14   Photomicrograph of a typical monolithic diffused resistor.

resistor diffusion.   Because the substrate is normally connected to the lowest potential of the circuit, conduction could occur if the p-n junction between the resistor and the n-type epitaxial layer became forward-biased through leakage or some other defect.   As can be seen, then, any current leakage between the substrate and the n-type layer would be multiplied by the β of the transistor and would act as a shunt leakage between the resistor and the substrate.   In a properly designed circuit, therefore, the n-type layer should be kept at the highest positive

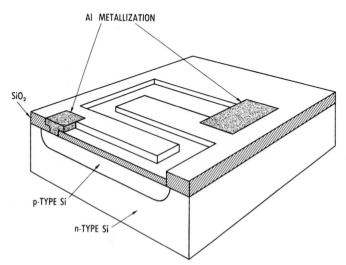

Fig. 10-15   Cross-sectional view of a diffused resistor for hybrid integrated circuits.

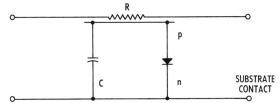

Fig. 10-16   Equivalent circuit of a diffused resistor for hybrid integrated circuits.

circuit potential to prevent such effects by maintaining a reverse bias on the p-n junction between the resistor and the n-type layer.

Other parasitic effects associated with diffused resistors are the distributed junction capacitances whose typical values for a 4,000-ohm resistor are indicated in Fig. 10-13.   The effects of these capacitances become significant at the higher frequencies.   Figure 10-14 is a photo of a typical monolithic diffused resistor.

Figure 10-15 is a cross-sectional view of a diffused resistor intended for hybrid integrated circuits.   The n-type substrate of 0.5 to 5 ohm cm provides the necessary bulk for mechanical strength and physical mounting, while the p-type layer, approximately 3 microns deep, determines the resistance value.   The equivalent circuit of the resistor is shown in Fig. 10-16.   A diode and the distributed capacitance of the p-n junction associated with the resistor are present as parasitic elements if a contact is made to the substrate material.   The reverse breakdown voltage of the diode is approximately 50 volts, while the leakage current of the junction is normally less than 10 nA.   The value of the distributed capacitance is a function of the substrate resistivity and normally varies between 0.2 and 0.05 pf/mil².   These values should be considered in the circuit applications because the maximum voltage across the resistor is limited by the reverse breakdown voltage of the diode, and the distributed capacitance effect is a factor at frequencies above 10 Mc.

Figure 10-17 is a photo of a tapped diffused resistor often employed in hybrid applications for the purpose of using a single structure for obtaining a variety of resistance values.

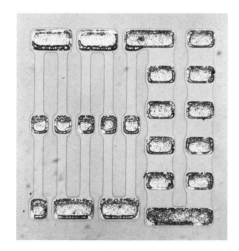

Fig. 10-17   Tapped diffused resistor for hybrid integrated circuits.   Resistors are made in tapped decade configurations from which close tolerance units can be obtained merely by bonding to the proper taps. The resistors are stocked in dice form, ready for mounting on a header and for bonding to the resistor taps that provide the specified resistance values.

Except for the parasitic capacitance and transistor effects, the hybrid and monolithic diffused resistors will have approximately the same performance characteristics. Properties such as power dissipation, temperature coefficients, and tolerances are the same for both types. However, as with capacitors, the hybrid resistors can have a continuous range of values, whereas the monolithic units are designed around values determined by the transistor design.

Range of Values. For a p-type diffusion, the sheet resistance R_S can vary from 10 to 500 ohms per square. In addition, n-type diffusions can be used to give values as low as 2.5 ohms per square. However, as indicated above, because of the characteristics desired for monolithic transistors, the monolithic diffused resistor is limited to values of 2.5 and 100 to 300 ohms per square. Although a resistance range of 2.5 ohms to 100 kilohms is possible for both hybrid and monolithic diffused resistors, a more practical range from an economic standpoint would be from 100 ohms to 30 kilohms. Figure 10-18 illustrates in graphic form the total isolation area required for different resistor configurations, which determines the practical upper limit for the values of integrated circuit resistors.

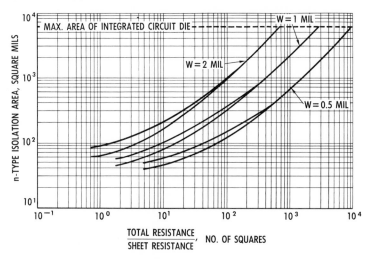

Fig. 10-18 Total isolation area required for a monolithic diffused resistor as a function of resistor value and construction.

Tolerances. For both hybrid and monolithic diffused resistors, three different operations determine the accuracy of the final resistance value. These are the initial layout and mask fabrication, the formation in the oxide of the proper length-to-width aperture by etching techniques, and the diffusion of the proper amount of impurity through this aperture to obtain the desired sheet resistance. Thus, the problem of resistor tolerances is divided into the control of pattern formation and the control of diffusion.

1. *Mask Tolerances.* Mask layouts for resistor patterns involve a number of considerations, in addition to the obvious length-to-width ratio which can be controlled to a tolerance of better than 0.5 per cent. For example, with low-value resistors, having low length-to-width ratios, the contact areas and bends in the resistor path will greatly influence the final value. Therefore, to take such varia-

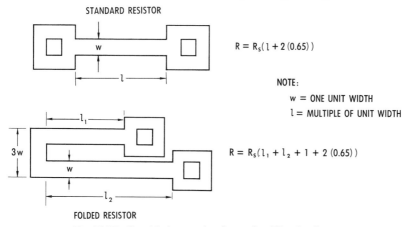

STANDARD RESISTOR

$$R = R_s(1 + 2(0.65))$$

NOTE:

w = ONE UNIT WIDTH

l = MULTIPLE OF UNIT WIDTH

$$R = R_s(l_1 + l_2 + 1 + 2(0.65))$$

FOLDED RESISTOR

Fig. 10-19 Empirical correction factors for diffused resistors.

tions into account, correction factors have been developed empirically for corners and various end configurations. Figure 10-19 illustrates these correction factors for determining a "compensated" pattern. Using such correction factors, mask errors can be held to within 1 per cent for both absolute values and ratios.

2. *Etching.* The operation of the etching of the oxide apertures prior to the diffusion process and the etching of the ohmic contact areas will result in further loss of resistor accuracy. This results primarily from overetching or underetching of the patterns. As an example, if we start with a length-to-width ratio of 10:1 (10 by 1 mils) and overetch in each direction by 0.1 mil, the resulting ratio is 10.2 to 1.2 mils, or 8.5:1, thus lowering the final value of the resistor. Typical tolerances for this operation are about ±2 per cent on absolute values and ±1 per cent on ratios where two or more resistor apertures are etched simultaneously.

3. *Diffusion.* The largest loss of accuracy in the absolute values of diffused resistors occurs during the diffusion operation. Here several factors, such as the amount of impurity predeposition and the junction depth, must be precisely controlled to maintain the desired sheet resistance. It is difficult, however, to control these factors with enough precision to obtain the exact resistance value desired. On the other hand, because the same operation takes place over an entire wafer, ratios of adjacent resistors are much more accurate. Typical tolerances are ±7 per cent for the absolute values and ±1 per cent for ratios.

Table 10-4 lists some typical values of tolerances that may be obtained at each step of the operation. Tighter tolerances are possible, but with lower yield and greater cost.

Table 10-4   Typical Tolerances of Diffused Resistors

Operation	Absolute values	Ratios
Drawing plus mask................	1%	1%
Etching.........................	2	1
Diffusion.......................	7	1
Overall process (worst case).........	$\approx\pm10\%$	$\approx\pm3\%$

Frequency Effects. As shown in the equivalent circuits of Figs. 10-16 and 10-13, both the monolithic and hybrid diffused resistors have an inherent distributed capacitance between the resistive element and the isolating substrate. It can be shown that this distributed capacitance acts as a shunting capacitance to the resistive element. Thus, at high frequencies, the effective impedance of the resistor is lowered.

As an example of this effect, Fig. 10-20*a* shows the response of a monolithic 3.2-kilohm resistor. These results were obtained with the n region at zero bias to produce the maximum distributed capacitance value. The plot illustrates the effect of the distributed capacitance on the resistor action as a function of frequency. The calculated value was obtained assuming the monolithic resistor to be represented by a 3.2-kilohm resistor, shunted by a 5-pf capacitor. The measured results were determined using the circuit shown in Fig. 10-20*b*.

As shown, these measurements indicate a drop-off at frequencies above 10 Mc. The behavior with frequency depends, of course, on the value of the resistor and the distributed capacitance shunting it. Diffused resistors have been used in both hybrid and monolithic RF amplifiers operating at above 100 Mc. The drop-off at

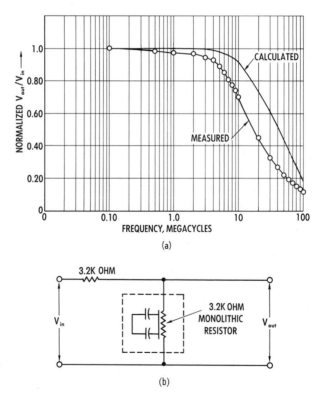

Fig. 10-20 (*a*) Transfer characteristics as a function of frequency for a 3,200-ohm monolithic diffused resistor; (*b*) circuit for measurement of transfer characteristics shown in *a*.

higher frequencies is more pronounced for diffused resistors in monolithic circuits than in hybrid circuits because of the additional parasitic capacitances through the substrate.

Temperature Coefficients.   The temperature coefficient of diffused resistors is another variable which must be considered in many circuit applications.   One of the most critical factors affecting the value of the temperature coefficient is the impurity surface concentration of the diffused area.   It has been shown that in a highly concentrated p-type layer, the total resistance is an inverse function of the hole mobility μ_p; explicitly,

$$R = \frac{l}{q\mu_p N_A X_j w} \tag{10-6}$$

where q = electron charge (1.6×10^{19} coul)
    N_A = acceptor concentration (effective value)
    μ_p = hole mobility, cm^2/volt sec
    X_j = junction depth
    w = pattern width
    l = pattern length

Gärtner[5] shows how the temperature sensitivity of the hole mobility is a function of the impurity concentration, becoming less with higher concentrations.   The mobility normally decreases with temperature, thus giving a positive temperature coefficient for the total resistance of the unit.   This effect is shown in Fig. 10-21 where various sheet resistances are plotted as a function of temperature.   Thus the temperature coefficient of the diffused resistor is determined to a great extent by the sheet resistance.

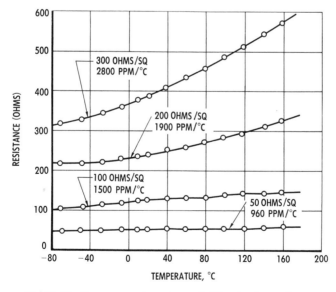

Fig. 10-21   Temperature dependence of diffused resistor values.

Power Limitations. For low-frequency applications, diffused resistors have some inherent limitations, primarily with respect to power dissipation and maximum voltage ratings. The permissible amount of power dissipation in the resistor is limited because excessive heating will result in a nonlinear current-voltage relationship. Measurements indicate that the maximum power dissipation for units mounted in a standard TO-18 can is on the order of 3 mw per square mil of diffused area.

The maximum voltage drop across the unit is limited by the reverse voltage breakdown of the p-n junction in the substrate. This value is normally in the vicinity of 20 volts, depending only upon the impurity concentration of substrate material.

Because of the small cross section of the diffused area, there is also a limitation on the maximum current, because of *current-limiting* effects which result from a thickening of the depletion layer of the isolating junction into the resistive elements. However, this effect is usually overshadowed by the heating action at high currents.

Values. Table 10-5 lists some of the values associated with the hybrid and monolithic diffused resistors.

Table 10-5   Range of Values for Diffused Resistors

Characteristic	Hybrid	Monolithic
Range of sheet resistance, ohms/sq	2.5–300	2.5 or 100–300
Maximum value	See Fig. 10-18	See Fig. 10-18
Temperature coefficient, ppm/deg C	500–2,000	500–2,000
Maximum power dissipation, watt	0.25	0.1
Tolerance, %	±5	±10

10-4   Thin-film Resistors

As with capacitors, it may be advantageous to use compatible thin-film techniques in the fabrication of integrated circuit resistors. In order to fabricate a thin-film resistor for hybrid circuits, a thin film of a metal or a semiconducting oxide is

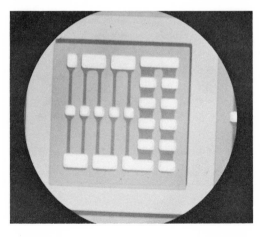

Fig. 10-22 Photomicrograph of a typical thin-film resistor.

deposited on an insulating substrate. For monolithic integrated circuits, the metal film is deposited directly on the silicon dioxide layer covering the integrated circuit. By means of masked etching, the desired geometry of the thin-film material is achieved. An insulating layer is then deposited on top of the resistor, and apertures for ohmic contacts are etched through the insulating layer. The contact metal is then evaporated over the insulating layer and through the apertures onto the resistor. The metal is then removed in all but the desired contact areas by means of masked etching. Figure 10-22 shows a photomicrograph of a typical thin-film resistor. Note the similarity between this resistor and the diffused resistor in Fig. 10-17. A number of materials are available for use in the fabrication of thin-film resistors. Those more commonly used are discussed below.

Tin Oxide (SnO_2). A material must, of course, exhibit conductive properties to be suitable for thin-film resistor fabrication. Although tin oxide as pure stannic oxide is an insulator, it can be made to exhibit a degree of "semiconduction."

When deposited by vapor-plating techniques, a film of SnO_2 becomes inherently an n-type semiconductor because of a deficiency of oxygen atoms within the growing SnO_2 film. The inclusion of trivalent ions, such as indium, during the vapor-plating process will decrease the conductivity of the film, and the inclusion of pentavalent ions, such as antimony, will increase the conductivity.

The tin oxide films have good adhesion to vitreous surfaces and can easily be etched by standard masked etching methods. Films with sheet-resistance values ranging from 80 to 4,000 ohms per square may be obtained by doping the film with varying amounts of indium or antimony during the vapor-plating process. This yields a total range of resistances from 40 ohms to 3 megohms. The temperature coefficient will vary from approximately 0 to $-1,500$ ppm/deg C over this range of values.

Tantalum (Ta). Tantalum films are deposited by the sputtering techniques. The desired sheet resistance is obtained with tantalum films by a process of anodization (see Chap. 13), which reduces the cross section of the metal film. The oxide film resulting from the anodization serves also as a protective layer for the resistors. This layer adheres tightly to the metal and has a high chemical and mechanical stability. The anodization, and therefore the thickness of the resistor, can be closely controlled. The temperature coefficient of resistance can be controlled by introducing varying amounts of nitrogen during the sputtering process.

Aluminum (Al). The vacuum evaporation (see Chap. 13) of aluminum from a multistranded tungsten filament gives deposits with high electrical conductivity ideally suited for contacts and interconnections. The films can also be used for the fabrication of resistors with very low resistance values. They show excellent adhesion to metals and glass.

A disadvantage of aluminum is the formation of an Al_2O_3 coating over the metal, caused by its high chemical reactivity with oxygen even at relatively low temperatures. This coating tends to make the metal difficult to use.

Chromium (Cr). Vacuum-evaporated chromium films adhere well to metals and glass. They have a poor conductivity and the geometric configurations cannot be controlled easily by conventional masked etching techniques. This is because of oxide film formation on the surface and the resulting difficult etching conditions.

For this reason, chromium alone is seldom used for fabrication of thin-film resistors.

Nickel (Ni). The adhesion of nickel to glass is poor. Hence, it is seldom used alone to fabricate integrated circuit resistors.

Nichrome*. Although neither chromium nor nickel is suitable for thin-film resistor fabrication, the alloy of the two metals, Nichrome, has excellent properties for this application. Nichrome films are deposited from an evaporant source consisting of 80 per cent nickel and 20 per cent chromium by means of vacuum evaporation. A high substrate temperature (300°C) is essential during evaporation in order to obtain films with stable resistance. Adhesion of the film is excellent because of an initial evaporation of chromium alone. The Nichrome films have a composition close to that of the alloy used as the evaporant source.

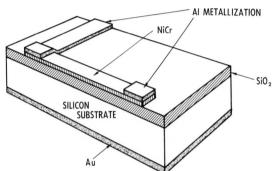

Fig. 10-23 Cross-sectional view of a Nichrome thin-film resistor.

Because, in a compatible integrated circuit, all portions of the thin-film resistors are deposited on the surface of the silicon dioxide, as shown in the cross-sectional view of Fig. 10-23, there is no inherent difference between the hybrid and monolithic structures. The NiCr resistors can be constructed on a substrate of either n- or p-type silicon. A layer of SiO_2 approximately 10,000 Å thick is grown on the silicon substrate, and the NiCr is deposited over the entire surface. The resistor patterns are then etched by a masked etching process which is compatible with the

Table 10-6 Characteristics of Compatible Thin-film Resistors

Characteristic	NiCr	SnO$_2$
Range of sheet resistance, ohms/sq	40–400	80–4,000
Maximum value, kilohms.	50	>500
Breakdown voltage, volts dc.	±200	±200
Maximum power dissipation, watt	0.5	0.5
Temperature coefficient, ppm/deg K.	<100	0 to −1,500
Tolerance, %.	±5	±5
Aging allowance, %	±7	±7

remainder of the circuit in the case of a monolithic circuit. NiCr resistors are available in a sheet resistance range of 100 to 400 ohms per square, depending on film thickness, thus giving a total resistance range of 20 to 50 kilohms. The temperature coefficient is less than 100 ppm/deg C.

---

* Nichrome is a trade name of the Driver-Harris Company, Harrison, N.J.

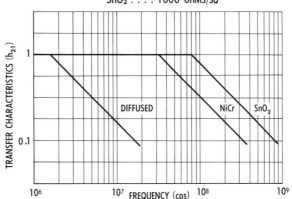

DIFFUSED . . . . 200 OHMS/SQ
NiCr . . . . 400 OHMS/SQ
SnO₂ . . . . 1000 OHMS/SQ

Fig. 10-24 Calculated transfer characteristics for a diffused, a Nichrome, and a tin oxide 10-kilohm resistor for integrated circuits.

Table 10-6 summarizes the characteristics of the two most frequently used compatible thin-film resistors.

Since thin-film resistors have fewer and smaller parasitic components than diffused resistors, their high-frequency transfer characteristics are superior to those of the diffused resistors. This is illustrated in Fig. 10-24, which shows the calculated transfer characteristics for a diffused, a Nichrome, and a tin oxide resistor.

10-5   Inductance

Inductors with practical values of inductance and Q are by far the most difficult components to fabricate by integrated circuit techniques—both by semiconductor and thin-film processes. Although considerable effort has been expended in this area, no really practical results have yet been achieved. For example, when a 20-turn flat spiral with an outside diameter of 0.330 in. was deposited on 50-ohm-cm silicon and on glass, the data shown in Table 10-7 were obtained.

Although inductors on glass offer an order-of-magnitude better Q than those on the silicon substrate, there is still much room for improvement. Therefore, until improved results are obtained, it seems likely that any necessary inductance will be placed external to the monolithic circuit.

Table 10-7   Characteristics of a 20-turn Flat Spiral on 50-ohm-cm Silicon and on Glass

Frequency, Mc	50-ohm-cm silicon		Glass	
	L, μh	Q	L, μh	Q
20	2.26	4.9	2.18	36.2
40	2.57	3.4	2.33	49.4
60	3.20	1.7	2.82	47.1
80	4.42	0.89	3.91	35.1

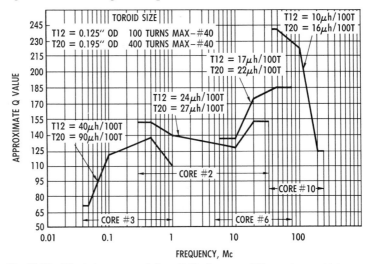

Fig. 10-25   The inductance and Q available from two different size toroidal cores compatible with the size of the TO-5 package.

Small Toroids.   The use of small toroidal coils made of powdered iron or special ferrites appears advantageous in integrated circuit systems.   They are comparable in size to the TO-5 package.   The available Q together with the inductance values obtainable make these useful components for hybrid integrated circuit applications.

Figure 10-25 shows the inductance and Q available from two different core sizes, both of which are compatible with the TO-5 package.

The coil may be either external to an integrated circuit package or installed within the taller of the TO-5 packages (see Fig. 10-26).   If the coil is mounted within the TO-5 package, the maximum processing temperature of the package is reduced because of temperature limitations imposed by the insulation used on the coil or wire.

Considerations discussed for single inductors apply also to RF transformers which can be wound on small toroid cores and mounted either within a tall TO-5 package or external to the integrated circuit.

Fig. 10-26   Toroidal coil mounted in the TO-5 package.

10-6   Piezoelectric Filters

One of the methods of frequency selection which does not require separate inductors is the use of the piezoelectric crystal element. Frequency selection using resonant piezoelectric ceramic or quartz materials is feasible in hybrid integrated circuits.

Ceramic resonant devices are commercially available at a very low cost. They may be ground to dimensions suitable for packaging within a standard TO-5 can and can operate on a fundamental frequency as low as 180 kc, and on the first overtone as high as approximately 2 Mc.

In addition to providing frequency selectivity, they can be designed to have *transformer action* for impedance matching purposes. Moreover, they can be cascaded to provide a complete, high-performance filter element. However, ceramic filters exhibit nonlinear phase characteristics; such devices do not exhibit the characteristics suggested by their simple equivalent circuits.

Quartz crystals appear to be suitable for use over a frequency range from 10 kc to 100 Mc in sizes compatible with integrated circuit techniques. But from a practical standpoint it must be realized that they are at present far more expensive than the ceramic elements.

10-7   Large-value Capacitors

When a circuit requires capacitance values in excess of those practically obtainable with diffused or compatible thin-film techniques, the requirements are normally met with the large-value tantalum capacitor which can be mounted either inside or outside a TO-5 package.

The use of a tantalum capacitor mounted in the TO-5 package imposes a maximum-temperature limitation on the circuit. However, in the hermetically sealed environment, it is a highly reliable circuit component. A volt-microfarad product of approximately 10 is reasonably obtainable for tantalum capacitors mounted within the TO-5 package. Values larger than this are best mounted externally, using normal commercial techniques.

Mounting Methods for Nonsilicon Elements. A component may be mounted internally in the TO-5 package by welding its leads to the TO-5 header posts; or if the component is large, it can be cemented to a ceramic wafer which is in turn brazed or welded in place in a multiple ceramic header, as shown in Fig. 10-26.

Since many components will not withstand the 300°C bake temperatures normally used before the can is welded to the header, allowance must be made for this. In the flat package, the 450°C final-seal temperature (together with the more limited internal height) virtually precludes the use of nonintegrated, nonsilicon components.

10-8   Other Components for Integrated Circuit Systems

Most electronic systems cannot be completely reduced to microminiature integrated circuit packages at the present state of the art; however, the percentage of circuit functions which can be integrated is surprisingly high, usually running 60 to 80 per cent.

Of considerable importance in complete systems is the interconnection problem. The development of reliable multilayer printed circuit boards allows the user to take advantage of the high packaging density available with integrated circuits. In some systems, the packaging density has reached the point of diminishing returns. For example, a small transmitter-receiver recently made in the laboratory has a total volume of six cubic inches, with the total transmitter and receiver electronics, including the crystal filter, occupying only slightly more than one cubic inch. The rest of the volume is occupied by the case, antenna, speaker, microphone, batteries, switches, and so forth.

10-9 Summary

In monolithic circuits, passive elements such as resistors and capacitors must be constructed by techniques which are compatible with the formation of transistors and other circuit elements; various methods such as compatible thin-film techniques may also be used.[6,7] However, the use of diffused resistors and junction-type capacitors is more desirable from the standpoint of fewer processing steps and higher yield. Because such elements may be formed at the same time and with the same steps required for the transistors, no additional process steps are required to obtain useful component values. There are limitations, however, in the range of values available with diffused resistors, and in the maximum value of capacitance that may be obtained from a p-n junction. Although these ranges are sufficiently great for many circuits, they cannot meet all possible requirements. Where larger values are called for, and where the circuit cannot be modified to utilize available values, the circuit designer must employ the more complex structures of compatible techniques involving a combination of semiconductor and thin-film technologies. Only in the extreme case (e.g., large-value capacitor or inductor) is it necessary to mount a component outside the integrated circuit.

REFERENCES

1. Spector, C. J.: A Design Theory for the High Frequency P-N Junction Variable Capacitor, presented at the 1958 Electron Devices Meeting, sponsored by the PGED–IRE, Washington, D.C., Oct. 30–31, 1958.
2. Registrar, J.: Silicon Junction Diodes as Variable Capacitors, *Electron. Eng.,* vol. 33, pp. 783–787, December, 1961.
3. Black, J. R., and G. R. Madland: Compatible Techniques for Integrated Circuits, Electrochemical Society, Pittsburgh, Pa., April, 1963.
4. Berry, R. W., and D. J. Sloan: Tantalum Printed Capacitors, *Proc. IRE,* vol. 47, pp. 1070–1075, June, 1959.
5. Gärtner, W. W.: "Transistors," D. Van Nostrand Company, Inc., Princeton, N.J., 1960.
6. Dicken, H. K., and D. C. Bailey: Integrated Devices for Hybrid Circuits, Professional Group on Electron Devices Meeting, Washington, D.C., October, 1962.
7. Dummer, G. S. A. (ed.): "Microminiaturization," Proceedings of the AGARD Conference, Oslo, July 24–26, 1961, Pergamon Press, New York, 1962.

Part **3**

INTEGRATED CIRCUIT FABRICATION

11

CRYSTAL GROWING AND THE EPITAXIAL PROCESS

The first step in the manufacture of any semiconductor device, whether it be an alloy diode or an integrated circuit, is the growth of a single crystal of semiconducting material. In the earliest procedures, the p-n junctions were formed during this process by additions of appropriate impurities to the melt as the crystal was being grown. This approach was rather quickly supplanted, however, by junction-forming techniques (such as diffusion), which operated on smaller pieces of single-crystal material cut from a more-or-less uniformly doped large crystal.

Recently the epitaxial technique has combined elements of both procedures, improving on both of them as well. Wafers cut from a large, uniform crystal are frequently used, and additional single-crystal material is then grown, but from a gas phase rather than a liquid phase. The advantages of epitaxy are numerous, but one of the most striking advantages is the possibility of growing sequences of n and p regions without impurity compensation and with unprecedented control over doping, thickness dimensions, and even impurity distribution or *profile* in the direction normal to the plane of growth. The ultimate advantages are realized, however, by judiciously combining epitaxy with other well-established techniques, particularly diffusion. So flexible are these combinations that the structural possibilities they open up have only been glimpsed thus far.

11-1 Crystal Growing

There are a number of methods for the production of single-crystal material.[1-3] The one most commonly used for growth of the single crystals for integrated circuits is that of Czochralski.[4] In this method, the charge of hyperpure silicon from which the single crystal is to be grown, along with any doping impurity which is to be added to the crystal, is placed in a high-purity quartz crucible set inside a graphite susceptor. The susceptor, crucible, and charge are placed in a controlled, inert atmosphere inside a quartz cylinder. RF induction coils are placed outside the quartz cylinder and around the graphite susceptor. RF power is applied to the coils, and the charge is heated until it is completely molten and the temperature has been stabilized just above the melting point of the silicon.

Once the temperature has been stabilized, a *seed* crystal (a small, highly perfect, and oriented crystal of silicon) is dipped into the melt. The seed is allowed to melt back a short distance to remove any surface imperfections which may have resulted from its preparation. The seed is then rotated and very slowly withdrawn from the melt. If the temperature of the melt is properly maintained, as the seed is withdrawn it grows as a single, oriented crystal. The effect is as though one were to "pull" a single crystal from the melt. It is common practice to refer to the growth of single crystals by this method as *crystal pulling*.

The finished crystal is typically about 1 in. in diameter and 8 to 10 in. long, with the exact dimensions depending on size of the charge, the rate of pulling, and the temperature of the surface of the melt during the growth period.

11-2 Wafering and Polishing

After the single crystal has been grown, the next step is to saw it into thin slices, commonly referred to as *wafers*. The crystal is first oriented according to crystallographic planes by X-ray techniques. This is usually a quite simple process, as the seed used for the crystal growth is accurately oriented before the crystal growth. Once the crystal is oriented, it is placed on a diamond saw which slices the crystal into wafers. The diamond saws in wide use today are the so-called "ID" saws (ID standing for inside diameter). The saw blades are annular, with the diamond cutting edge being the inside edge. The saw blade is clamped, then, at the outside edge. This technique permits the use of much thinner blades than does the older center-spindle system, significantly reducing the kerf, or cutting loss.

The wafers, after being cut, are lapped on abrasive lapping machines to the thicknesses required for integrated circuits. The lapped wafers are then polished to a mirror finish with graded diamond polish, the final polish being done with quarter-micron diamond paste. The finished polished wafers are sent on to epitaxial processing.

11-3 Epitaxy

The word epitaxy is derived from the Greek words *epi* meaning "upon" and the past tense of the verb *teinen* meaning "arranged." This is about as good a definition of epitaxy as can be stated ... an arranging of atoms in single-crystal fashion upon a single-crystal substrate so that the lattice structure of the resulting layer is an exact extension of the substrate crystal structure. Figure 11-1 illustrates this growth process. A gas-phase reaction, discussed below, is represented schematically in the upper portion of the diagram. The overall reaction gives rise to free silicon atoms. Atoms from the gas phase skid about on the surface of the growing epitaxial film until they find a correct position in the lattice before becoming fastened into the growing structure.

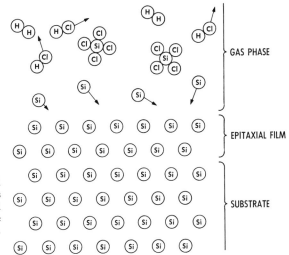

GAS PHASE

EPITAXIAL FILM

Fig. 11-1 The growth of an epitaxial film of single-crystal silicon from the gas phase. Note that the atoms in epitaxial film form an exact extension of the arrangement of the atoms of the substrate.

SUBSTRATE

Epitaxy versus Diffusion. The diffusion process works from the outside of the semiconductor body; that is, impurity concentration changes within a semiconductor material are accomplished by applying a high concentration of impurity atoms to the surface and then causing some of these atoms to diffuse at elevated temperatures into the semiconductor material.

Figure 11-2a shows a typical impurity profile for the diffusion of n-type impurities into n-type silicon. Although the shape of this profile can be varied by using different impurity-atom surface concentrations, and different diffusion times, the profile always resembles a declining exponential function, at least in the deeper portions. Linear profiles cannot be produced by diffusion.

Figure 11-2b shows an impurity concentration profile resulting from a diffusion of p-type impurities into n-type silicon, and Fig. 11-2c shows the resultant impurity

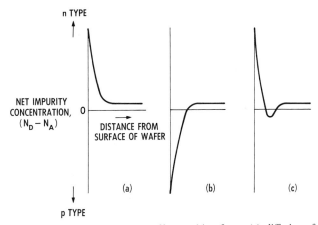

n TYPE

NET IMPURITY
CONCENTRATION,   0
$(N_D - N_A)$

DISTANCE FROM
SURFACE OF WAFER

(a)   (b)   (c)

p TYPE

Fig. 11-2 Typical impurity profiles resulting from: (a) diffusion of n-type impurities into n-type silicon; (b) diffusion of p-type impurities into n-type silicon; (c) diffusion of n-type impurities into the p-type portion of b.

profile when n-type impurity atoms are diffused into the p-type portion of Fig. 11-2*b*. From these two curves it is evident that junction formation can occur only by impurity-atom compensation. For example, in Fig. 11-2*b*, a p-n junction occurs at the plane where the concentration of p-type atoms N_A is equal to the concentration of n-type impurity atoms N_D, or where $N_D - N_A = 0$.

The compensation factor may be deleterious for a number of reasons. During the fabrication of a multijunction device, every diffusion step introduces many impurity atoms into the semiconductor body. During each successive diffusion (needed for the formation of successive junctions) the number of impurity atoms that must be introduced to compensate for the previously introduced impurity atoms increases exponentially. The solid-solubility limits for useful impurities in silicon are such that more than three consecutive diffusions into a silicon surface are not practical. Since the active impurity concentration is a difference between two large numbers of opposite-type atoms, buried layers of low impurity concentration (high resistivity) are difficult to achieve and control.

Moreover, the mobilities of holes and electrons decrease with increasing total impurity content of the semiconductor material. This mobility decrease in materials containing large concentrations of both n- and p-type impurities may affect adversely all the electrical characteristics of devices made from that material.

With epitaxy, however, one is not constrained to work from the outside of a crystal previously formed. This is apparent from Fig. 11-3. Impurity atoms are incorporated into the crystal lattice while the film is growing. The ratio of silicon atoms to impurity atoms in the gas phase is controlled so that the film contains the desired impurity content. By changing the type of impurity or the impurity concentration in the gas phase, the characteristics of the epitaxial film can be changed almost without limit, and this can be accomplished without resorting to compensation.

This means that it is possible to fabricate semiconductor devices without many of the compromises necessary in simple diffused structures. For example, consider

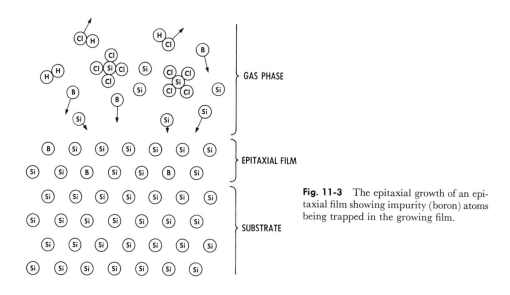

Fig. 11-3   The epitaxial growth of an epitaxial film showing impurity (boron) atoms being trapped in the growing film.

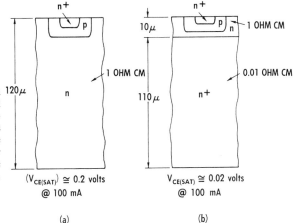

Fig. 11-4 A comparison between (*a*) a transistor made by diffusion alone and (*b*) one made by a combination of epitaxy and diffusion. Both transistors have the same BV_{CBO}; however, note that the epitaxial-diffused transistor has a $V_{CE(SAT)}$ an order of magnitude lower than the simple diffused transistor.

the problems involved in making a diffused silicon transistor with a high collector breakdown voltage BV_{CBO} and a low saturation voltage $V_{CE(SAT)}$. To obtain a high BV_{CBO}, the collector region of the device must be made of high-resistivity material, which results in a high series collector resistance, thereby yielding a high $V_{CE(SAT)}$. Although the $V_{CE(SAT)}$ could possibly be reduced to a desired low level by reducing the thickness of the high-resistivity collector region, there are physical limitations governing the minimum thickness, below which the wafer (which constitutes the collector region) becomes too thin and brittle to be handled without excessive breakage. Thus, for a given minimum wafer thickness (normally a thickness of 120 microns is required for adequate mechanical strength), the impurity concentration must represent a compromise between a high BV_{CBO} (high resistivity) and a low $V_{CE(SAT)}$ (low resistivity).

The epitaxial process eliminates the need for such a compromise. Starting with a relatively thick substrate (say 110 microns), of very low resistivity material, it is possible to grow epitaxially a thin layer (say 10 microns) of high-resistivity material on top of the substrate. The epitaxial layer has the high resistivity required for a high BV_{CBO} but is thin enough to yield a low $V_{CE(SAT)}$. The basic substrate, because of its extremely low resistivity, is essentially metallic and does not degrade the electrical characteristics of the device. It does, however, provide the necessary bulk to make the wafer safe to handle without undue breakage.

A comparison between such transistors made by the diffusion and epitaxial processes is shown in Fig. 11-4. It can be seen that, for the case illustrated here, the epitaxial process permits a reduction in $V_{CE(SAT)}$ of an order of magnitude.

If an epitaxial film of one conductivity type is grown epitaxially on a substrate of the opposite conductivity type, an excellent starting material is obtained for the fabrication of monolithic integrated circuits. The impurity profile of such a wafer is shown in Fig. 11-5. Transistors can be fabricated in the n-type epitaxial film by the diffusion process. The individual transistors and other components can then be electrically isolated from each other by the p-type diffusion procedure treated in Chap. 5. The isolation diffusion builds a wall from substrate to surface around the components. Although similar electrically isolated parts could be fabricated

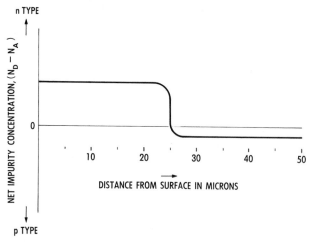

Fig. 11-5 Impurity profile for an epitaxial wafer suitable as starting material for the fabrication of integrated circuits.

in a nonepitaxial wafer through the use of three consecutive diffusions plus the isolation diffusion, such devices would again be subject to serious performance compromises.

It is possible to fabricate good transistors by means of the epitaxial process alone, but such a procedure by present methods is more complex than the combination of epitaxy and diffusion as described above. Therefore, most modern high-frequency transistors are made by this combination process.

As noted in Sec. 3-1, an intrinsic limitation of the commonly used epitaxial process is that the growth of an epitaxial layer is always accompanied by the diffusion phenomenon which causes an exchange of impurities between the substrate and the growing film. This causes a *blurring* of an otherwise sharp transition in net doping and prevents the fabrication of an ideal step junction.

This is illustrated in Fig. 11-6 which shows an actual resistivity profile for a 12-micron-thick 4-ohm-cm n-type epitaxial film grown on an antimony-doped 0.01-ohm-cm substrate wafer at a temperature of 1200°C. Considerable diffusion has taken place, as evidenced by the gradual change in resistivity. An appreciable fraction of the total epitaxial film is needed to change completely from 0.01 ohm cm to the desired value of 4 ohm cm. This imposes a limitation in applications requiring a perfect step junction.

The effect of diffusion on an epitaxial structure can sometimes be given a simple analytical treatment which is accurate enough to be useful. When a lightly doped film is grown on a heavily doped substrate, the final impurity distribution can be calculated from Eq. (3-12), which is repeated here for convenience:

$$N(x) = \frac{N_o}{2}\left(\text{erfc}\,\frac{x}{2\sqrt{Dt}}\right) \tag{3-12}$$

In this case, $x = 0$ is taken at the original interface, and the positive x axis extends into the film. N_o is the impurity concentration in the substrate. Thus it is possi-

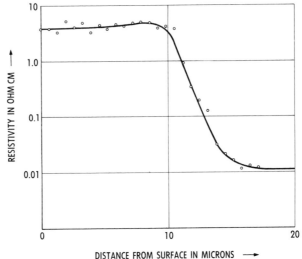

Fig. 11-6 An actual resistivity profile for a 12-micron-thick 4-ohm-cm n-type epitaxial film grown on an antimony-doped 0.01-ohm-cm substrate wafer at a temperature of 1200°C. Note the gradual change in resistivity resulting from the diffusion which has taken place during epitaxial growth.

ble to estimate the extent of the substrate-to-film diffusion that will occur during film growth or during any subsequent processing, and to grow films having the required thickness of high-resistivity material.

The temperature at which epitaxial growth takes place is by far the most important factor in determining how much diffusion occurs. The rate of diffusion increases about an order of magnitude for an increase of 100°C. If one could reduce the epitaxial growth temperature by 200°C while maintaining the growth rate corresponding to 1200°C, then the associated diffusion depth could be reduced by a factor of 100 and a much sharper transition could be achieved. Unfortunately, lower temperatures are associated with lower growth rates. For a given film thickness, therefore, the total amount of diffusion is about the same.

The Epitaxial Process. The system for production growth of epitaxial wafers incorporates a reaction chamber consisting of a long cylindrical quartz tube with inlet and outlet at opposite ends, encircled by an RF induction coil. Single-crystal silicon wafers of the desired diameter, surface planarity, and bulk electrical properties are placed upon a quartz sleeve encasing a long rectangular graphite rod called a *boat*. The boat is then placed within the reaction chamber where the graphite can be heated inductively. A control console permits the introduction of the wide variety of gases needed to produce epitaxial films with the various properties required for integrated circuits and semiconductor devices. This system is shown in Fig. 11-7.

The basic chemical reaction used for the epitaxial growth of pure silicon is the hydrogen reduction of silicon tetrachloride.

$$SiCl_4 + 2H_2 \overset{1200°C}{\rightleftharpoons} Si + 4HCl$$

This reaction has a number of advantages. The silicon tetrachloride is easy to purify, nontoxic, and inexpensive. The reaction is almost entirely heterogeneous; that is, the reaction forming silicon from silicon tetrachloride takes place only at a

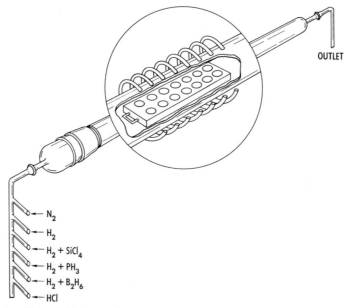

OUTLET

N₂
H₂
H₂ + SiCl₄
H₂ + PH₃
H₂ + B₂H₆
HCl

Fig. 11-7 A diagrammatic representation of a system for production growth of silicon epitaxial films.

surface, not in the gas phase. Conditions can be arranged so that the reaction takes place only at a silicon surface and not on the boat or reaction chamber walls.

The growth of intrinsic silicon epitaxial layers is not the common requirement, however. Epitaxial films with specific impurity types and concentrations are normally needed. This requires two simultaneous reactions properly proportioned to provide the desired amount of impurity concentration in the film. This is accomplished by introducing phosphine for n-type doping or diborane for p-type doping into the silicon tetrachloride–hydrogen gas steam. Phosphine and diborane undergo decomposition reactions similar to that of silicon tetrachloride. This results in the incorporation of phosphorus or boron atoms in the growing silicon lattice. These reactions are excellent for the formation of a variety of structures, such as n on n^+, p on p^+, and alternating n and p layers.

However, this system suffers from the disadvantages associated with the diffusion during growth mentioned in the preceding section. Where it is necessary to produce epitaxial films with abrupt impurity concentration changes, it is possible to use another reaction system, the thermal decomposition of silane. It will proceed at about the same rate at 1000°C that the silicon tetrachloride reaction exhibits at 1200°C. The silane reaction is

$$SiH_4 \overset{1000°C}{\rightleftharpoons} Si + 2H_2$$

Silane is a very difficult and dangerous material to handle, and therefore, despite the apparent advantage of this reaction over the silicon tetrachloride reaction, it is seldom used.

The cleanliness of wafers used for the growth of epitaxial films is of paramount importance. Final cleaning of substrate wafers, therefore, is done in the reaction chamber with vapor-phase HCl. This HCl is the purest obtainable.

For integrated circuit applications, epitaxial wafers with the particular resistivity profile shown schematically in Fig. 11-5 are frequently used. Such a wafer consists of an epitaxial film with approximately 10^{16} donor impurity atoms/cm³, and 25 microns thick, grown on a substrate wafer which contains approximately 10^{15} acceptor impurity atoms/cm³. The epitaxial film has a resistivity of 0.5 ohm cm and is n type. The substrate has a resistivity of 10 ohm cm and is p type. With integrated circuits, the substrate and film are of opposite type because the substrate in integrated circuits must help provide isolation between components.

The operations necessary to produce such an epitaxial film are as follows: The substrate wafers, after mechanical polishing and ultimate cleaning, are placed on the boat, and the boat is placed in the reaction chamber. The system is closed, and nitrogen is admitted to flush out the air present. Hydrogen is then admitted to the reaction chamber, and its flow rate is set at 30 liters/min. The RF heating is turned on, and the substrate wafers are heated to 1200°C $\pm 2°$. When the temperature has been stabilized, HCl is admitted to the reaction chamber. The hydrogen-to-HCl ratio is 100:1 and the reaction is allowed to proceed for 6 min, during which time 3 microns of substrate surface is etched away. At this point the HCl is shut off, and the $SiCl_4$ and phosphine are turned on. The hydrogen-to-$SiCl_4$ ratio is 800:1, and the hydrogen-to-phosphine ratio is 5×10^8:1. This reaction is allowed to proceed for 50 min, after which a 25-micron n-type film has grown on the p-type substrate. The phosphine and silicon tetrachloride are turned off, and the wafers are cooled in pure hydrogen. This process yields material in which the thickness and resistivity are controlled consistently to within ± 5 per cent.

Process Control. The process must produce epitaxial films with the following important properties:

1. Perfection of the crystallographic structure
2. Accuracy in thickness and resistivity values
3. Uniformity of thickness and resistivity across a single wafer, and from wafer to wafer down the tube.

Single crystals of high perfection are an absolute necessity for the fabrication of integrated circuits. Only in such material can the impurity content be sufficiently uniform for high-yield manufacture.

Many factors can affect the crystalline perfection of silicon epitaxial films. The reaction used for this process must be heterogeneous. If reaction occurred in the gas phase to form silicon atoms, these atoms could agglomerate to form a cluster. This cluster could fall on the growing film but could not be accommodated in the crystal lattice, and a polycrystalline region would result. The silicon tetrachloride reaction, however, is one which occurs only on a surface and not in the gas phase. The most probable mechanism for the reaction is a two-step process involving first the reduction of the silicon tetrachloride to silicon dichloride, and second, the heterogeneous disproportionation of the silicon dichloride to silicon and silicon tetrachloride:

1. $SiCl_4 + H_2 \rightleftharpoons SiCl_2 + 2HCl$
2. $2SiCl_2 \rightleftharpoons Si + SiCl_4$

The first step takes place in the gas phase. The second step can only take place when the two silicon dichloride molecules meet in the presence of a third body. The probability of a three-body collision in the gas phase is vanishingly small, but the probability of having two $SiCl_2$ molecules come together on a surface is excellent. In this way, single atoms of silicon are released onto the crystal-growing interface, and the probability of a high-perfection crystal is good.

The growth of single crystals is normally a slow process since a near-equilibrium must be achieved between layer growth and removal of imperfectly placed atoms to eliminate incipient imperfections. As the reaction temperature is increased, however, the atoms which are descending to the growing interface possess more energy and can travel over the surface more readily to find their proper positions in the lattice. Thus it would be expected that higher temperatures would make higher growth rates consistent with perfect-crystal growth. This is indeed true. At 1100°C it is not possible to grow high-perfection epitaxial films at rates greater than 0.1 micron/min. At 1200°C, growth rates of 1 micron/min are possible. At 1270°C, growth rates of 5 microns/min produce excellent crystals.

The permissible growth rate is also a function of the purity of the reactant gases. If these gases were to contain even as little as 25 ppm of oxygen, water vapor, or long-chain carbon compounds, perfect crystals could not be grown at any rate at any temperature.

The cleanliness and perfection of the substrate wafer are of paramount importance. No matter how well the substrate wafer is cleaned before placement in the reaction chamber, mechanical imperfections, silicon dioxide, residual dust, and other contaminants are retained on the wafer surface. These surface defects nucleate crystal imperfections which manifest themselves as bumps, pits, and stacking faults in the growing film.

These defects can best be understood through a brief study of crystallography. Crystals grow in certain preferred directions, and their geometric shapes are governed by their slowest-growth directions. The faces of the crystal are perpendicu-

PLANE ABCD = (001) PLANE
PLANE AEG = (111) PLANE
PLANE BDEG = (110) PLANE

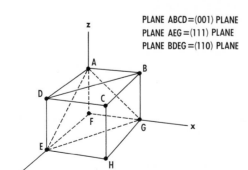

Fig. 11-8   The unit cell of the simple-cubic crystallographic system.

lar to the slowest-growth direction and are a macroscopic manifestation of the atomic structure. The crystal faces are parallel to atomic planes of symmetry. In Fig. 11-8 is shown a unit cell in the simple-cubic crystallographic system. Plane $ABCD$ is a plane of symmetry since on either side of it is another plane of atoms, each of which is a mirror image of the other. This plane can be wholly defined by Miller indices which are the reciprocals of its intercepts on the x, y, z axes. Plane $ABCD$ intersects the x and y axes at infinity and the z axis at one unit. The Miller index for this plane is (001). The (100)

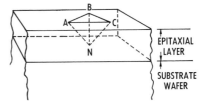

Fig. 11-9 A minor defect at N may cause the stacking order of the atoms above N to be off by one atomic plane. This nucleates a stacking fault which propagates with the growing crystal. Note that when the epitaxial growth is in the (111) direction the stacking fault intersects the surface as an equilateral triangle ABC.

and (010) planes are easily distinguished. Other easily seen planes are the (111) and the (110).

The silicon or diamond lattice is considerably more complex than this simple structure. The best way to visualize the silicon crystal lattice is to place an extra atom in the middle of each face of the simple cell; take another *face-centered cubic* cell and press it about halfway into the first cell. In the simple-cubic crystallographic system the atoms of each succeeding plane are positioned exactly above those of the plane beneath. In the silicon lattice, if we consider the direction perpendicular to the (111) plane (plane AGE in Fig. 11-8), silicon atoms repeat their positions, but only in every sixth plane do they assume completely equivalent positions (see Fig. 1-6).

If a minor defect, such as a small dust particle or other contaminant at the substrate of an epitaxial wafer grown in the (111) direction, causes this stacking order to be off one plane of atoms at that point with respect to the rest of the growing crystal, then a stacking fault is initiated and the fault propagates with the growing crystal. This is shown in Fig. 11-9. The portion of the crystal growing within the tetrahedron is out of step with the rest of the crystal. The actual *fault* resides in the planes bounding the tetrahedron where crystalline mismatch exists. The regions both inside and outside these planes may be perfect-crystal regions, but their perfection is interrupted at the three triangular planes shown in Fig. 11-9. A stacking fault can be made visible by etches which attack perfect regions and defective regions at differing rates. A stacking fault in a wafer of (111) orientation usually manifests itself as an equilateral triangle, as Fig. 11-9 suggests. A sample with numerous faults will present an array of triangles of uniform size and orientation.[5, 6]

A gross disturbance of the substrate surface, such as a scratch, would cause a corresponding disturbance in the final surface. This affects the uniformity of results in subsequent steps such as diffusion and masking, and clearly leads to defective integrated circuits or devices. The effect of the stacking fault is more subtle. If a junction is fabricated in material containing stacking faults and that junction is reverse-biased, light is emitted at the edges of the stacking fault; this is evidence of localized breakdown. Such junctions usually exhibit high leakage currents.

It has been found that if vapor-phase HCl is passed over the substrate wafers before epitaxial growth, to etch away a few microns at the surface of the wafers, then scratches, dust, and contaminants are removed to a remarkable extent. Epitaxial films grown upon substrate wafers so treated are completely free of bumps and pits. The stacking fault density is reduced several orders of magnitude, from 10,000/cm^2 to less than 10/cm^2.

The growth rate of epitaxial films is dependent upon the flow rate of SiCl$_4$, the ratio of H$_2$ to SiCl$_4$, and the temperature. All these variables can be controlled to within reasonable limits. Growth rates are normally maintained constant, and time is used to control the film thickness.

The resistivity and conductivity types of the epitaxial film are dependent upon the kind and amount of impurity added to the gas stream during the growth cycle. Very dilute mixtures of the dopant gases in hydrogen are used. One hundred parts per million is a typical concentration for either phosphine (n type) or diborane (p type). These gases are commercially available in high-pressure cylinders.

The relationship between the impurity concentration in the gas phase and the resulting impurity concentration in the growing film is extremely complex. Involved are the chemical kinetics of the reduction of silicon tetrachloride and the impurity phosphine or diborane, as well as gas flow and temperature. In this case empirical relationships are easier to obtain than theoretical relationships. Figure 11-10 shows the relationship between the gas-phase composition and the epitaxial film impurity content when phosphine is used as the dopant. Figure 11-11 shows the relationship between the gas-phase composition and the epitaxial film impurity content when diborane is used as the dopant.

The thickness of the epitaxial film across a wafer is affected to an important degree by flow rate. When the gas flow is extremely fast but still nonturbulent, the epitaxial film tends to assume a mounded growth shape. Under such conditions, the

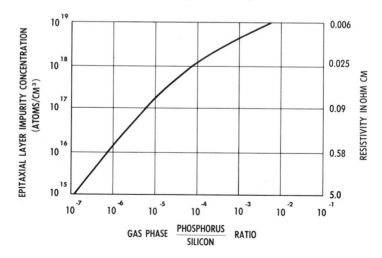

Fig. 11-10 The relationship between gas-phase composition and the epitaxial film impurity content when phosphine is used as the dopant.

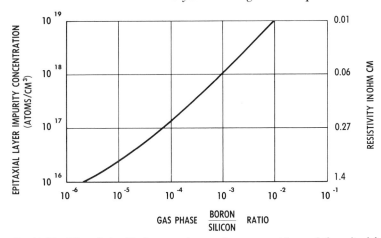

Fig. 11-11 The relationship between the gas-phase composition and the epitaxial film impurity content when diborane is used as the dopant.

film at the edges of the wafer nearest the tube walls is thinner than elsewhere on the wafer. The opposite is true for very slow reactant gas-flow rates. By choosing an intermediate flow rate, films of uniform thickness are achieved.

The most difficult thickness control factor concerns the *front-to-back* problem. The tendency is that the leading wafers have films which are *thicker* than the last wafers in the tube. The phenomenon of thickness variation is related to the fact that $SiCl_4$ becomes depleted as the reagent stream flows toward the exit end of the tube.

The front-to-back problem also applies to resistivity, causing a variation in doping along the length of the tube. For n films on n^+ substrates or p films on p^+ substrates, the downstream films are the more heavily doped. The explanation is as follows: At the elevated temperature of this process, impurity atoms diffuse out of the bottom surfaces of the substrate wafers and into the gas stream. This occurs on all wafers throughout the system, but the enrichment of the gas stream by this mechanism increases progressively down the tube, leading to the observed result. Where film and substrate are of opposite type, the result of this effect is compensation. The sequence of events just outlined is sometimes termed *autodoping*. Where lightly doped substrates are used, such as the usual integrated circuit situation, autodoping is a negligible effect.

The elimination of the entire front-to-back effect is a problem in gas-flow patterns. By tilting the boat 5 to 10° away from the direction of flow of the reagent gases (by raising the trailing edge of the boat), one ensures that each wafer sees a fresh supply of nondepleted, nonenriched reactant gas; as a result, uniformity of both thickness and resistivity from wafer to wafer down the reaction chamber is considerably enhanced.

Conclusion. The process of epitaxy is still in its infancy. Serious work in this field has only been going on since 1960, although the conception of the process occurred much earlier.[7] Much progress has been made. We have learned to grow films with a high degree of crystal perfection and to control the thickness and resistivity of the films with precision. We can vary the resistivity and type of these films in the vertical direction almost at will. A primary need is the development of a process which can operate safely at lower temperatures than the silicon tetrachloride reduction reaction. This will reduce the diffusion that now occurs during epitaxial growth to a point where its effect becomes negligible, so that truly abrupt impurity concentration changes become possible.

REFERENCES

1. Teal, G. K., and J. B. Little: Growth of Germanium Single Crystals, *Phys. Rev.,* vol. 78, p. 647, June 1, 1950.
2. Verneuil, A.: *Compt. rend.,* vol. 135, p. 791, 1962.
3. Hannay, N. B. (ed.): "Semiconductors," Reinhold Publishing Corporation, New York, 1959. (Note: This volume has an extensive bibliography.)
4. Czochralski, J.: A New Method for the Measurement of the Velocity of Crystallization of the Metals, *Z. physik. Chem. Leipzig,* vol. 92, p. 219, 1917.
5. Light, T. B.: Imperfections in Germanium and Silicon Epitaxial Films, in "Metallurgy of Semiconductor Materials," Metallurgical Society Conferences, vol. 15, p. 137, 1962.
6. Queisser, H. J., R. H. Finch, and J. Washburn: Stacking Faults in Epitaxial Silicon, *J. Appl. Phys.,* vol. 33, pp. 1536–1537, April, 1962.
7. Christensen, H., and G. K. Teal: Method of Fabrication of Germanium Semiconductors, U.S. Patent 2,692,839 (to Bell Telephone Laboratories, Inc.), issued Oct. 26, 1954.

12

WAFER PROCESSING

The portion of modern semiconductor integrated circuit manufacturing which we call *wafer processing* deals with operations performed upon the semiconductor wafer before it is separated into smaller subwafers or dice. The original silicon wafer, as cut from the grown crystal, can be thought of as a system with virtually no information content . . . a homogeneous piece of material, each minute segment of which is intended to have identical properties. The purpose of the wafer processing sequence is to impart to the wafer information in the form of a certain desired array of semiconductor junctions and connections.

The theory of junctions has been explored in Chap. 2. The purpose of this chapter is to provide a practical working knowledge of the various techniques used to form junctions in semiconductor crystals, and the methods by which the resulting regions can be connected selectively to form circuits.

Semiconductor wafers can be processed in one of two basic ways. In one, the processing is done on each individual die in order to form the desired junction device, as in the fabrication of microalloy transistors; in the other, the processes are performed simultaneously on all elements of the wafer, as with most diffused types of transistors. In the microalloy transistor (see Fig. 12-1), the semiconductor wafer is cut into small pieces before any other processing is done. Each individual die is

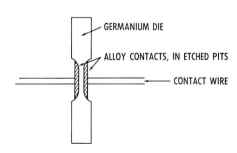

GERMANIUM DIE

ALLOY CONTACTS, IN ETCHED PITS

CONTACT WIRE

Fig. 12-1 Cross section of a microalloy transistor.

then suitably etched on both sides to form pits. These pits are formed opposite each other so that they nearly punch through the semiconductor chip. A metal of the appropriate type, such as a p-type metal for a p-n-p transistor, is then alloyed into each pit. Alloy junctions are formed at these points by the phenomenon of *regrowth,* which will be discussed later.

In the second case, the process steps used result in the simultaneous fabrication of many elements on a large wafer, and this is the procedure used in an integrated circuit. See Sec. 5-4 for a concise summary of the wafer processing and assembly processing steps employed in fabricating a monolithic integrated circuit.

For completeness it should be pointed out that there are certain processes which represent a combination of these two; in other words, one or more steps are performed on a large wafer which represents many potential devices, followed by additional processing steps on the individual dice after they have been separated from the large wafer. An example of such a process is the microalloy-diffused transistor, where a heavy base layer is first diffused into the entire wafer, after which processing procedures very similar to those for the microalloy transistors are employed.

The process steps most commonly employed in integrated circuits manufacturing —epitaxial growth, impurity diffusion, oxidation, photo masking, and vacuum evaporation—are all performed on the wafers as a whole. Some of these processes are employed more than once in the sequence. The basic masking technique, which imparts *selectivity* to each of the other processes, is a photolithographic process in which patterns are actually photographed on an emulsion covering the wafer. The process is alternatively called the *photo-resist process.*

It is appropriate at this point to review very briefly the processing leading to the existence of the silicon wafer, which is the starting point for integrated circuit fabrication. The basic starting material is silicon in a highly pure but polycrystalline form. This polycrystalline silicon is melted in a crucible, and a seed of single-crystal silicon of the desired crystallographic orientation is immersed into the melt and gradually withdrawn, producing a large, single crystal which is nearly perfect. The silicon melt can be *doped* with a suitable n- or p-type impurity to provide a finished crystal which is n-type or p-type to any desired conductivity, limited only by the solubility of the desired impurity in silicon.

The final crystal is frequently ground to a uniform diameter by means of a technique known as centerless grinding. The orientation of the crystallographic structure of the crystal is determined by some method, such as X-ray diffraction. Then a small flat area is ground along the length of the crystal, parallel to one of the crystal planes. This flat surface is used later as a reference in the scribing process. The crystal is then sawed into wafers using a diamond-impregnated blade. The wafers are mechanically lapped with a suitable abrasive such as Al_2O_3 or diamond, and one surface may be polished with an even finer abrasive.

At this point the wafers contain a large number of surface imperfections resulting from the lapping and polishing operations. These imperfections generally extend several microns into the wafer and can be removed by a chemical or gas etching technique.

With this brief introduction to wafer processing and the preceding operations, we can now proceed to a more detailed consideration of the individual wafer processing steps. They will be considered in the order in which they are performed on integrated circuit wafers.

12-1 Epitaxy

Epitaxial growth, as discussed in Chap. 11, is a process whereby a thin film of single-crystal silicon is grown from a vapor phase upon an existing single-crystal wafer of the same material. In contrast to the procedure used for producing bulk semiconductor crystals in which a single crystal is grown from the liquid phase, the epitaxial process involves growth from the gas phase, and no portion of the system is at a temperature anywhere near the melting point of the material.

The epitaxial layer may be of the same or the opposite conductivity type as the substrate wafer. The impurity concentrations in the epitaxial layer can be controlled within wide limits, and complex impurity profiles may be grown. Furthermore, impurity compensation can be avoided in epitaxial layers, a feature which cannot be achieved in diffused layers which form junctions.

12-2 Diffusion

The solutions of the diffusion differential equation take different forms depending on the boundary conditions, but they are always roughly exponential in character (see Figs. 3-2 and 3-4). As noted in Chap. 3, when an impurity diffuses into a solid, the impurity concentration has a maximum value near the surface of the solid, falling off in a gaussian or complementary error function fashion within the wafer itself. If the diffusion cycle is allowed to proceed for a sufficiently long time, the impurity becomes uniformly distributed throughout the sample. However, in the practical case, when it is desired to form junctions in the sample, the diffusion cycle is terminated long before saturation occurs; hence, the graded distribution of the impurities is *locked in.*

A most useful property of certain impurity diffusants commonly used in silicon is that their diffusion constants are much greater in silicon than in silicon dioxide. For this reason silicon dioxide layers are widely used as *masks* in diffusion procedures, and the growth of these layers is intimately associated with impurity diffusion technology.

Oxidation. In the oxidation process, nonoxidized wafers or partially oxidized wafers are placed in the central tube of a diffusion furnace maintained at very high temperature (typically 900 to 1200°C). The wafers are pushed into the hot zone of the furnace on a quartz carrier, or boat, attached to a quartz pushrod which extends the length of the tube. An oxidant, such as oxygen gas or steam, is then passed over them and combines with the silicon of the wafer to form a layer of SiO_2. As the layer forms, the rate of growth decreases with time because of the time necessary for the silicon or oxygen (or both) to diffuse through the SiO_2 so that the reaction can take place. Thus, the thicker the layer, the slower the process becomes.

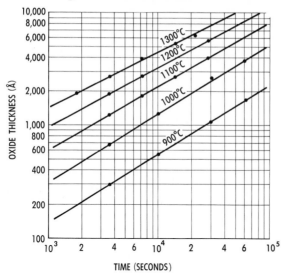

Fig. 12-2 Oxide thickness versus growth time for a silicon surface of (111) orientation exposed to dry oxygen at various temperatures. (*After Evitts, Cooper, and Flaschen.*[1])

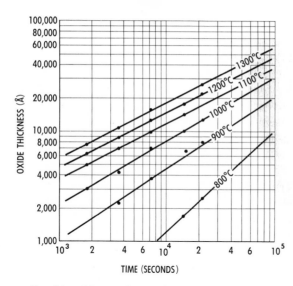

Fig. 12-3 Oxide thickness versus growth time for a silicon surface of (111) orientation exposed to steam at various temperatures. (*After Evitts, Cooper, and Flaschen.*[1])

Considerable work has been done on the study of accelerated oxide growth.[1] Figures 12-2 and 12-3 indicate the growth rates of SiO_2 on Si in atmospheres of dry O_2 and steam, respectively. It can be seen that the slope of the line for steam oxidation differs from that of dry O_2 oxidation, indicating a difference in the activation energy for the oxidation reaction by the two methods.

Masked Diffusion. Once an oxide layer has been grown on the silicon wafer, it is possible to etch apertures of selected size and shape through the use of the photolithographic techniques treated in Chap. 5 and also later in this chapter. When a wafer so prepared is exposed to a diffusant, the impurity will penetrate into the silicon where it has been exposed by etching. It is possible in this way to modify the properties of the wafer in localized regions, and in a controllable fashion. If an

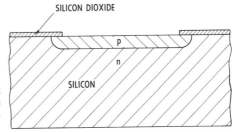

SILICON DIOXIDE

p

n

SILICON

Fig. 12-4 Cross section showing the result of a masked boron diffusion into n-type silicon. The undermask penetration of the impurity is approximately equal to its vertical penetration.

impurity of suitable conductivity type is employed, the conductivity type of the crystal can be locally inverted by means of a selective diffusion, forming a junction in local regions. This process is termed *masked diffusion*.[2]

Figure 12-4 depicts a specimen which has undergone such a masked diffusion using boron as a diffusant. In the right-angle cross section it can be seen that the diffusant has entered the silicon only at the opening or "window" in the oxide. However, because diffusion is a three-dimensional process, some of the boron has diffused under the edge of the oxide mask. Allowance must be made for this effect when laying out the patterns for all integrated circuits since the closest spacing between components in an integrated circuit is limited by this underoxide diffusion. As a first approximation, it can be assumed that the distance which the diffusion penetrates under the mask is equal to the vertical penetration of the impurity.

Masked diffusions are the heart of the modern semiconductor process. It should be pointed out that not all impurities have the property of slow diffusion in SiO_2 and rapid diffusion in silicon. Boron and phosphorus both have this useful property and are widely used because of it. Gallium, on the other hand, diffuses readily through SiO_2 and hence cannot be used in processes requiring the masked termination of a p-type impurity.

Arsenic is also masked by silicon dioxide, but because of its very low diffusion constant in silicon, it is less widely used. However, the use of arsenic as an n-type impurity can be advantageous because it tends to "stay put" during subsequent heat-treatment steps, such as further diffusion processes. This property is sometimes highly desirable.

Boron and phosphorus are almost universally employed as the p-type and n-type impurities, respectively, in silicon. Some of the reasons for this, in addition to the fact that they do not penetrate silicon dioxide, are that they have nearly equal diffusion constants in silicon, and that they both have very high solid solubilities in silicon, permitting a high surface concentration.

Diffusion Apparatus. In all cases one requires a high-temperature furnace having a flat temperature profile over a useful length (Fig. 12-5). (A temperature *profile* is a plot of temperature versus position along the axis of the hot zone of the furnace.) The flatness required in the profile will be a function of the precision required in the properties of the final diffused layers. For example, if the tolerance on the penetration of the diffused layer is ± 50 per cent, then a temperature profile which is flat only to $\pm 5°C$ is adequate. However, if the tolerance permissible in the penetration is only ± 5 or ± 10 per cent, then a temperature profile flat to within $\pm \frac{1}{2}°C$ might be required. In practice it is possible to obtain profiles

Fig. 12-5 High-temperature diffusion furnace suitable for integrated circuit work.

with short-term temperature stability of $\pm\frac{1}{2}°C$ over a zone of 20 in. Such a profile is shown in Fig. 12-6.

Precise control of the hot-zone temperature is required for integrated circuit diffusion work. A diffusion run in which wafers are distributed throughout a zone which varies in temperature from one end to the other will produce wafers with varying depths of impurity penetration, the wafers on the hot end having a deeper diffused layer. This occurs because the diffusion constant of the impurity increases very rapidly with increasing temperature. If the profile of a furnace shows excessive temperature variation, adjustments are made on one or more of the temperature controllers associated with given portions of the furnace length. Then another

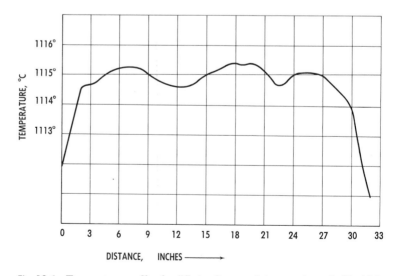

Fig. 12-6 Temperature profile of a diffusion furnace of the type shown in Fig. 12-5.

profile is taken, after waiting a suitable time, before a run is made. Since the absolute temperature of the hot zone will vary gradually with time, this must be checked and adjusted periodically.

The hot zone of a typical furnace is heated by three individually controlled, adjacent resistance elements. The use of the three zones generally provides sufficient control over the flatness of the temperature profile to permit $\pm\frac{1}{2}°C$ performance in a 20-in. zone. If a longer hot zone or more precise control were required, additional heaters would probably be necessary. However, it is unlikely that a zone much longer than 20 in. would be desirable for this application because it is possible to run hundreds of wafers in a zone of that size, and each wafer may contain hundreds of circuits. Thus the number of circuits invested in a single diffusion run in a single furnace can be very large indeed. Since there is always a chance of a malfunction or mistake, it would of course not be prudent to increase the total number of circuits invested without limit. Just where the optimum number lies will vary from case to case, but a 20-in. zone at the present state of the art usually accommodates this many or more.

Typical Diffusion Systems. Impurities are rarely diffused from their elemental forms. For instance, compounds such as B_2O_3, BCl_3, and BBr_3 are used as sources of boron, and P_2O_5 and $POCl_3$ can be used as sources of phosphorus. The compounds used as impurity sources can be gases, liquids, or solids. At room temperature, P_2O_5 is a solid, BCl_3 is a gas, and BBr_3 is a liquid. The nature of the impurity source determines how the impurities are delivered to the wafers. For example, a solid diffusion source, such as P_2O_5, can be heated in a chamber upstream from the wafers being diffused. This chamber is generally heated to a much lower temperature than that of the wafers, and a carrier gas such as oxygen is passed over the vaporizing P_2O_5, carrying it to the wafers. A gaseous source may be used directly or diluted with some other gas. With a liquid source, the carrier gas can be passed over or through the liquid which is maintained at a constant temperature.

In all the above cases, the impurity is carried to the wafers in a gas stream. However, certain other techniques are occasionally employed. One of these involves the placing of a heavy deposit of the impurity directly upon the wafers at room temperature, by means of plating, evaporation, or paint-on techniques. The wafers are then heated and the impurities diffuse into the wafer directly from this deposit. These techniques are rarely used for integrated circuit processing because of the surface damage which usually results from such heavy deposits. The one exception is the case of gold diffusion, which will be described later.

Consider a typical system for diffusing phosphorus in silicon, using P_2O_5 as a source. P_2O_5 is a solid material which is extremely deliquescent and must be protected from moisture. It vaporizes at relatively low temperatures, and has a significant vapor pressure when heated to approximately $200°C$. In practice, the pure P_2O_5 is placed in an open quartz container within the diffusion tube but out of the hot zone. Surrounding the diffusion tube at this point is a small, low-temperature heater for heating the source to the desired temperature. A carrier gas, such as dry oxygen, is passed over the vaporizing P_2O_5, sweeping it into the high-temperature zone of the furnace. A quartz carrier, or boat, containing a number of carefully cleaned wafers is pushed into the hot zone from the opposite end of the diffusion tube. Only a small amount of the vaporized P_2O_5 actually diffuses into the wafers; the rest is carried out the other end of the tube. (A suitable exhaust system must be provided to prevent the toxic vapors from entering the room.) After a specified time the wafers are withdrawn, and the diffusant source is removed. Then the wafers are usually pulled into a cool zone within the diffusion tube and allowed to cool to a temperature suitable for handling. In certain diffusions it may be desirable to perform a controlled, programmed cooling of the wafers to anneal out dislocations. However, programmed cooling is used rather infrequently because of the difficulty in maintaining good temperature profiles on the furnaces.

A more recent technique for phosphorus diffusion employs the compound $POCl_3$. It is a liquid at room temperature, rather than a solid as is P_2O_5, and many of its advantages stem from this fact.

Typical apparatus for $POCl_3$ diffusion is shown in Fig. 12-7. A carrier gas is bubbled through the liquid diffusant source. Typically this gas is a mixture of nitrogen and oxygen in the ratio of $3:1$. This particular ratio leads to the formation of the moderate film of phosphorus-silicon glass necessary for surface protection, and yet avoids excessive oxide formation.

Using a single-step procedure provides a complementary error function (erfc) distribution with a high surface concentration suitable for emitter fabrication. On the other hand, a two-step procedure consisting of a *predeposition* step followed by a *drive-in* step leads to gaussian distribution of lower surface concentration suitable for a transistor base. Typically the predeposition for the base of a p-n-p transistor is done at $900°C$, and the subsequent drive-in is done at $1100°C$. This method enables one to control surface concentration within the range of 5×10^{17} to 1×10^{21} cm^{-3} with a junction depth of 3 to 4 microns.

The advantages of $POCl_3$ over P_2O_5 include:

1. Easier source handling
2. Simpler furnace requirements—one zone is needed rather than two
3. Identical glassware for low and high surface concentration diffusions
4. Total atmosphere control for the wafers in process
5. Better control of impurity density from wafer to wafer and from run to run.

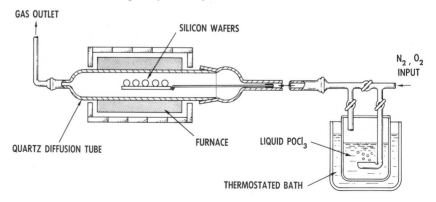

Fig. 12-7   Schematic representation of typical apparatus for $POCl_3$ diffusion.

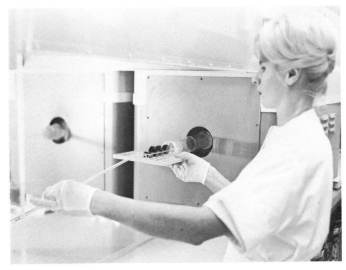

Fig. 12-8 Diffusion furnace for boron drive-in procedure.

In a typical boron diffusion, the solid B_2O_3 is employed as a source of boron. However, the properties of B_2O_3 are quite different from those of P_2O_5. At low temperatures such as 200 to 300°C, the vapor pressure of B_2O_3 is not sufficient for diffusion. Therefore, a method called the *platinum box* technique may be used, utilizing a box made out of platinum sheets with a loosely fitting platinum cover. First B_2O_3 is sprinkled over the inner surface of the platinum lid and fired at high temperature in flowing hydrogen. During this procedure, the B_2O_3 liquefies and, upon cooling, bonds to the surface of the platinum in the form of a thick glassy layer. This procedure is called *source preparation*, and must be repeated at intervals because the layer is depleted during use.

The next step is the predeposition of boron on the wafers. The wafers to be boron-diffused are placed flat on a quartz carrier. This carrier is placed in the platinum box, which is then covered. Next, the entire assembly is pushed into the furnace hot zone and brought up to diffusion temperature. Once again hydrogen gas is used. The vapor pressure of B_2O_3 from the glass layer results in the deposition of a heavy layer of boron glass on the surface of the wafer.

After a suitable time the wafers are withdrawn, cooled, and then placed in another furnace (Fig. 12-8), which is brought up to a different and usually higher temperature, and the boron is driven in. A gas containing no impurities is passed over the wafers, and the heavy boron glass which was predeposited in the previous step acts as a diffusion source of boron.

The properties of the diffused boron layer formed by this process are a function of the time and temperature cycles during both the predeposition and drive-in steps, as well as the gases used during these steps. For example, if a gas such as hydrogen is used during drive-in, the amount of impurity which enters the silicon will be quite high because no oxidation is taking place. On the other hand, if the diffusion is done in oxygen, a significant portion of the total impurity deposited on the wafers will end up in the oxide that forms, since boron has a high solubility in this oxide. Thus, if unusually deep or high-surface-concentration diffusions are required, hydrogen will be used in part or all of the cycle. There are many other sources which can be used for boron, some of which do not require this two-step procedure; each of the systems has its own advantages.

Since the nature of the oxide layer formed during the diffusion step is related to the type of diffusion process used, it is often necessary to consider subsequent steps, such as photo-resist procedures, when doing a diffusion. For example, certain of the oxide layers which might be formed during diffusion have surface properties which make it difficult to obtain good adhesion of photo-resist coatings. Further, the etch rate of some doped oxides is extremely low, and it is often impossible to obtain good etching of the oxide using the photo-resist process without severe undercutting. Problems of this nature will be considered in detail later.

Gold Diffusion. As mentioned in Chaps. 3 and 7, the introduction of gold into the silicon lattice structure, usually by diffusion, is widely employed as a means of lowering the carrier lifetime. A gold atom located in the crystal constitutes a trap, or site, at which carrier recombination may occur. If many such traps are present, the probability of a carrier's being intercepted by such a trap in its diffuse, random motion through the crystal is high, and the resultant lifetime of minority carriers will be low.

The need in some instances for extremely low carrier lifetime is a result of the phenomenon known as *charge storage*. In high-speed saturated switching transistors this charge, which saturates a portion of the crystal during forward conduction, provides a lingering current after turn-off. If carrier lifetime in the crystal is very low, this effect will be markedly diminished. If carrier lifetime is extremely high, then the effects of charge storage may be so pronounced as to render the device useless in many applications. The range of carrier lifetimes which can be achieved using gold diffusion is quite broad, extending from below one nanosecond up to the neighborhood of a microsecond with good control, and hence this technique is widely used in both integrated circuit and discrete device fabrication. Transistors of the 2N834, 2N709, and 2N2369 variety are commonly made using this process.

Gold is one of the few materials which is generally diffused from the elemental form. In practice, a thin film (less than 500 Å) is deposited upon the wafer by means of vacuum evaporation. The wafers are then brought up to diffusion temperature, typically about 1000°C, and remain at this temperature for approximately 15 min. The diffusion constant of gold in silicon is so high at this temperature that 15 min is sufficient to establish an appreciable concentration of gold through the crystal. Then the wafers are quickly cooled or *quenched* by quick withdrawal from the hot zone of the furnace, in order to prevent out-diffusion or precipitation of the gold, as described in Chap. 3. Although vacuum evaporation is the deposition method usually used, alternative techniques for depositing controlled quantities of gold have suggested the possibility of localized gold doping.[3]

Carrier lifetime can be "killed" in other ways. Among these are high-energy particle bombardment and high-temperature shock treatments which introduce dislocations into the crystal. However, devices in which lifetime has been killed by these methods undergo considerable *annealing* at temperatures as low as 50°C, with an attendant increase in carrier lifetime that partially offsets the bombardment effect. In annealing, the damaged crystal partially heals itself by atom rearrangement.

Gold diffusion has emerged as the most promising method for lifetime control in silicon technology because it does not suffer nearly so much from annealing as do the other methods. In order for the lifetime to be increased in a gold-diffused integrated circuit or device, it is necessary for some of the gold to precipitate in electrically inactive aggregations. Although the diffusion constant of gold in silicon is exceedingly high at temperatures above 500°C, it falls off to a low value at temperatures below 300°C, the normal maximum operating range for most devices, and hence gold-doped structures are stable with respect to carrier lifetime.

Diffusion Evaluation. After the diffusion is completed, the wafers are checked. A commonly used procedure is to remove a sliver from one or more of the wafers by scribing. The sliver is beveled by attaching it with wax to a beveling post. Figure 12-9 is a photograph of the beveling post. So mounted, the sliver is then polished by moving the post and its holder over a glass plate covered by a slurry of a fine Al_2O_3 abrasive. This operation produces a polished facet on the specimen which is inclined very slightly to the original surface.

Figure 12-10 depicts a beveled specimen containing a junction. The specimen has been beveled at an angle of 11°, or approximately ⅕ rad, leading to a magnification of the depth dimensions by a factor of 5. The intersection of the junction with the beveled surface forms an elliptical pattern in this case. That is, the beveled surface presents a distorted profile of the junction. Diffused silicon specimens are frequently beveled in this manner for detailed study of their structure, though usually at even smaller angles. When an angle of 0.5° is used, for example, it is clear that the junction pattern is further distorted into a very nearly rectangular shape, rather than the elliptical shape shown in Fig. 12-10.

Chemical staining methods delineate the n and p regions, making junctions visible. Because typical depth dimensions are frequently quite small in comparison to lateral dimensions, it is often convenient to portray a structure as it would appear in beveled section, and this is done frequently in diagrams appearing elsewhere in this book. The reader can readily determine whether a beveled or right-angle section is intended by noting whether the undermask portion of the junction is depicted in rectangular (beveled section) or circular (right-angle section) fashion.

Fig. 12-9 Beveling post used to produce a polished beveled facet on a silicon specimen for detailed examination of junction patterns.

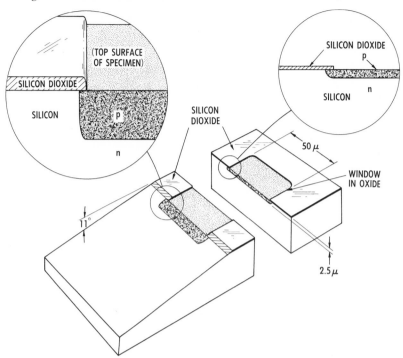

Fig. 12-10 Beveled specimen containing a junction, showing the magnification of the depth dimensions.

By means of an interferometer it is then possible to determine the depth of the diffused layer, usually to an accuracy of ± 0.05 micron. In addition to junction depth, the sheet resistance is measured after a diffusion run. As explained in Chap. 3, this is essentially a measurement of the total integrated diffusant density. A four-point probe (Fig. 3-10) is used if the diffused layer is of the conductivity type opposite to that of the bulk of the silicon wafer. If the diffusion is performed on a wafer of the same conductivity type (for example, a phosphorus diffusion into an n-type wafer), then it is necessary to employ a *test bar* in the run. This is a wafer of opposite conductivity type which will be used only for the purposes of measuring sheet resistance and junction depth. If it is assumed that the nature of the impurity-concentration-versus-distance profile within the wafer is as predicted by theory, then the measurement of sheet resistance and junction depth is adequate to specify the diffused layer completely.

12-3 Photo Resist

The basis for the masking process is the photo-resist technique. Photo resist, devised by Kodak many years ago, is a photosensitive emulsion first used for photo-engraving and for the etching of large metal parts, such as aluminum aircraft panels. In the electronics industry it is also used in the fabrication of printed circuit boards. The procedure was called *metal etching,* and the term *photo resist* was derived from the fact that the process is primarily photographic in nature, and the emulsions are resistant to certain corrosive etches.

In the semiconductor industry, the same emulsions are used to form selectively etched patterns on oxide-coated wafers. The etch commonly used for this process in the semiconductor industry is hydrofluoric acid, an extremely reactive agent. The emulsion itself is a polyvinyl alcohol (PVA) which is soluble in various solvents such as trichloroethylene. This material can be polymerized by ultraviolet light, heat, and certain other means. In semiconductor applications, the PVA is polymerized by means of high-intensity ultraviolet light. Once the material has been polymerized, dissolving it is virtually impossible.

It has been found that there is a certain degree of surface-activated polymerization which occurs because of interaction of the emulsion with the walls of its container. Thus, it is important to filter the liquid frequently in order to remove these solid particles and assure good coatings on the wafer to be etched. This is conveniently done using a high-pressure apparatus such as a Krueger filter. It is also important that the emulsion be stored in a cool, dark place.

In the photo-resist process the first step is to clean the oxide-coated wafer with a solvent such as trichloroethylene. In general, the purest grade of solvents and acids (referred to as *electronic* or *semiconductor grade* by the chemical industry) are used in all semiconductor processes. Contamination of the wafers at any step of the process lowers the yield of good devices. This is especially true in large power transistors or integrated circuits in which the probability of contaminating a given device or circuit is high.

After cleaning, the wafer is placed on a vacuum chuck which can be rotated at high speed by a motor (Fig. 12-11). After the wafer is centered on the chuck, it is

Fig. 12-11 Vacuum chuck which can be spun at high speed. Liquid photo resist is placed on a wafer which is secured by the chuck, and the spinning action flattens and smooths the photo-resist film.

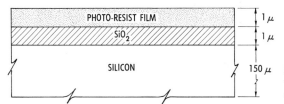

Fig. **12-12** Schematic cross section of a wafer having a photo-resist film applied over an SiO$_2$ layer.

secured by a vacuum. Then a quantity of liquid photo resist is deposited on the wafer with an eye dropper. When the motor is turned on, most of the liquid is spun from the wafer. The combination of surface tension and the forces resulting from spinning causes the liquid to spread into a uniform, thin film from which the solvents used to liquefy the compound quickly escape by evaporation. With the wafer spun at 8,000 rpm for 10 sec, the resulting film is approximately 1 micron thick, and flat to within ±10 per cent. The wafer is then carefully removed from the spinner and placed in a 60°C oven with a nitrogen atmosphere for 30 min to *cure* the photo-resist film and drive off any remaining solvents.

The coated wafer (Fig. 12-12) is placed in an alignment tool consisting basically of another vacuum chuck, provided with x, y, and θ movements (Fig. 12-13). A carrier containing a glass mask is then placed in a holder above the wafer (Fig. 12-14). This holder is capable of z movement only. Mounted above this assembly is a high-power microscope and a movable ultraviolet source. The glass mask is an ordinary high-resolution photographic plate which contains the pattern

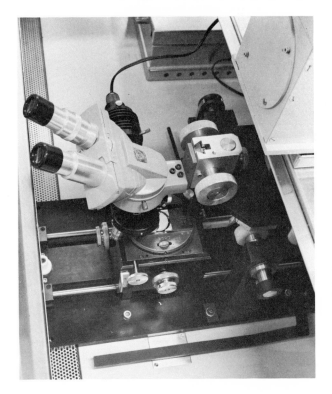

Fig. **12-13** Tool for aligning and orienting a photographic mask upon a patterned wafer.

Fig. 10-14 Mask holder and mask for use in alignment tool shown in Fig. 12-13.

to be placed upon the wafer.   This pattern usually consists of an array of identical elements such as integrated circuits or transistors, spaced on centers consistent with their size.   At certain positions in the array a device pattern is replaced by a special key pattern, which serves as an alignment aid for registration of successive patterns upon the wafer.   Examples of these can be seen in the masked wafer (Fig. 12-15).

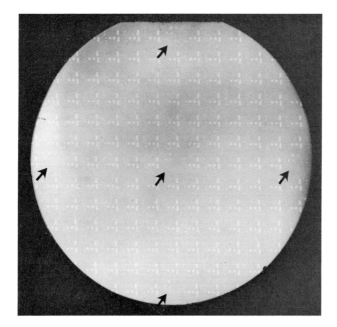

Fig. 12-15 Masked integrated circuit wafer. Arrows indicate positions of key patterns for subsequent mask alignment. This wafer is ready for the p-type isolation diffusion; the small light areas are SiO_2 diffusion masks.

During the first masking step there is no existing set of patterns on the wafer. Thus, it is merely necessary to align the array parallel to the *flat* on the wafer. The flat is the short, straight edge on the wafer produced by grinding an oriented flat surface on the side of the silicon crystal prior to slicing. This serves as a crystallographic reference. After this has been done, the mask is lowered into contact with the wafer, and the ultraviolet source is brought into place above the mask. Typical exposure times are about 30 sec. Wherever the emulsion on the mask is black, the ultraviolet light does not penetrate to the wafer; where it is clear, some of the ultraviolet can reach the wafer, although it is attenuated considerably by the mask.

After exposure, the light source is removed, the mask is lifted from the wafer, and the wafer is carefully removed from the alignment tool. The wafer is then developed by rinsing in Kodak developer or trichloroethylene. The developer dissolves the unexposed and hence unpolymerized portions of the photo-resist film from the wafer. The rest of the film is undisturbed. The developed wafers are then given a final bake at 200°C for 30 min to harden the remaining photo resist and ensure its adhesion to the oxide.

After bake, the wafer is immersed in an etching solution consisting primarily of ammonium fluoride, water, and hydrofluoric acid. The ammonium fluoride is required to prevent lifting of the photo resist from the oxide. (The exact details of this etch are given in Appendix B. These materials must be handled with caution. Safety considerations for these and a number of other materials common in semiconductor processing are outlined in Appendix C.) Etching takes place at room temperature and usually takes from 10 to 250 sec, depending upon the thickness and impurity doping of the oxide. After etching, the wafer is inspected to be sure that all the oxide has been removed in the desired areas. If the wafers pass this inspection, they are then cleaned. If not, additional etching may be employed.

Removal of the polymerized photo resist in order to ready the wafers for subsequent diffusion is extremely difficult. The polymerized photo resist is insoluble in virtually any known chemical; therefore, removal of this layer is essentially a mechanical abrasion process. The wafers may be boiled in hot sulfuric acid to loosen the film and then scrubbed with water or solvent. After cleaning, they are thoroughly inspected for possible residues. Any vestige of photo resist that might cling at the edges of the openings cut by the etching process can impair results in subsequent diffusion steps, as described in more detail below.

After removal of the polymerized photo resist, the wafer is ready for a diffusion through the apertures cut in the oxide by the photo-resist process. During this dif-

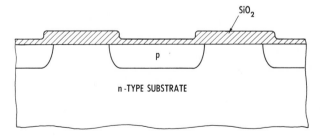

Fig. 12-16 An array of p-n junctions formed in a typical masked diffusion operation.

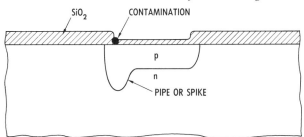

Fig. 12-17 A junction pipe or spike caused by contamination accompanying a diffusion process.

fusion, a new oxide is usually grown in the apertures. If, for example, the original wafer were n-type material and a boron diffusion had been performed, an array of p-n junctions would be present in the material (Fig. 12-16). If the object of this particular process sequence were the formation of transistors, it would be necessary to carry out a second photo-resist and diffusion sequence to form the required second (emitter) junction. It is necessary that the new aperture lie within the area of the original base aperture. In performing this operation, the steps previously described are repeated, except that the alignment key patterns must be used.

The alignment keys reproduced on the wafer by the first masking process are now used in conjunction with a second set of keys on the second mask for alignment. After alignment, the remainder of the process steps are identical, and the newly etched wafers are again diffused, this time using an impurity of opposite conductivity type, such as phosphorus.

Figure 12-17 shows a cross section of the wafer in which a particle of contamination has caused local alloying of the impurities at the edge of the opening, forming a liquid source for enhanced diffusion. The cross-sectional view of the resulting junction shows the *pipe* or *spike* caused by such contamination. If a similar cross section had been taken at a different portion of the junction, no pipe would have been observed. That is, this deep diffusion does not represent a long trough along the edge, but merely a localized region.

If such pipes occur during an early diffusion step, such as base diffusion, they are usually of little consequence because they penetrate into a thick region. However, when they occur in a second or third diffusion step as shown in Fig. 12-18, the device may be susceptible to *punch-through*. The electrical result of this is

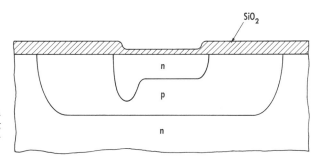

Fig. 12-18 A spike associated with an emitter junction. The resulting transistor is subject to collector depletion layer punch-through.

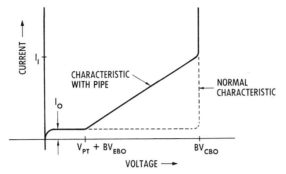

Fig. 12-19 *I-V* characteristic of the collector junction in a transistor exhibiting punch-through caused by an emitter spike of the type shown in Fig. 12-18.

shown in Fig. 12-19. Here the lower junction (collector-base junction) has been reverse-biased, setting up a depletion layer. When the voltage V_{PT} is reached, the depletion layer touches the bottom of the pipe, establishing a connection between the two n regions. With further increase in voltage, the emitter will continue to float at a voltage which differs from the collector voltage by approximately V_{PT}, and the emitter junction will go into reverse bias. When the emitter-base voltage exceeds BV_{EBO} (usually a small value), then the collector-base I-V characteristic will begin to depart from that of a normal transistor because a connection exists from collector to base through the pipe, the emitter, and the avalanching emitter junction. The dominant resistive element in this path is the pipe itself.

The resistive portion of the punch-through characteristic (Fig. 12-19) represents the resistance of this pipe. Once the avalanche breakdown of the collector-base junction is reached, the punch-through characteristic and the normal characteristic once more coincide. Section 4-6 gives a description of the punch-through phenomenon from a slightly different point of view.

The photo-resist process is prone to certain difficulties resulting from previous process sequences. A commonly encountered problem is lack of adherence. It has been found experimentally that the surfaces of oxides grown under certain specific conditions (e.g., in the presence of heavy impurity contamination) inhibit adherence of the photo-resist emulsions. When this happens, the etching solution may penetrate under the edges of the photo resist. This phenomenon, known as *undercutting*, causes removal of oxide where such removal is not desired. Thus, in subsequent diffusion cycles, impurities will penetrate into the silicon in these areas. If the effect is severe enough, it may result in a shorted device.

Pinholes are a second common problem. These may be the result of lack of integrity in the photo-resist film on the wafer. They usually occur at random on the wafer and are usually very small (1 to 3 microns in diameter, typically). Where such pinholes occur, the etching solution can attach the oxide and form a small pit which may penetrate the oxide partially or entirely. These pinholes have serious consequences when they occur in critical portions of the wafer. Their effect is discussed in more detail later in connection with metallizing.

12-4   Oxide-Silicon Interface Effects

During the fabrication of integrated circuit structures, diffusion steps usually follow or are accompanied by the growth of a silicon dioxide layer, as the preceding discussion of wafer processing has shown. The growth of these oxide layers can have a pronounced effect on the distribution of impurities within the wafer, principally near the oxide-silicon interface. A dopant such as aluminum has a stronger affinity for silicon dioxide than for silicon. Thus, during oxide growth on a sample which is aluminum-doped, the concentration of aluminum near the surface of silicon tends to decrease because the aluminum migrates from the silicon into the silicon dioxide layer. Boron, however, tends to regard both phases with equal favor and shows little change in surface concentration as a result of oxide growth.

On the other hand, the n-type impurities, phosphorus in particular, have little relative affinity for the oxide phase, and therefore accumulate on the silicon side of the oxide-silicon interface. That is, silicon is consumed during the oxidation of its surface, and the phosphorus atoms encountered in this process are rejected into the silicon, enriching its doping near the surface. The tendency for n-type impurities to pile up near the surface is often referred to as the *snowplow* effect.[4,5] The relative distributions of aluminum, boron, and phosphorus are illustrated in Fig. 12-20.

A second mechanism can also cause changes in the conductivity of the silicon near this surface. Depletion or enhancement of the carrier concentrations near the surface can be caused by the presence of fixed charges associated with the oxide. Note that *carrier* concentrations change in this case and not *impurity* concentrations as in the previous case. This fundamental difference makes it possible to determine practically which effect is predominating in a particular situation. (They can of course coexist.) Snowplow-type surface conductivity perturbations are not affected by removing the oxide. On the other hand, in charge-induced surface perturbations, the surface tends to return to normal when the oxide is removed.[6]

Charge-induced changes toward either n-type or p-type surface conductivity are possible. Changes toward n-type behavior are more common, however, indicating prevalent fixed positive charges associated with the oxide. These positive charges attract electrons toward the surface and repel holes, accounting for the observed n-type effect. The higher the resistivity of the silicon, the more pronounced the effect, simply because there are fewer majority carriers in high-resistivity silicon; hence, the effects of the surface charges are more significant.

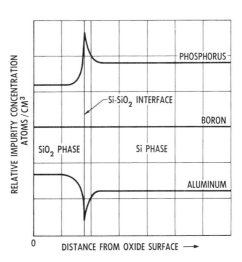

Fig. 12-20 Representation of effects associated with silicon surface oxidation. Phosphorus (and other n-type impurities) show the "snowplow" effect, or pile up near the oxide-silicon interface. Boron is almost unaffected. Aluminum concentration is diminished near the interface. (*After Cooper et al.*[5])

Transistor collector regions are particularly vulnerable to these surface problems because the collector region often has a high resistivity in order to provide high collector breakdown voltage and low parasitic capacitance. In an n-p-n transistor, charge-induced enhancement of the n-type collector conductivity at the surface can seriously reduce collector breakdown voltage. In a p-n-p transistor, a small change of the collector surface region toward n type may simply lead to higher p-type resistivity and hence is not serious. It is more probable, unfortunately, that the surface will actually *invert* in conductivity type. That is, an n-type region will form on the collector surface and form an extension of the n-type base region. This charge-induced n-type region, often called a *channel,* can degrade a transistor's performance profoundly. In particular, if it communicates with the fractured edge of the die as shown in Fig. 12-21, it can carry a large current when the collector is reverse-biased. The collector-base junction exhibits what appears externally to be a large leakage current.

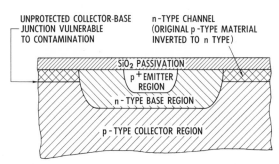

Fig. 12-21 A p-n-p transistor with an oxide-caused channel on the collector surface.

A third type of surface conductivity change may occur simply if the masking oxide is not thick enough to avoid penetration by an impurity during diffusion. However, this problem is not common and certainly is easier to avoid than the preceding ones.

Many of these detrimental effects are circumvented by a new fabrication process, known as the Annular* process. In the Annular process, no attempt is made to eliminate the channel. In fact, the process is arranged so as to induce a channel. However, this channel is then terminated by means of an annular ring of p-type impurity which surrounds the base-collector junction, as shown in Fig. 12-22. This impurity ring is of such heavy concentration (approximately 10^{20} atoms/cm^3) that it is impossible for a channel to exist in this region. Thus the channel is terminated beneath the oxide, maintaining the passivation of the collector-base junction. The effective resistivity of the channel is very high, and thus does not represent a limiting factor in breakdown voltage.

In practice, this impurity ring can be formed during the emitter diffusion. Thus it is possible to include this desirable feature in a transistor without introducing additional processing steps.

---

*The Motorola Annular process provides true silicon oxide passivation and eliminates uncontrolled *channeling* and leakage to the edges of the transistor die. Patents pending.

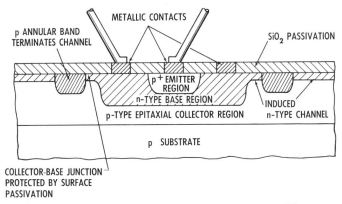

Fig. 12-22   Structure resulting from the Annular process. The p-type annular region formed at the same time as the emitter terminates the n-type channel on the collector surface.

12-5   Formation of Ohmic Contacts

Masked diffusion can produce structures with the desired electrical characteristics. To utilize these structures, however, contacts must be made to various parts of the structure. Because it has been found impractical to attach wires directly to silicon, an intervening metal film is nearly always employed. The properties desired in this metal film are as follows:

1. It must be capable of making a good ohmic (nonrectifying) contact to the semiconductor.

2. It must be an excellent conductor.

3. It must have metallurgical properties suitable for the lead-attachment procedures to be used.

Many metals have been used for the formation of ohmic contacts to semiconductor devices. The most common are gold, aluminum, nickel, lead, silver, and chromium. In silicon devices, aluminum has been found to be preferable. However, when using aluminum one must be careful to avoid the formation of a p-type region that can result when aluminum is alloyed into silicon. The phenomenon of regrowth, which causes this problem, can be understood by examination of Fig. 12-23, a phase diagram of the aluminum-silicon system.

As shown, an alloy consisting of 89 per cent aluminum and 11 per cent silicon has a lower melting point than any other combination of the two metals. This minimum point is called an *eutectic;* one or more eutectics are commonly observed in the phase diagrams of various bimetallic systems. Such mixtures are not true chemical compounds.

Figure 12-24 is a schematic representation of what is happening at the interface when two metals are heated to a temperature just higher than the eutectic point. As the critical temperature is approached, atoms of each metal begin diffusing at the interface. When the eutectic point is reached, a very thin liquid layer forms at the interface, and this liquid phase very rapidly dissolves both metals in the

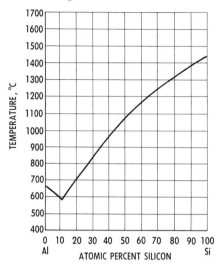

Fig. 12-23   Phase diagram for the aluminum-silicon system. The eutectic alloy consisting of 11 per cent silicon and 89 per cent aluminum melts at 576°C.

appropriate proportion to form a large volume of eutectic alloy. If a limited amount of one of the two metals is available, this process will cease when the entire amount of the limited material has been consumed. This is the situation, for example, when a film of aluminum on the order of one micron thick is deposited by vacuum evaporation onto a silicon substrate which is hundreds of microns thick. When this system is heated beyond the eutectic temperature (576°C), all the aluminum present rapidly gets "used up" by the liquid phase. The aluminum in this case is clearly the limiting factor because the aluminum film is much thinner than the silicon regions and because the eutectic alloy requires a much greater percentage of aluminum than of silicon.

Now, if such a system is heated to a temperature higher than the eutectic, more and more silicon is dissolved in the liquid phase as seen on the phase diagram. If the system is now cooled to a point below the eutectic, this additional silicon is rejected from the liquid during cooling, forming a *regrowth layer* of silicon in the interface. This regrowth layer contains a small percentage of aluminum, as determined by the solid solubility of aluminum in silicon (approximately 0.001 per cent). The liquid aluminum-silicon alloy will "freeze" and form an ohmic contact to the silicon, provided that the original silicon is either p type or heavily doped n type. If it is p type to start with, there is no difficulty because the aluminum which has segregated out into the regrowth layer tends to make it more p type. If it is n type to start with, then there must be more n-type atoms than p-type aluminum atoms per unit volume in the regrown crystal; otherwise, a p-n junction will be formed

METAL "A"   ORIGINAL INTERFACE

METAL "B"   LIQUID SHEET

Fig. 12-24   Schematic representation of the situation obtained when two metals in contact with each other are heated slightly above their eutectic temperature.

ALUMINUM ALLOYED CONTACTS

SiO$_2$

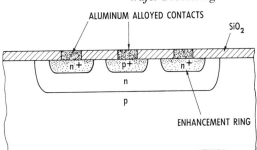

ENHANCEMENT RING

Fig. 12-25 Localized n-type enhancement diffusion to permit aluminum metallizing for ohmic contact to an n-type region.

at the interface between the regrowth layer and the original undisturbed silicon. The amount of aluminum present in the regrowth layer is approximately 5×10^{18} atoms/cm^3. Thus, unless there is an n-type species present in the regrowth layer in excess of this concentration, a rectifying contact will be formed.

Aluminum is useful as an ohmic contact to both the emitter and base regions in n-p-n transistors. In such devices the base doping may be less than 5×10^{18} atoms/cm^3, but it is already p type. The emitter is n type, but its doping is normally in the order of 10^{21} atoms/cm^3. In a p-n-p transistor, the emitter contact is again no problem because it is both heavily doped and p type. However, the base doping may be less than 5×10^{18} atoms/cm^3, and since it is n type, the use of aluminum will normally result in a rectifying contact. This can be prevented, as shown in Fig. 12-25, by performing a masked n$^+$ enhancement diffusion prior to metallization.

In practice, a typical metallizing sequence is as follows:

After all diffusions have been completed, openings are cut in the oxide by the photo-resist technique in the areas where ohmic contacts are to be formed. The wafers are then cleaned and placed in a vacuum evaporation apparatus. The clean, etched wafers are placed under a tungsten filament in the bell jar and the ohmic-contact metal desired (e.g., aluminum) is coiled around the tungsten filament. After the bell jar has been evacuated, the aluminum is first melted and then vaporized by the heated filament. A thin film of aluminum metal is deposited on the wafers as well as on all interior parts of the system.

After all the metal has been evaporated, the bell jar is backfilled, and the wafers are removed. At this point the wafers appear in cross section as in Fig. 12-26. The metallized wafers are again coated with photo resist, exposed with a new mask which is essentially the inverse of the preceding mask, and developed. At this point, an appropriate etch such as sodium hydroxide is used to remove the alumi-

ALUMINUM FILM

SiO$_2$ LAYER

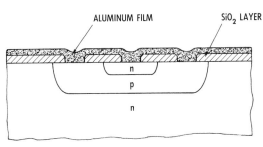

Fig. 12-26 Cross section of a wafer immediately after metallization.

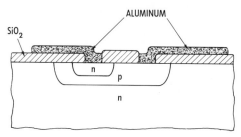

Fig. 12-27 Cross section showing overlay metallization.

num in the unwanted areas. The metal is now alloyed into the surface of the silicon by heating the wafers to a temperature above the eutectic temperature.

A variation of the ordinary metallization procedure just described is a process known as *overlay metallizing,* which is useful in integrated circuits. In overlay metallizing the same basic principles apply as in ordinary metallizing. However, in addition to forming an ohmic contact to the silicon, the metal deposit forms extensions of the ohmic contact over the oxide. This is shown in cross section in Fig. 12-27. Note that the metal deposit actually crosses the junctions but does not short-circuit them because of the intervening insulating oxide. The overlay contact adds about 0.03 pf/mil^2 of parasitic capacitance. With this technique two new degrees of freedom are achieved. First, it is possible to make large ohmic-contact areas to extremely tiny junction areas. Second, it is possible to interconnect two or more otherwise isolated junction areas directly on a wafer without short-circuiting the junctions.

The choice of contact metal is much more restricted in the overlay process because the metal used must have the additional property of making a good mechanical bond to the SiO$_2$ without complete penetration of the oxide. Only two materials have been found satisfactory for this purpose: aluminum and chromium. Both aluminum and chromium are active reducing agents and can combine with the oxygen from the silicon dioxide layer. This reaction results in a disturbance of the surface of the layer, and creates a good bond between the oxide and metallic film. Since it is difficult to use chromium because of its high melting point and certain other properties, aluminum is practically the only contact metal used for overlay metallizing. With the use of n$^+$ enhancement diffusions for making contact to high-resistivity n-type regions, aluminum has proved satisfactory in all cases.

Pinholes formed during the photo-resist process can seriously affect overlay metallized devices. Examination of Fig. 12-28 shows the effect of pinholes in the

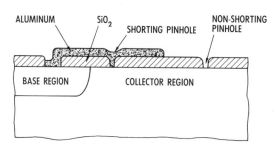

Fig. 12-28 Cross section showing an oxide layer with pinhole defects. Pinhole in the region of overlay metallization may short-circuit a junction. Pinhole in a more remote position may be harmless.

passivating oxide covering the collector region. In the figure are two pinholes; one is outside the area of overlay metallization, and the other is beneath the overlay metallized layer. Obviously, the pinhole outside the overlay region does not affect the operating characteristics of the device. However, the other pinhole has allowed penetration of the aluminum base contact to the collector region of the transistor, causing a short from base to collector. Since integrated circuits employ large amounts of overlay metallization, the pinhole count must be kept extremely low to avoid loss of a significant number of devices.

REFERENCES

1. Evitts, H. C., H. W. Cooper, and S. S. Flaschen: Rates of Formation of Thermal Oxides of Silicon, presented at the Semiconductor Symposium of the Electrochemical Society National Meeting, Boston, September, 1962.
2. Frosch, C. J., and L. Derick: Surface Protection and Selective Masking during Diffusion in Silicon, *J. Electrochem. Soc.,* vol. 104, pp. 547–552, September, 1957.
3. Adamic, J. W., Jr., and J. E. McNamara: Studies of the Diffusion of Gold into Silicon and Silicon Dioxide Films, presented at the Semiconductor Symposium of the Electrochemical Society National Meeting, New York, October, 1963.
4. Atalla, M. M., and E. Tannenbaum: Impurity Redistribution and Junction Formation in Silicon by Thermal Oxidation, *Bell System Tech. J.,* vol. 39, pp. 933–946, July, 1960.
5. Cooper, H. W., E. I. Doucette, and R. A. Mehnert: Oxidation-induced Diffusion in Silicon, presented at the Electronics Division of the Electrochemical Society National Meeting, Chicago, May, 1960.
6. Atalla, M. M., E. Tannenbaum, and E. J. Scheibner: Stabilization of Silicon Surfaces by Thermally Grown Oxides, *Bell System Tech. J.,* vol. 38, pp. 749–783, May, 1959.

13

THIN FILMS IN INTEGRATED CIRCUITS

Thin films are used in almost every type of integrated circuit for interconnection and isolation. In addition they may be used in the fabrication of resistors and capacitors. For many applications thin-film resistors and capacitors offer certain distinct advantages over their p-n junction counterparts. To use these advantages to the fullest, silicon and thin-film technologies are being combined in the same integrated circuit in a variety of ways.

Thin films must be deposited, modified (in some cases), patterned, adjusted (in some cases), and must be provided with contacts before they can perform useful electronic functions. Active (oxidized silicon) and passive (glazed or unglazed ceramic) substrates may both be utilized. The thin-film elements and their interconnections must be compatible with the rest of the integrated circuit in which they appear, with the various chemical and thermal processing and sealing steps, and they must withstand accelerated life-test procedures. In other words, we must be able to treat thin-film and silicon component parts of an integrated circuit as equivalent with respect to some processing steps, all packaging steps, and in reliability expectation.

The term *thin* as it applies to thin films is quite ambiguous. It is used to define layer thicknesses in the range from one monolayer (about 5 Å) to approximately 1 micron. The term *thick film* is sometimes used to describe films with a larger thickness dimension. For the purpose of this chapter, every *deposited* layer of interest will be termed a thin film, even though it be a mil or more thick.

The thin-film circuit elements of major consequence at the present time are the resistor and capacitor (see Chap. 10). These are depicted schematically in Fig. 13-1, which illustrates the insulating substrate, metal film contacts, and resistive and dielectric films. Resistors may be made with contacts above or below the resistive film.

Conventional thin-film circuits are made by depositing thin-film capacitors and resistors on a passive substrate such as glass or ceramic, and subsequently adding

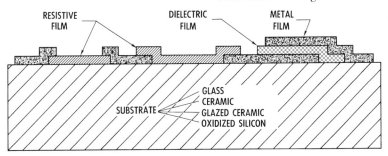

Fig. 13-1 Cross-sectional representation of thin-film resistors and capacitors showing the insulating substrate, metal film contacts, and resistive and dielectric films.

complete prefabricated active components to the thin-film structure. Such a circuit is illustrated in principle by Fig. 13-2*a*, and an actual circuit is shown in Fig. 13-2*b*. Compatible thin-film techniques, discussed in this chapter, involve processes through which the desired thin-film components are fabricated on top of the passivated

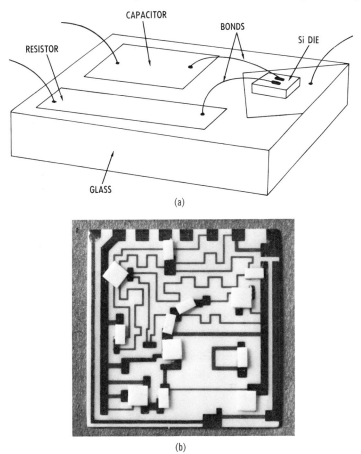

Fig. 13-2 (*a*) Schematic representation of a complete thin-film circuit. (*b*) Photomicrograph of a complete thin-film circuit.

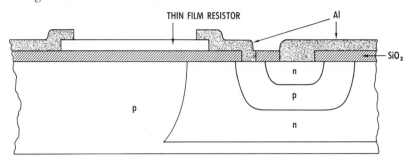

Fig. 13-3   A compatible thin-film integrated circuit showing a thin-film resistor in series with the base of a monolithic transistor.

silicon monolithic circuit (see Fig. 13-3), and interconnected with the silicon components beneath the silicon dioxide passivating layer.

The combination of thin-film and semiconductor technologies provides a greater degree of design freedom, a wider range of component values, improved tolerances, and better electrical performance than either technology can provide separately.

13-1   Deposition of Thin Films

The various methods for thin-film deposition are listed in Table 13-1.   General requirements for good thin films are uniformity of film thickness and composition, and good adhesion to the substrate and to other films with which the deposited film makes contact.

Table 13-1   Thin-film Deposition Methods

I. Vacuum evaporation:	III. Gas plating:
Hot filament	Hydrogen reduction
Flash filament	Thermal decomposition
Electron bombardment	IV. Electroplating
Electron beam	V. Electroless plating
II. Sputtering:	VI. Silk screening
High pressure	
Reactive	

Several of these methods are used for thin-film deposition on a commercial scale, and many other techniques under investigation appear to have important future applicability.[1]   Major emphasis will be placed on vacuum evaporation, gas plating, and silk screening as deposition techniques, respectively, for Nichrome* (NiCr) resistors, aluminum silicate ($Al_2O_3 \cdot SiO_2$) dielectrics, and moly-manganese (Mo-Mn) contacts; other materials and processes will be discussed briefly.

Vacuum Evaporation.   Vacuum evaporation is used to deposit many types of thin films.   In a highly evacuated glass (or metal) bell jar (Fig. 13-4) a tungsten filament is brought to a high temperature by passing an electric current through it.   The material to be evaporated, which is in contact with the filament, is heated sufficiently

*Nichrome is a trade name of Driver-Harris Co., Harrison, N. J.

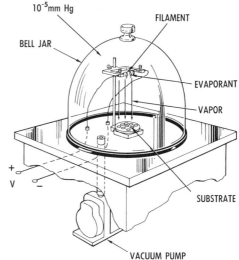

Fig. 13-4 Drawing of a high-vacuum bell-jar system for vacuum evaporations.

to vaporize it quickly. In a high vacuum (usually 10^{-6} to 10^{-5} torr), the mean free path of evaporated molecules is many times the diameter of the bell jar. Hence, the evaporated material radiates in all directions from the source, shadowed by all objects in its path. The substrate, which is usually heated during evaporation to promote adhesion and to control the film structure, is placed a considerable distance (usually several inches) from the source. The effective substrate temperature, primarily determined by the substrate heater, is modified by radiant energy from the heater and the kinetic energy of the impinging particles.

Different shapes of evaporation heaters (Fig. 13-5) are used with different materials. The helical filament is most commonly used for metals which, in the form of small wire U's, are hung over the tungsten wire. Gold, aluminum, and silver

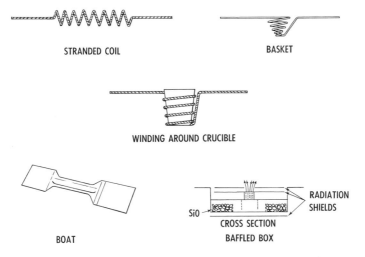

Fig. 13-5 Various types of heaters for high-vacuum evaporation of various materials.

are frequently evaporated in this way. The basket and boat configurations can be used for materials not readily available in wire form. The basket evaporates material in all directions and the boat (because of its shape), only upward. Materials which react with tungsten at high temperatures may be evaporated by placing them in a crucible (made, for example, of carbon or alumina) heated by a tungsten coil. If the material to be evaporated tends to splatter and thus disturb the continuity of the deposited film, a shielded source may correct the problem. This is done with silicon monoxide which is commonly evaporated from the baffled box.

The above sources work well for many elementary materials and for some compounds. Other compounds fractionate at high temperatures, and so it is necessary to evaporate them quickly, using a very fast-heating "flash" source. Still other materials are so refractory, fractionate so badly, or react with tungsten so quickly, that electron bombardment (of extremely high power densities) is necessary to vaporize them properly. The source material is often contained in a water-cooled metal crucible which, because it is not in the electron stream, remains cold and therefore does not react with the molten source. This is the technique commonly used for Nichrome evaporation.

In the electron beam technique, a narrow electron beam is focused on one part of the source, vaporizing it quickly. If necessary, the beam may be scanned over the source during evaporation. Some of the more refractory cermets will require this technique in order that deposited films coincide in composition with that of the source.

Film thickness and rate of deposition are sometimes monitored by placing a quartz crystal which is oscillating in an electronic circuit in the path of the evaporant. The film deposited on the quartz crystal changes its frequency. Thus, the thickness of the film may be determined directly. For thin-film resistor deposition, a monitor which reads film resistivity directly is often inserted, close to the substrates. In addition to these in-process measurement techniques, there are methods for measuring the thickness of finished films. The most common is monochromatic interference micros-

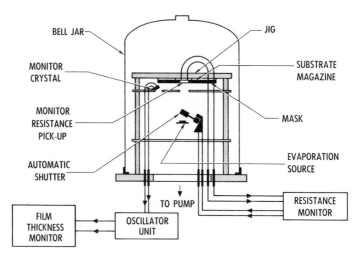

Fig. 13-6 Diagram of a high-vacuum evaporation apparatus illustrating the flag, crystal, and resistance monitors.

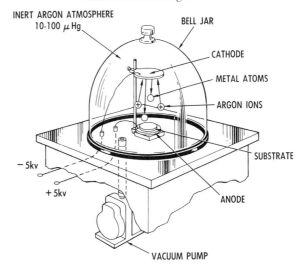

INERT ARGON ATMOSPHERE
10-100 μ Hg

BELL JAR

CATHODE

METAL ATOMS

ARGON IONS

SUBSTRATE

− 5kv

+ 5kv

ANODE

VACUUM PUMP

Fig. 13-7 Bell-jar-type apparatus for cathode sputtering of thin-film materials.

copy which works well for films thicker than about 1000 Å. For transparent dielectric films, room light interference often gives a good indication of uniformity variations down to about 200 Å.

Frequently, a metal "flag" is placed between source and substrate during the early phases of evaporation to intercept the more volatile impurities from the source. The flag is then moved aside to initiate deposition and returned to stop deposition when the desired film thickness has been attained. Figure 13-6 illustrates the flag, crystal, and resistance monitors. To increase the capacity of an evaporator, intricate mechanical feeders may be inserted in the bell jar to present several groups of substrates in succession for deposition.

The film deposited on a surface by vacuum evaporation is usually polycrystalline, with crystallite size being controllable to some extent. For example, fine-grained film structures are encouraged by a high rate of evaporation which produces a large number of nuclei; such a fine-grained film has a more predictable sheet resistance than a coarser one. On the other hand, evaporation onto a surface at grazing incidence favors the formation of large grains oriented in the direction of incidence. This is usually undesirable.

In procedures where the source material is completely evaporated, the thickness of the film is determined by the mass of the source metal and the distance between source and substrate, assuming a normal angle of incidence.[2] Both normal incidence and complete evaporation are frequently employed for the sake of simplicity and uniformity.

Cathode Sputtering. Sputtering is performed using equipment (Fig. 13-7) similar to that for evaporation. A low vacuum (generally 0.04 to 0.1 torr) is maintained by bleeding a gas, usually argon, into the bell jar while pumping on it with a high vacuum. A glow discharge is initiated by applying a high voltage between cathode (source) and anode. The substrate may rest on the anode, or be placed in the glow region. Argon ions (A^+) produced by the discharge are accelerated toward the cathode and gain sufficient energy to knock atoms (or molecules) out of the cathode.

Atoms knocked loose from the cathode by the impinging ions have sufficient velocity so that when they hit the substrate they usually adhere well.

Sputtering is generally slower than evaporation, depositing a micron-thick film in minutes to hours, compared to seconds to minutes for evaporation. Sputtering can be used to deposit films of refractory metals, such as tantalum. Usually dc (but sometimes asymmetrical ac) voltages as high as 5,000 volts are applied between the cathode and the anode.

The term *reactive sputtering* is used where a second gas, which becomes incorporated into the deposited film, is bled into the bell jar. It is proposed that the second gas (at least partially) picks up a negative charge in the plasma and hence impinges on the substrate with considerable energy. However, the exposure of a freshly deposited film layer to an active gas is often sufficient to cause a reaction between them. Reactive sputtering can be used to deposit SiO_2 (silicon cathode, oxygen gas); however, its most common application to integrated circuits is in the deposition of Ta + N (tantalum nitride), using a tantalum cathode in a nitrogen atmosphere.

Gas Plating. Vapor-phase deposition consists essentially of reducing or decomposing a volatile metal halide such as aluminum chloride, or silane, so that a film of the metal is deposited on a heated substrate. The source compound should be capable of being readily broken up into its component atoms by dissociation or reduction at temperatures below the melting point of the film or of the substrate, but it must be stable enough to reach the deposition surface before decomposition takes place. A film made under these conditions at atmospheric pressure and at relatively high temperature frequently has better adhesion and stability than a film deposited by other methods at lower temperatures. The process has great flexibility, inasmuch as even semiconductor-type films can be deposited on the substrate by means of the interaction of reactive gases with other volatile compounds. The processes can be carried out in an apparatus made of Vycor* or Pyrex* glass, quartz, porcelain, or in some cases, stainless steel; the choice is dependent on the corrosiveness of the reactants. Two gas-plating methods are of special interest: hydrogen reduction and thermal decomposition.

Figure 13-8 shows the flow chart of a typical hydrogen reduction apparatus. Purified hydrogen is passed over a liquid metal halide (for example) which is heated to the temperature required to give the desired partial pressure of metal halide vapor. The gas mixture passes over the heated substrate in the plating chamber where the metal halide is thermally decomposed to the free metal plus halogen. The metal then deposits onto the substrate and reaction chamber walls. The effluent gases are condensed, the unused metal halides are recovered, and the waste gases are exhausted. With this process, films with any desired thickness up to 20 microns may be formed. For most systems deposition begins at a substrate temperature in the neighborhood of 600°C and proceeds at a slow rate. The rate of reaction increases with increasing temperature and can be regulated as conditions require. The normal operating temperature range is 750 to 1000°C. The substrate temperature has a pronounced effect on the nature of the deposit, which is fine-grained when deposited at the lower temperatures, and becomes coarser with increasing temperature. A high rate of gas flow produces more uniform films. Uneven plating can be

*Vycor and Pyrex are trade names of the Corning Glass Works.

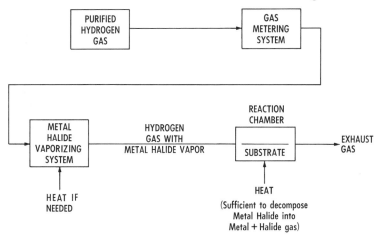

Fig. 13-8   Flow chart of a typical hydrogen reduction gas-plating apparatus.

caused by cracks and flaws in the substrate.   Good adhesion depends mainly on the purity of the gases used.   However, absorption by the film of gases which come from the walls of the plating chamber or from the reaction itself will also be detrimental. For more complex films, volatile organometallic compounds are used.   For example, $Al_2O_3 \cdot SiO_2$ dielectric layers are deposited from a mixture of triethylaluminum and tetraethylorthosilicate.   Reactions in gas plating take place from room temperature to 1200°C, with 300°C or below being a common range used for compatible thin-film elements.

The principles involved in thermal decomposition are the same as in the hydrogen reduction process, but argon replaces hydrogen as a carrier gas, and a liquid halide or a solution of the halide in water is sprayed onto the heated substrate.   Halides for doping can be mixed into the solutions, and thus the electrical properties of the film can be controlled.   The gas flow and the substrate temperature are important in the deposition of a uniform film.   Figure 13-9 shows a nozzle-type apparatus for thermal decomposition.

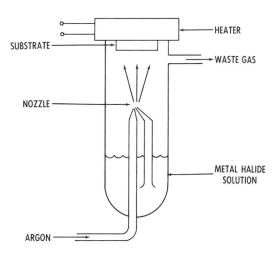

Fig. 13-9   Nozzle-type apparatus for thermal decomposition gas plating.

Electroplating.   Electroplating[3,4] is another process for coating an object with one or more relatively thin, tightly adherent layers of different metals.   An ionic compound such as the metal salt, copper sulfate, dissociates when dissolved in water into the divalent cation Cu^{++} and the divalent anion SO_4^{--}.   When we insert two copper electrodes into an aqueous solution of copper sulfate and connect them to a voltage source, the ions will transport an electric current through the electrolyte, and the following chemical reactions will take place:

At the cathode:

$$Cu^{++} + SO_4^{--} + 2e^- \longrightarrow Cu^0{\downarrow}(\text{deposited}) + SO_4^{--}$$

At the anode:

$$Cu^0 \text{ (electrode)} + SO_4^{--} \longrightarrow Cu^{++} + SO_4^{--} + 2e^-$$

This is a typical electroplating-bath reaction.   As can be seen, only the copper ions are affected by the passage of the electric current.   Faraday's law applies to the process.   Summarized and simplified, this law states: The weight of the metal deposited at the cathode or dissolved from the anode is proportional to the quantity of electricity and inversely proportional to the valence (the number of charges carried) of the metal ion.

The efficiency of the reaction can be influenced by various factors.   These factors are: (1) temperature (which changes the solubility of the salts), (2) the viscosity of the bath, (3) the current, (4) the size and stability of the crystalline deposit on the cathode, (5) agitation (which increases the transport of fresh ions to the cathode, permits an increase of current density, and removes gas bubbles from the anode), (6) concentration (which influences the conductivity of the bath and the rate of deposition of the plating), (7) polarization (which results from concentration changes in the bath near the electrodes), (8) overvoltage (which results from the formation of hydrogen on the cathode), (9) the pH of the solution, (10) the cleanliness of the cathode surface, and (11) the formation of pores and defects on the cathode (which can be caused by absorption of hydrogen).   All these conditions can be tightly controlled, and thin films of excellent adhesion and of any desired thicknesses can be deposited.

Electroless Plating.   In the electroless deposition of thin metal films,[5,6] a metal ion in solution is reduced to the free metal and deposited as a metallic coating without the use of an electric current.   The process may be used to deposit metals on any substrate, including glass, ceramics, plastics, etc., and films may be built up to a considerable thickness.   If properly performed, this process can yield a nonporous thin film of uniform thickness and density.   Electroless plating involves reduction (the gaining of electrons) of a metal ion by the simultaneous oxidation (an electron loss) of a chemical reducing agent.   For nickel chloride in an acid solution for example, and in the presence of a convenient reducing agent, such as the hypophosphite ion, there will be the following reactions:

Reduction: $Ni^{++} + 2e^- \longrightarrow Ni^0{\downarrow}$

Oxidation: $PO_2^{-3} + H_2O \longrightarrow PO_3^{-3} + 2H^+ + 2e^-$

Total: $\quad\quad \overline{Ni^{++} + PO_2^{-3} + H_2O \longrightarrow Ni^0{\downarrow} + PO_3^{-3} + 2H^+}$

To provide control of the rate at which this oxidation-reduction reaction proceeds, electroless plating solutions are formulated with the concentration of metal salt, the reducing agent, and the acidity such that the spontaneous reduction of the nickel is prevented. Plating is initiated by the use of catalysts which limit the plating reaction to preferred surfaces only.

If the metal to be deposited serves as its own catalyst, deposits may be built up as thick as desired. This "autocatalytic" effect is produced by nickel, cobalt, iron, copper, and chromium, and the metals of the platinum group. Where the metal being deposited does not have this autocatalytic property, rapidly decomposing plating solutions are employed. This is done in silver and gold plating. An effective reducing agent should have a positive standard oxidation potential, such as does the hypophosphite ion, and should work in a suitable acidity range. On nonreactive surfaces, *activators* (salts of certain heavy metals) may be introduced onto the surface to be plated. These are reduced to a very thin film of the free metal which then functions as the catalyst. On chemically active surfaces, the initial deposit will act as the catalytic surface.

A number of other bath additives are used, such as complexing agents, wetting agents, stabilizers, and buffers. The treatment of the surfaces before plating metallic and nonmetallic materials is quite important. Numerous procedures are available for roughening, cleaning, sensitizing, and activating the surface.

Silk Screening. The silk-screen process used in thin-film work is an adaptation of that used for years by printers and artists. An example of the use of silk screening for integrated circuits is in the preparation of the interconnecting and die bonding patterns on the ceramic substrate for hybrid integrated circuits, as shown in Fig. 13-10. All the areas of the screen except for the pattern to be deposited are blocked out on the screen. A 320-mesh stainless steel screen is used more frequently today than the classic silk screen. The screen is then placed in intimate contact with the ceramic substrate, and a thin layer of the *moly-manganese,* consisting of a mixture of powdered molybdenum and manganese metals typically in the ratio of 95 parts Mo to 5 parts Mn, suspended in a vehicle such as pine oil, is squeezed through the openings of the screen onto the ceramic substrate.

Fig. 13-10 A ceramic substrate for hybrid integrated circuits with the lands and interconnecting metallization prepared by silk screening techniques.

After the suspension has dried onto the substrate, it is fired in a damp hydrogen atmosphere at a temperature of 1400 to 1600°C. The exact temperature and time of firing depend on the type of ceramic used and the ratio of Mo to Mn used. Following the firing steps, the moly-manganese lands are electroless-nickel- and gold-plated by the processes discussed earlier. The gold-plated ceramic substrate is then ready to receive the silicon dice for the fabrication of the hybrid integrated circuit.

Resistive elements known as *cermets* may also be deposited by the silk screen method. The term cermet is derived from a combination of the words *ceramic* and *metal*. In practice, cermets are mixtures of highly conducting materials (i.e., metals) and insu-. lating materials (i.e., refractory oxides, glasses). Some examples of cermets in present-day usage are SiO + Cr; Ag + Pd + glass.

Complete thin-film circuits are also prepared on larger (typically 0.75 by 0.75 in.) ceramic substrates by very similar techniques. After the silk-screened moly-manganese lands have been prepared, Nichrome resistors and alumina or SiO_2 capacitors are fabricated on the ceramic substrate. Individual silicon dice are then die-bonded to the appropriate lands and interconnected by wire bonding (see Chap. 14). Finally the circuit may be encapsulated in a suitable plastic material or hermetically sealed in a manner very similar to that used for the flat package discussed in Chap. 15.

13-2 Modification of Thin Films

After the thin film has been deposited, it is usually necessary to perform additional operations on it in order to make it a useful circuit element. Perhaps the best-known film-modification procedure in integrated circuit work is the conversion of part of a tantalum film to tantalum oxide to serve as a capacitor dielectric.[7] This is accomplished by anodic oxidation, as illustrated in Fig. 13-11. Electrical contact is made to the tantalum film, which serves as the anode. An oxide builds up on the tantalum, stopping at a thickness determined by the applied voltage. A mild acid electrolyte,

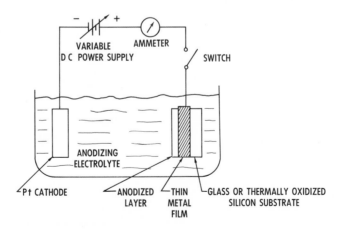

Fig. 13-11 Anodic oxidation apparatus for the formation of anodized thin films on metals.

such as acetic acid, is used. Typical anodizing conditions are in the neighborhood of 50 volts and 2 mA/cm², which can give a uniform, nonporous film.

13-3 Patterning of Thin Films

In order to become useful electronic circuit elements, it is necessary that the thin films be properly patterned. Perhaps the simplest patterning method is the silk-screen process discussed earlier, in which the deposition of the thin film and its patterning occur simultaneously. Physical masking used during evaporation has the same advantage. Photo resist, inverse photo resist, and inverse metal masking are also commonly used in the patterning of thin films.

Physical Masking. Physical masking, accomplished by placing a mask (usually a thin metal sheet with an etched pattern) between the evaporant source and substrate, is often used in vacuum evaporation. Since the evaporating material travels in straight lines, masking is sharp. The mask is placed very close to the substrate in order to minimize fuzzy or diffuse edges caused by the finite size of the source. Physical masking is limited as to the shapes of patterns which can be handled. For example, a circular opening with a solid center is impossible (unless two overlapping masks are used, generally requiring two separate evaporations). Also, intricate patterns are difficult with metal masks because of the fine, poorly supported regions that result. Fine metal masks are quite expensive, but, once made, their patterning efficiency is excellent. With repeated use, the openings in a metal mask are made narrower by the accumulation of evaporant, and it must be periodically cleaned. Metal masks are commonly used to pattern NiCr, SiO, and metal "interconnect" films in thin-film circuits.

Even where the material flow during deposition has poor directionality (sputtering, vapor plating, thermal spray decomposition), patterning can be obtained by placing the mask in contact with the substrate, but the definition so obtained is relatively poor when compared to that obtainable with other schemes.

Photo Resist. Photo-resist techniques are finding increasingly wide application to thin-film patterning. The direct photo-resist technique involves depositing a thin-film layer over the entire substrate, applying a coat of photo resist (usually KMER or KTFR is used) over the film, using a glass mask to produce a pattern of polymerized resist where the film is to remain, and etching the film away through holes in the photo resist where the film is not desired. This sequence of processes can be used only where the etchant used to remove parts of the deposited film does not attack the material (which may be the substrate or a different thin film) beneath the film, or react with the polymerized photo resist. Direct photo-resist patterning is commonly used with Al, SiO_2, SnO_2, $Al_2O_3 \cdot SiO_2$, and sometimes with Ta.

Inverse Photo Resist. Inverse photo-resist patterning is performed by placing the photo resist on the substrate and exposing and developing the photo resist in the conventional manner. Holes are thus formed in the photo resist where it is desired to have the deposited film remain on the substrate. The thin film is then deposited over the entire wafer. When the polymerized photo resist is removed from the substrate, it takes the overlying thin film with it, leaving a film pattern on the substrate corre-

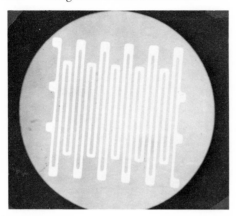

Fig. 13-12 Tapped Nichrome resistor patterned by means of inverse metal masking.

sponding to the openings that were present in the photo-resist pattern. This technique is used for materials which are difficult to etch without attacking the photo resist or substrate, such as gold and chromium. This method is limited to rather low substrate temperatures during evaporation to prevent deterioration of the photo-resist mask. Preevaporation cleaning of the exposed substrate regions must be done through (sometimes small) holes in the resist mask without damaging the resist, an often difficult job.

Inverse Metal Masking. Inverse metal masking requires depositing a metal film over the entire substrate, depositing a photo-resist layer over the metal and exposing and developing it, etching through the metal film a pattern corresponding to the openings in the photo resist, and removing the polymerized photo resist. The substrate is thus coated with a thin metal film with openings corresponding to the desired thin-film pattern. The desired thin-film layer is then deposited, and the metal masking layer etched off, taking the superimposed thin film with it. This technique is used successfully with NiCr. If the film is too thick, tearing at the edges during separation creates a ragged contour. Very fine definition, however, can be obtained with NiCr films several hundred angstroms thick, as shown in Fig. 13-12.

13-4 Adjustment of Thin Films

After deposition and patterning, thin-film elements are sometimes adjusted to make tighter tolerance units. For resistors, adjustment reduces the effective cross-sectional area, thereby increasing the resistance. It may be performed after contacting metal films are applied, and sometimes before, using probe contacts for measurement. Abrading away part of a resistor with a fine sandblast tool is usually effective for coarse geometries. Fine geometries can be mechanically modified by providing, in multiple parallel paths, fine-increment resistors, some of which may be scratched open to add slight increments to the total resistance.

Film resistors may be adjusted in value by anodic oxidation. Also, for some materials, simply heating in air can be performed with sufficient control to provide effective resistor adjustment. The surface oxides so formed are insulating, so that the effective resistor film thickness is reduced and resistance increases.

Capacitors can be adjusted (reduced in value) by reducing the area of the upper electrode. Although mild abrasion or etching can be used in some cases, it is usually necessary to make a revised upper electrode mask.

13-5   Contacts to Thin Films

One of the most difficult technological tasks connected with thin films in integrated circuits is making electrical contact to the thin-film element. The metal contact to a resistor must form a linear, low-resistance junction. The contact to a capacitor must form a low-loss interface. In active substrate structures, any contacts to the silicon (n-type or p-type) must be ohmic. This set of boundary conditions is, in itself, not too difficult to meet, but when we combine technologies to produce the more complex structures, then the same interconnecting metal film may have to establish satisfactory contact to a number of different elements, i.e., thin-film resistor, capacitor, and silicon.

It is comparatively easy to make good connections to the metal-alloy (e.g., NiCr) resistors with a metal such as aluminum, the main concern being that no oxide exists on the resistor where contact is desired. Actually, a thin oxide (which forms at room temperature on many metals) may be tolerated, provided the contact metal alloys through it when heated for adherence. Aluminum, which is an active metal, is excellent in this respect. Wide bandgap semiconductor resistors (e.g., SnO_2), however, can pose difficulties, especially when they are of high resistivity. Here a high-recombination interface sometimes provides a "barrier-free" contact. Care should be taken to avoid reactions between the contact-metal film and resistor film which, when heated during contact deposition or for adherence, may produce undesirable compounds that will prevent the contact from being ohmic. For example, Al on SnO_2 resistors can, when heated, react and produce an insulating Al_2O_3 interface, essentially opening the resistor. Thus it is necessary to insert an intervening layer of Ni metal between the SnO_2 and the Al. The Ni reacts with neither the Al nor the SnO_2, thus assuring that a stable contact is formed. SnO_2 thin-film resistors with Al contacts over Ni are shown in Fig. 13-13. Similar contact situations can occur with capacitors, the reactions sometimes producing a lossy layer which degrades the capacitor.

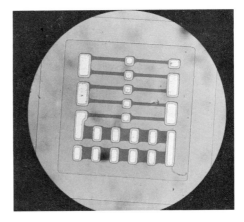

Fig. 13-13   Tapped SnO_2 resistor using aluminum contacts over nickel.

13-6   Substrate Preparation

The cleanliness of the substrate has a major influence on the ultimate performance of a thin-film device. Surface contamination manifests itself in pinholes which can cause open resistors or localized high resistances. In capacitors, pinholes may cause shorts or a poor adherence of the film. For this reason, a thin-film deposition should always be preceded by a careful cleaning procedure:

1. Gross contaminants are removed by solvent degreasing.
2. Tightly adherent organic contaminants are removed by ultrasonic agitation in detergent.
3. The detergent is removed by running water.
4. Traces of impurities are eliminated by treating with boiling deionized water.
5. Possible inorganic contaminants are etched away from the surface by acids.
6. Water vapor is removed by drying the substrate in hot filtered air and then baking it at 600°C or higher.
7. Subsequent contamination is avoided by storing the substrate in a dust-free container until the thin film is deposited.

A substrate should be free from scratches, cracks, fissures, or other imperfections. Imperfect surfaces will cause flaws and irregularities in the properties of the deposited films.

Most thin films of metals or oxides which have been freshly deposited or formed show some instability of resistance, both at room temperature and at elevated temperatures. These changes in electrical properties can be attributed to a structural imperfection acquired during the deposition process. These defects can be removed by a heat treatment for the purpose of annealing the structure.

The composition and thickness of a thin film determine its electrical and mechanical characteristics. Both properties can be controlled during processing by close control of the following: temperatures, pressures, concentrations, deposition rates, flow rates, purity of raw materials, geometrical configurations, and structure of the deposit.

13-7   Design of Compatible Circuits

Compatible thin-film circuit components should be considered when the silicon components alone will not perform the required monolithic circuit function. Monolithic circuit design is somewhat simplified by using thin-film components since no parasitic diode or transistor action is present. However, circuit fabrication is usually more complex because additional masking steps are required to produce either the thin-film resistors or capacitors.

Advantages of the thin-film resistor over a diffused resistor are:

1. Better frequency response
2. Improved tolerance
3. No need for compromise in monolithic transistor characteristics

The thin-film resistors have higher frequency response than diffused resistors for two reasons. One is the reduction of capacitance per unit area (0.09 to 0.2 pf/mil^2

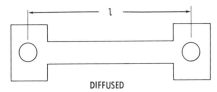

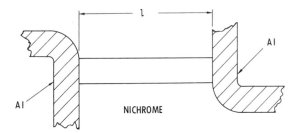

Fig. 13-14 Mask layout for Nichrome thin-film resistor as compared to the mask design for diffused resistor.

for a diffused resistor versus 0.03 pf/mil² for a thin-film resistor), and the other is the higher sheet resistance attainable in thin films (so that smaller areas are adequate for a given resistance value).   In some high-frequency circuits, the integrated circuit operation is further improved by the use of thin-film resistors since no compromise need be made in the transistor base diffusion to accommodate the production of the desired values of resistance.   High-frequency transistors require low r_b' which calls for a base sheet resistance of 100 ohms per square or less.   Frequently, however, a base sheet resistance of 200 ohms per square is used in the all-silicon integrated circuits in order to reduce the area necessary for the resistors, resulting in an increase in transistor r_b'.   The use of thin-film resistors eliminates the need for this compromise.

Mask layouts for thin-film resistors are usually not the same as for diffused resistors (see Fig. 13-14).   With Nichrome, for example, the contacts are made directly to the Nichrome film rather than through an opening cut in the silicon dioxide.   Thus, for the fabrication of compatible thin-film resistors it is necessary to use at least one additional mask.

Several additional steps involving masked etching may be required for thin-film capacitors where the complete capacitor is formed on top of the passivating film of the monolithic circuit.   The following operations are required as a minimum:

1. Masked etching to shape the bottom plate
2. Masked etching to shape the dielectric
3. Masked etching to shape the top plate

Thus, three additional masks are required in the fabrication of a thin-film capacitor over the passivating oxide layer of a monolithic integrated circuit.

13-8   Compatibility of Thin-film Circuits

The integrated circuit, including thin-film components, has certain high-temperature requirements placed upon it after completion.   Die bonding (which often takes place at temperatures exceeding 400°C) and wire bonding are necessary.

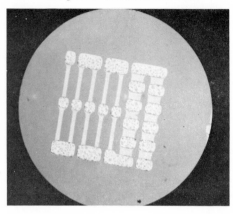

Fig. 13-15 Photomicrograph of a cermet resistor which has been aged at 450°C for 2 hours.

Packaging often requires high temperatures; flat packages are often sealed at temperatures between 400 and 500°C. After assembly and packaging are completed, high-stress tests at temperatures up to 500°C are necessary for reliability evaluation with a reasonable number of units in a reasonable length of time. Possible changes that occur upon exposure to high temperatures may be categorized into bulk, metallurgical, and surface effects. Changes within the bulk of a material may be, in most cases, ignored since they occur so slowly. Where they do occur (e.g., Au diffusion in Si), they are often well enough understood so that their effects during long-term high-stress aging may be calculated.

Metallurgical effects (i.e., effects pertaining to contacts and interconnections) can become very pronounced at high temperatures. Figure 13-15 is a photograph of a completed cermet resistor, with contacts, which has been aged for 2 hours at 450°C. Figure 13-16 shows the same unit after a very mild abrasion (rubbing with a cotton swab). The contacts have reacted with the cermet, creating a very crumbly compound, whereas the cermet material itself has been unaffected by the high-temperature cycle. The "purple plague" is a solid-state reaction that occurs between aluminum (metallizing) and gold (wire) upon extended heating at high temperatures (see Sec. 14-2). A similar reaction occurs between silver wires and aluminum. The two materials need not be in contact for gross metallurgical reactions to occur. In

Fig. 13-16 Photomicrograph of the same cermet resistor shown in Fig. 13-15 after rubbing with a cotton swab, showing degradation of the contacts.

Fig. 13-17 A gold wire with whiskers of silver growing from it. The silver was originally a thin film deposited elsewhere in the system, but apparently has been transported as the result of reaction with the atmosphere in the package.

the closed environment of a hermetically sealed package, vapor-phase reactions can occur. Figure 13-17 shows a gold wire with silver whiskers growing from it. The silver was originally a thin film deposited somewhere else in the system, but the (probably humid) gas in the package reacted with the silver to form a volatile compound, and deposited it on the gold wire. This is a cyclic reaction, so that a small amount of gas can move a large amount of material.

The advantages of a high-temperature-compatible metallurgical system for all types of integrated circuits are so great that a search was initiated for materials that do not undergo solid-state reactions with one another at elevated temperatures. Many systems were investigated simply by evaporating a film of one metal on top of another, and aging in various ambient gases at elevated temperatures. Figure 13-18a shows one metal film, evaporated in the pattern of a split ring with central spot, deposited on another metal on a glass slide. Figure 13-18b shows a change which is typical of many of the drastic solid-state reactions; it occurred during 300°C aging for a matter of hours.

These investigations showed that there are relatively few compatible metal systems. Since the metals have to be compatible with thin-film resistors and capacitors, silicon, and package leads (usually Kovar), the number of suitable systems is very limited. An all-aluminum system is the most convenient of these, and

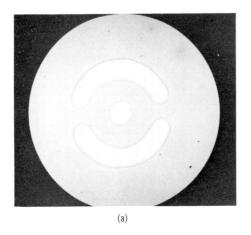
(a)

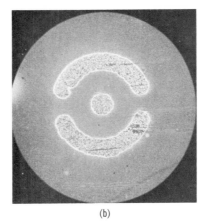
(b)

Fig. 13-18 (a) A metal film, evaporated in the pattern of a split ring with a central spot, deposited on another metal. (b) The same film as in a after several hours of aging at 300°C, showing a typical solid-state reaction.

(a)

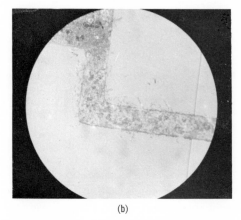
(b)

Fig. 13-19   (*a*) A complete high-speed MECL gate after 48 hours of aging at 500°C.   (*b*) A greatly magnified portion of the MECL gate shown in *a*, showing the reaction which occurs between the aluminum interconnection pattern and the SiO_2, limiting even this system to a long-term aging temperature of about 500°C.

is suitable for general use. An example of its capabilities (Fig. 13-19*a*) is a completely bonded high-speed MECL gate, shown after 48 hours of aging at 500°C. Figure 13-19*b* is a greatly magnified section of the aluminum interconnection pattern on the SiO_2 film, showing the slow reaction which occurs between these materials, limiting even this system to a long-term aging temperature of about 500°C.

13-9   Summary of Thin-film Processes

Table 13-2 gives a brief summary of some of the more common materials used for thin-film components and the methods of depositing these materials.

Figures 13-20 through 13-24 show some of the various circuits which have been prepared by thin-film techniques. These are only a few of the types which are possible by thin-film and compatible-thin-film techniques.

Table 13-2   Thin-film Materials and Processes

Application	Material	Process
Resistors	Nichrome	Vacuum evaporation
	SnO_2	Gas plating
	Tantalum	Sputtering
Dielectrics.	Al_2O_3	Gas plating, anodic oxidation of aluminum films
	Ta_2O_5	Anodic oxidation of tantalum film
	SiO_2	Gas plating, high-temperature steam oxidation, reactive sputtering
	SiO	Vacuum evaporation, reactive sputtering
Metallization on ceramic substrates . .	Nickel	Electroless plating
Plating on headers.	Gold	Electroplating

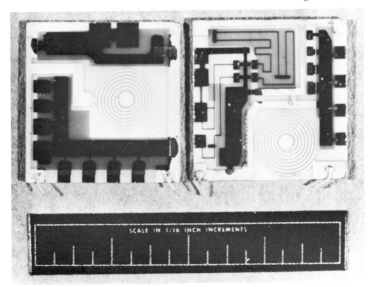

Fig. 13-20 A thin-film circuit with thin-film resistors, capacitors, and spiral inductors.

Fig. 13-21 A thin-film 2-Mc RF amplifier.

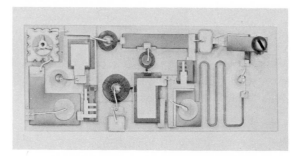

Fig. 13-22   A thin-film UHF tunnel diode mixer.

Fig. 13-23   A thin-film stair-step signal generator.

Fig. 13-24   A thin-film integrated circuit with attached elements, showing variable capacitors to permit tuning after package sealing.

REFERENCES

1. Javitz, A. E. (ed.), S. A. Halby, and L. V. Gregor: The Materials of Thin Film Devices, *Electro-Technol., New York,* vol. 72, pp. 95–122, September, 1963.
2. Bond, W. L.: Notes on Solution of Problems in Odd Job Vapor Coating, *J. Opt. Soc. Am.,* vol. 44, pp. 429–438, June, 1954.
3. Graham, A. K., and H. L. Pinkerton: "Electroplating Engineering Handbook," Reinhold Publishing Corporation, New York, 1955.
4. Blum, W., and G. B. Hogaboom: "Principles of Electroplating and Electroforming," 3d ed., McGraw-Hill Book Company, New York, 1949.
5. American Society for Testing Materials: Symposium on Electroless Nickel Plating, *ASTM Spec. Tech. Publ.* 265, 1960.
6. Saubestre, E. B.: Electroless Plating Today, *Metal Finishing,* pp. 67–73, June, 1962.
7. McLean, D. A., and F. S. Power: Tantalum Solid Electrolytic Capacitors, *Proc. IRE,* vol. 44, pp. 872–878, July, 1956.

14

ASSEMBLY PROCESSING

The fabrication of integrated circuits on semiconductor wafers represents only part of the total manufacturing process. Since each wafer may contain up to several hundred complete integrated circuits, these must be separated into individual dice, and each circuit or die must be individually packaged. These procedures constitute assembly processing. The package serves the combined functions of a heat sink (a heat-transfer path from the junctions to the surroundings), a means of interconnecting one circuit with another circuit or circuit element, and a means of protecting the circuit against chemical contamination and mechanical damage. The performance of any packaging scheme with respect to these factors must be weighed against requirements at hand. Additionally, consideration must be given in assembly processing to the metallurgical compatibility of the various materials used, and to the effect of parasitic elements added by the package on the electrical characteristics of the circuit.

14-1 Die Separation and Attachment

A number of schemes have been designed for cutting the large semiconductor wafer into individual chips or dice. A few of the more successful forms are these:

1. Scribing and cleaving: A diamond tool is used to cut lines into the surface of the wafer in a grid pattern. The wafer is fractured along these lines by flexure, producing dice (see Fig. 14-1).
2. Etch cutting: The dice are masked with wax or photo resist, and the regions between them are removed by etching.
3. Ultrasonic dicing: A plane metal tool with numerous holes having the shape of the desired dice is placed in firm contact with a silicon wafer which is bathed in an abrasive slurry. An ultrasonic transducer drives the tool and causes it to grind completely through the thickness of the silicon wafer, producing individual dice.

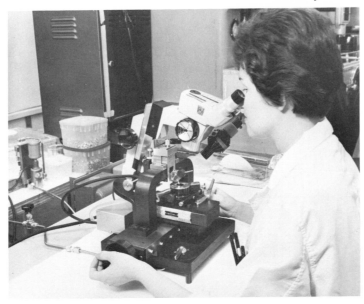

Fig. 14-1   Diamond scriber in operation.

Of these methods, the scribing and cleaving process is by far the most common for integrated circuits because of its relatively high speed and its freedom from waste.

Scribing and Cleaving. With this method, the finished wafer is placed on a vacuum chuck, which is capable of translation in both horizontal directions and rotation about a vertical axis. A diamond stylus loaded with a suitable weight is then drawn across the wafer to form a series of parallel lines between the circuit dice. After the entire wafer has been scribed in one direction, it is rotated 90° and the procedure is repeated (see Fig. 14-2). The wafer is then removed from the chuck, and the individual dice are separated by applying pressure to the wafer (Figs. 14-3 and 14-4). Finally, the finished dice are cleaned in a solvent such as trichloroethylene to remove scribing dust and other foreign matter which may have adhered to the surface. A comparison between a scribed die and one separated by the etch-cut method is shown in Fig. 14-5.

After cleaning, the die is ready for mounting in the package. In a monolithic circuit, the die normally requires no isolation from the package or header, even if the header is metallic, because the substrate of the monolithic circuit is always at the lowest circuit potential and is often grounded. In hybrid circuits, however, the individual circuit elements must be electrically isolated from one another and cannot be mounted directly on a common metallic base. This is normally accomplished by mounting the circuit elements on a thin ceramic wafer made of alumina or beryllia. To permit brazing or soldering of the dice to the ceramic, a metallic pattern of "lands" (Fig. 14-6), consisting of a molybdenum-manganese material, is first fired on the ceramic at a high temperature. These metallized lands readily accept a brazing alloy or solder and provide a suitably isolated base for each silicon die.

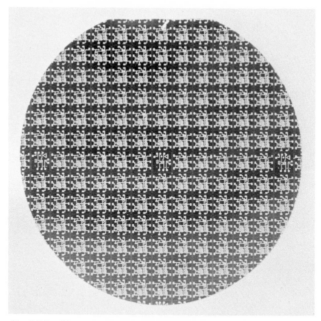

Fig. 14-2 Photomicrograph of an integrated circuit wafer which has been scribed with a diamond scribing needle.

Fig. 14-3 Dish of individual dice after fracturing of wafer.

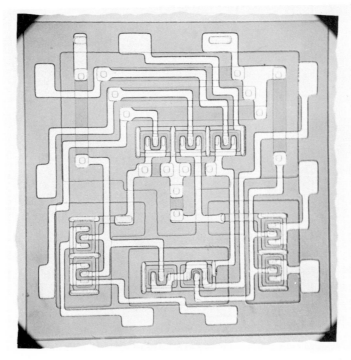

Fig. 14-4   Photomicrograph of individual integrated circuit die after fracturing of wafer.

Fig. 14-5   Comparison of etch-cut germanium die and scribed-fractured silicon die.

Fig. 14-6   Isolated header for hybrid integrated circuits.

Some typical packages utilized for today's integrated circuits are shown in Fig. 14-7. A more detailed discussion of package fabrication is given in Chap. 15.

Die Attachment. The attachment of the die to the package is usually accomplished by soldering, using a soft solder such as a lead-tin alloy, or by brazing, using a eutectic brazing alloy such as gold-germanium. The most commonly used eutectics are binary alloys (with perhaps trace quantities of other materials).

Use of a eutectic brazing alloy for die attachment is desirable because these alloys usually have a higher melting point than the so-called "soft" solders, and

Fig. 14-7   Some of the variety of packages available today for mounting of integrated circuits.

therefore, they produce a bond of high integrity at higher temperatures.   Moreover, it has been found that soft solders tend to fatigue upon extended thermal cycling, whereas the brazed joints appear to be relatively free from this problem. The disadvantages of the eutectic alloys are that they are generally expensive because they contain gold or some other noble metal, that they are quite brittle and difficult to form into unusual shapes, and that they cannot be vacuum-evaporated to form thin films.

Two differing basic methods are used to attach the die to its package.   One is the belt-furnace or continuous processing method, and the other employs the single-station die attachment machine.   The former method uses a furnace which consists of a long hollow tube surrounded by a suitably controlled heating element and containing a moving belt for conveying parts in and out of the hot zone

Fig. 14-8   Furnace for belt die bonding.

(Fig. 14-8). Riding on the belt are metal or graphite jigs (Fig. 14-9), which have been loaded with headers, brazing preforms, and dice. These jigs then progress through a furnace whose thermal profile has been designed to bring them up to the bonding temperature and then to cool them so that they can be safely handled (Fig. 14-10). The furnace is constructed so that an oxygen-free gas blanket or atmosphere can be maintained in the hot zone. Typically, hydrogen is used.

The single-station die attachment machine consists of an individually heated station in which a single header or package is placed (Fig. 14-11). The dice are picked up individually by an operator, using a mechanical micromanipulator, and are placed on the package for bonding. The operator can observe the operation directly through a microscope. A nonoxidizing gas blanket is maintained over the heated part, but in this case hydrogen cannot be used because of the danger of explosion. Figure 14-12 shows a cross section of a die-bonded die.

Each method has its own advantages and limitations. In the belt-furnace method, the production rate is extremely high because the operator is merely performing the loading and unloading of the furnace. Also, it is possible to use a hydrogen atmosphere, which always results in minimum oxidation of the constituent parts of the assembly. In the single-station method, however, it is possible to obtain much greater flexibility in the die attachment process because the operator has direct control over the placement of each part. This permits placement of the part in any position desired, so that dice which were imperfectly scribed can also be used providing they are electrically good. (Conversely, in the belt-furnace method a nearly perfect die is required to avoid hang-up in the jig.) In addition, in a single-station scheme, the time during which the parts are maintained at high

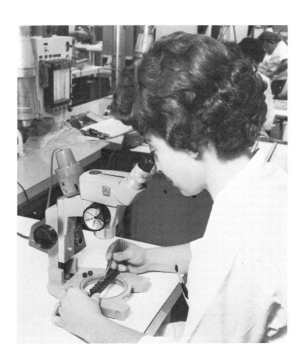

Fig. 14-9 Operator loading dice in die-bonding jigs.

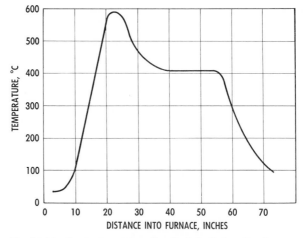

Fig. 14-10 Static thermal profile of a belt die-bonding furnace as a function of distance. The dice carried through the furnace on the belt at a constant speed are quickly heated by the high-temperature peak at about 23 in. They approach a temperature of 400°C as they move through this region, and then are held at this temperature for several minutes as they move from 40 to 55 in. through the furnace. During this time, the brazing takes place and the die is bonded to the header. As the die passes the 55-in. point, it begins to be cooled, and so by the time it emerges from the furnace it is cool enough to be handled.

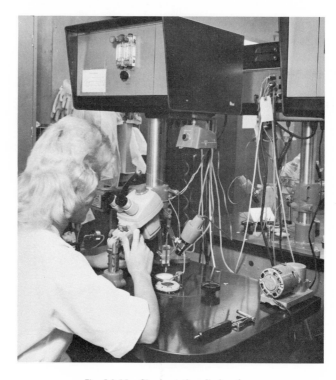

Fig. 14-11 Single-station die bonder.

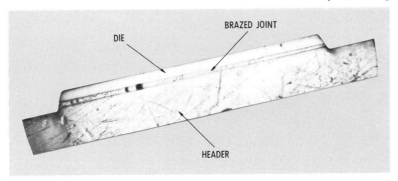

Fig. 14-12 Cross section of a die-bonded die.

temperature can be held to an absolute minimum because the operator controls the bonding operation directly and removes the part when a good bond has been achieved.

14-2 Lead Attachment

After the integrated circuit die has been attached to the package, it is necessary to make electrical connections between the ohmic-contact areas of the circuit and the package leads. In hybrid circuits it is also necessary to make electrical connections between the individual circuit elements.

Although semiconductor technology has developed a variety of ways of accomplishing this, the most commonly used method for integrated circuits today involves the bonding of extremely fine wires to the various areas to be interconnected, in a process which is known as *thermocompression* bonding.[1] This process involves the simultaneous application of heat and stress, and these lead to the deformation of at least one of the members being joined. A variety of bonding machines, including the so-called wedge bonders, nailhead or ball bonders, and stitch bonders, have been developed to accomplish thermocompression bonding.

Wedge Bonding. A typical wedge bonder is illustrated in Fig. 14-13. In the wedge-bonding procedure, the header containing the die-bonded die is mounted on a heated column and micropositioned so that the ohmic contact to which a lead attachment is desired is brought directly under a cross hair in the microscope. This cross hair has been previously aligned with the terminal position of a swinging hammer, or wedge, which is to do the bonding. After the contact area is positioned under the cross hair, a second micromanipulator is used to bring the wire from a wire feeder into the position over the ohmic contact. By pushing a button, the operator automatically brings the bonding wedge down upon the wire to attach it to the contact. The header is then manipulated so that the cross hair is over the lead on the package, and a second bond is made at this point. Figure 14-14 illustrates schematically the wedge-bonding procedure, and Fig. 14-15 shows a wedge-bonded transistor die.

Ball Bonding. In the nailhead or ball bonder a different principle of alignment is used (Fig. 14-16). In this machine the bonding tool consists of a capillary tube whose bore is slightly larger than the bonding wire to be used. The bonding wire is initially fed through this capillary. A flame is used to melt the end of the wire, to

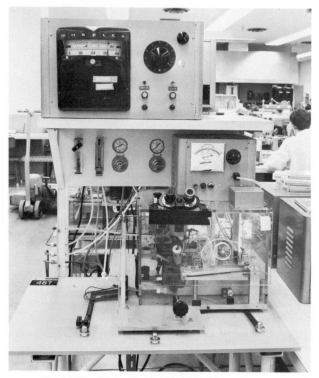

Fig. 14-13   Wedge bonder for lead wire attachment.

form a ball whose diameter is approximately twice that of the wire. This ball is then automatically drawn back snug against the end of the capillary, and the capillary is manipulated to the point at which bonding is desired. Then, in one continuous motion the capillary is lowered and zeroed in on the target, and the ball is firmly compressed against the contact area of the die, deforming the ball into a nailhead thermocompression bond. The capillary is then withdrawn an appropriate distance, and the flame is used to sever the wire and also to form a new ball.

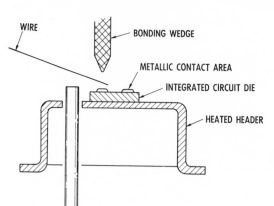

Fig. 14-14   Schematic representation of wire attachment by wedge bonding.

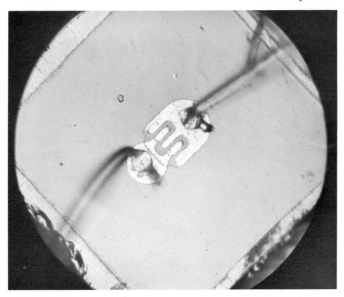

Fig. 14-15 An example of a transistor with wedge-bonded leads.

Thus, after the required bonds have been made on the circuit, the header is with-drawn from the bonder, and the bonded leads which are now free at one end are attached to the stems or leads on the package with a miniature hand-held resist-ance welder. This operation is often called *tweezer welding*. Figure 14-17 shows a ball bonder, and Fig. 14-18 shows a silicon power transistor with leads attached by ball bonding.

Each of these machines possesses certain advantages and limitations. With the wedge bonder, both bonds (to the semiconductor die and to the package) are made in the machine in direct sequence, eliminating the need for a second separate bonding operation. Also it is possible to hit much smaller contact areas in wedge bonding because the bond size is inherently smaller and because it is possible to use fine wires; capillaries for ball bonding with a bore less than 0.001 in. are diffi-

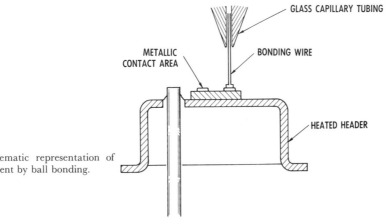

Fig. 14-16 Schematic representation of lead wire attachment by ball bonding.

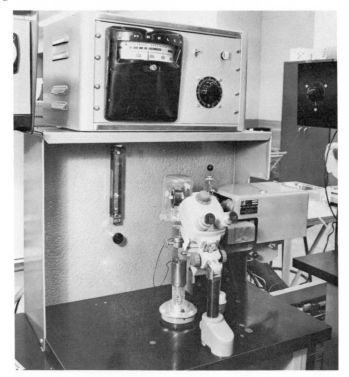

Fig. 14-17 A typical ball bonder.

Fig. 14-18 Silicon power transistor with leads attached by ball bonding.

cult to obtain and even more difficult to thread with fine wire. Thus higher-frequency devices can be fabricated using the wedge bonder. An additional advantage of the wedge bonder is that a larger spectrum of bonding wire types can be accommodated because it is not necessary to form a ball with a flame.

The ball bonder is essentially limited to the use of gold wire, since most other metals would be badly oxidized by the flame. On the other hand, the bond formed with a ball bonder is often sturdier because of its larger area. Also, the ball bonder does not require individual registration of the stripe, wire, and bonding tool during bonding. Thus it is not necessary to make as many adjustments in ball bonding as are required in wedge bonding.

Stitch Bonding. More recently, a new machine has come into widespread use. This new design, essentially a combination of the wedge and ball bonder concepts, is called a *stitch bonder* (Fig. 14-19). The stitch bonder promises to be the most versatile of all bonding machines. In principle it retains the capillary idea of the ball bonder, but bonding is done entirely without ball formation. The bonding wire is initially fed through the capillary and bent at a 90° angle. This 90° bend serves the same purpose as the flame-formed ball, in that it provides a metallic surface upon which the capillary edge can impinge to form a thermocompression bond. After a bond is formed, the capillary is withdrawn and moved to the next target. The bonding procedure is repeated at this point. If this is the last bond to be performed in the sequence, the capillary is withdrawn slightly and a scissorlike cutter is used to cut off the wire, leaving a new 90° bend. Thus the machine is now ready

Fig. 14-19 Operator using a stitch bonder.

for a new bonding sequence. It has been found that small wires can be used with this type of capillary, even though the bore size is generally large. Also there is no limit on the type of wire to be used because ball formation has been obviated. Finally, the desirable single-registration feature of the ball bonder has been retained. The minimum bonding-target size required for the stitch bonder lies between that of the wedge and ball bonders.

Metallurgical Compatibility. An important consideration in the lead attachment process is the metallurgical compatibility of the various constituents in the bonding system. This is especially important in silicon semiconductor systems where high-temperature operation and storage are important, for some bimetallic systems (i.e., gold-aluminum) are quite unstable at high temperatures, especially in the presence of certain other materials which may act as catalysts to compound formation. The gold-aluminum system, in particular, has stimulated considerable interest in the industry because of the widespread use of aluminum as a contact material for silicon and the great desirability of gold as a bonding wire on account of its ductility, electrical conductivity, and corrosion resistance. When gold and aluminum are placed in intimate contact, as in a weld or thermocompression bond, and the combination is heated to modest temperatures (greater than 200°C), chemical changes take place. These changes can be further complicated by the presence of silicon and oxygen. If a pure gold-aluminum system is heated to 300°C, a purplish material begins to appear at the interface between the two metals. This material has been analyzed and been found to be the chemical compound $AuAl_2$. This compound, which is a good electrical conductor and is strong mechanically, has been widely referred to as the *purple plague*.

Initially, it was felt that the $AuAl_2$ compound was responsible for the failure of bonds on silicon transistors metallized with aluminum, but it is now believed that this is not the case. To support this contention, an interesting experiment (Fig. 14-20) was recently described.[2] In the experiment a silicon wafer was heavily oxidized to form a thick layer of SiO_2. The SiO_2 layer was then removed from half of the wafer. Small aluminum hemispheres were placed over the entire wafer, and the system was heated beyond the melting point of aluminum (660°C). On the half of the wafer on which the oxide remained, the aluminum merely melted and resolidified. On the other half of the wafer, the aluminum alloyed into the silicon, changing the composition of the hemisphere to the aluminum-silicon eutectic composition, 89 per cent aluminum and 11 per cent silicon. (Figure 12-23 gives the phase diagram of the aluminum-silicon system.) After cooling, a thin film of pure gold was evaporated over the entire wafer. After this, the wafer was heated to 300°C for approximately 10 hr, and then cooled. A surface grinding operation was performed to cut through the gold film and halfway through the aluminum hemispheres. Upon examination of this section, it was found that on the side of the wafer retaining the oxide, the familiar purple phase existed. On the other side of the wafer a new white phase existed in addition. This white phase was analyzed and was found to be Au_2Al. Ostensibly, this new compound had formed in the presence of silicon as a catalyst. This compound was found to be a poor electrical conductor and was extremely fragile. Thus it is this *white plague* which is believed to be responsible for the failure of bonds.

(a)

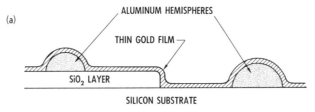

ALUMINUM HEMISPHERES

THIN GOLD FILM

SiO₂ LAYER

SILICON SUBSTRATE

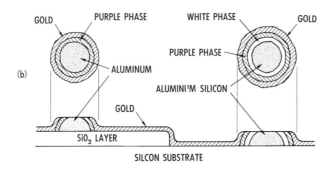

GOLD   PURPLE PHASE   WHITE PHASE   GOLD

PURPLE PHASE

(b)   ALUMINUM

ALUMINUM SILICON

GOLD

GOLD

SiO₂ LAYER

SILICON SUBSTRATE

Fig. 14-20 Summary of a definitive experiment on purple plague: (*a*) Cross section of specimen as originally prepared; (*b*) cross section of specimen after heating to 660°C. Both regions show the relatively strong and conductive purple phase. The brittle and resistive white phase has occurred where silicon was available. (*After Schmidt.*[2])

In order to circumvent these problems, there has been a general trend toward changing from the commonly used gold-wire-to-aluminum-contact-area bonding system to the more compatible aluminum-wire-to-aluminum-contact-area system. Today, the use of aluminum-alloy bonding wires is widespread in the industry. However, the suppliers of the fine bonding wires have found it necessary to intro-duce a trace of silicon into the aluminum melt in order to draw the wire to the fine diameters required. This means that when such aluminum wires are used for bonding to gold or gold-plated regions as on the package lead wires, there could be a plague problem. However, it has been found experimentally that the quantity of silicon in the wire is small enough that the white plague formation is usually negligible.

There are now in the developmental stages several methods other than wire bonding for making contact to the integrated circuit die. One of the more promising of these is a method in which brazed-clip contacts are used in place of the bonded wires. An experimental unit with brazed clips is shown in Fig. 14-21.

Fig. 14-21 Experimental integrated circuit with brazed-clip contacts.

14-3   Final Encapsulation

In the TO-18 and TO-5 packages commonly used for integrated circuits, total protection for the dice is provided by means of a hermetically sealed welded can, which completely surrounds the device. The devices and cans are generally baked out at a high temperature before welding, in order to drive off any solvents or other contaminants on the surface. They are then brought into a controlled-atmosphere dry box, and the cans are welded to the header, sealing in a portion of this controlled atmosphere. Figure 14-22 shows a bake-and-weld apparatus. Figure 14-23 is a cross-sectional photograph of a resistance weld or *hot weld*. It should be noted that it is necessary to use a hard metal or alloy for making a good resistance weld; hence a compromise of thermal conductivity may be necessary with a hot-welded package. The hot weld is an excellent seal; extremely low leak rates are easily achieved. However, it is important to recognize that certain substances can still diffuse through such a package, and further that it is never possible to remove all the contamination from the system before sealing. Just because a hermetic seal has been provided does not necessarily mean that the semiconductor die has been protected for all time from its surroundings. In addition to these considerations, it should be obvious that many forms of high-energy particles can easily penetrate the package and induce profound effects in the device.

Fig. 14-22   A typical bake-and-weld apparatus.

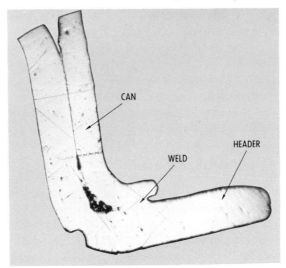

CAN

WELD

HEADER

Fig. 14-23 Cross section of a resistance weld, or hot weld.

In addition to the welded hermetic seal, it is also possible to form such seals by a combination of welding and brazing; however, it is not, in general, satisfactory to make the final seal a soldered or brazed joint because of minute blowholes that occur upon cooling of the system. The major portion of the seal can be a brazed joint, providing that an open tubulation is provided on the package. After cooling, the interior of the package can be evacuated or filled with some inert gas by means of the tubulation, with a final seal being achieved through pinching off or welding the tubulation.

Finally, it is also possible with certain materials, such as copper, to effect a *cold weld* seal by using tremendous pressures upon two adjacent pieces of material. Such cold welds are entirely satisfactory and can be fabricated with leak rates equivalent to those of the conventional hot-weld seal. Figure 14-24 is a cross-

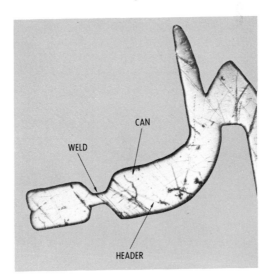

CAN

WELD

HEADER

Fig. 14-24 Cross section of a cold weld.

section photograph of a cold-weld seal. Cold-welded packages are often very desirable in devices requiring significant power dissipation because copper with its excellent thermal conductivity can be used throughout.

A very important new family of packages for integrated circuits employs ceramics and glasses which can be devitrified in a controlled way. These new methods have made it possible to achieve unorthodox package shapes with numerous leads and a new order of compactness. A popular flat-package example is described in detail in Chap. 15.

14-4 Parasitic Elements

Earlier in this chapter, means of providing electrical contact to the various areas of an integrated circuit were discussed. These connections also create certain parasitic elements (Fig. 14-25). The two most significant parasitics are inductance and capacitance. The shunt conductance of modern seals and feed-throughs, as well as the series resistance in the leads, is usually so low as to be negligible. However, it is very difficult to build leads which are large enough to carry the current required and long enough for easy fabrication, and yet which possess negligible inductance as required in high-speed switching circuits or high-frequency amplifiers. Such inductance results in a degradation of performance. Thus, the first aim in the design of a new package for high-frequency elements should be to keep leads as short as possible.

In addition to the parasitic inductances, there are shunt capacitances associated with the leads because of their proximity to one another, and because the space between leads is sometimes filled with a material of high dielectric constant. The loss factor of these capacitances can also become important at extremely high frequencies, which means that care should be exercised in the choice of the dielectric. Until recently the capacitance associated with feed-throughs and leads has not been an important factor in package design. However, with the advent of modern semiconductor devices of extremely small junction area, it is now often possible for the feed-through capacitance to approach and even exceed the junction capacitance. Thus the placement of the leads is an important factor in package design. Finally,

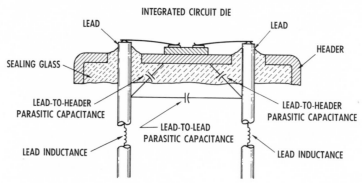

Fig. 14-25 Schematic representation of some parasitic electrical properties associated with packages.

it should be mentioned that some work has been done toward providing transmission-line packages for semiconductor devices. These have taken the form of coaxial or strip-line packages. With such techniques it should be possible to incorporate the inductance and capacitance into a transmission line with an attendant enhancement of high-frequency performance.

14-5 Thermal Considerations

For higher-power elements it is often imperative that the package also provide a good thermal path for heat transfer to the atmosphere or to an external heat sink. This consideration influences the electrical design of the package. A good example of this influence is the material for the ceramic substrate that serves as an insulated base for mounting the elements of a hybrid circuit to provide proper isolation. The ceramic must have practically zero electrical conductivity, but must have good thermal conductivity. The best materials known for this purpose are the ceramics, alumina and beryllia. When metallized, these materials possess a thermal conductivity between one-fifth and one-tenth that of copper. Copper is usually used as a reference because it is the best thermal conductor in common use.

An additional problem which occurs in the thermal design of a package is the fact that the thermal coefficient of expansion of silicon differs from that of many materials to which it is attached in the package. The largest disparity occurs between silicon and copper. If the semiconductor chip is small enough, it can be bonded directly to copper without ill effects. However, if the die is large, such a bond will nearly always result in fracture of the silicon, either during assembly or during thermal cycling of the finished parts. Thus, a thin piece of "buffer" material may have to be placed between the silicon and copper. Such materials as molybdenum and tungsten are suitable for this purpose. However, these materials are expensive and extremely difficult to handle. For this reason, special alloys such as Kovar* have been developed which match the thermal expansion coefficient of silicon quite well. Kovar may be used as a buffer or even as the actual package material if the ultimate in thermal conductivity is not required. Common TO-5 and TO-18 headers are made of this material.

REFERENCES

1. Anderson, O. L., H. Christensen, and P. Andreatch: Technique for Connecting Electrical Leads to Semiconductors, *J. Appl. Phys.,* vol. 28, p. 923, August, 1957.
2. Schmidt, R.: Mechanism of Lead Failures in Thermocompression Bonds, *IRE Trans. Electron Devices,* vol. ED-9, p. 506, November, 1962.

* Kovar is a trade name of Westinghouse Electric Corporation.

15

INTEGRATED CIRCUIT PACKAGING

A suitable package for an integrated circuit must satisfy a series of difficult and partially conflicting requirements. It must be strong enough mechanically to withstand the stresses occurring during assembly, during connection to other packages, and during use. Yet it should be small and of a shape which permits stacking or some other kind of compact aggregation. Obviously it has to provide easily established and reliable electrical connection from the circuit inside to the outer world. In spite of the high packing density of the conductors enforced by small overall dimensions, parasitic inductance and capacitance must be held to a minimum. The electrical insulation of many elements is of course a rudimentary requirement, and yet the thermal resistance from the circuit to its outer environment should be as low as possible. The package must maintain an interior environment which is stable and congenial to the circuit. The package is usually called upon to shield the circuit from light, and occasionally from magnetic fields. Realistically, the package is usually not called upon to shield the circuit from nuclear radiation. But one of the significant fringe benefits of the remarkably small size of integrated circuit systems is that effective external nuclear-radiation shields are now feasible, where weight or cost ruled them out before.

Two basic packages are currently in wide use for integrated circuits. One is the comparatively new flat package, and the other is a multileaded TO-5 package. The latter is of course a modification of a well-established transistor package. Figure 15-1 compares one version of each of these two package types in terms of their outlines and important dimensions, and Fig. 14-7 provides a further comparison of appearance. This photo shows flat packages of the 10-lead and 14-lead varieties and of differing sizes.

These two major package types perform basically the same function, of course. Their most obvious difference has to do with compactness, and so a brief quantitative comparison is in order before we proceed to a consideration of sealing and of the fabrication of both. One of the common flat packages has a ceramic body, which

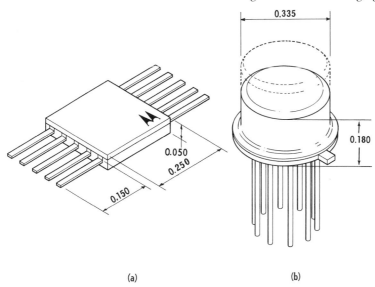

Fig. 15-1   A comparison of the (*a*) flat package and (*b*) the 10-lead TO-5 package in appearance and outer dimensions.

measures 0.250 by 0.250 by 0.050 in., cover included.   Its leads are 0.004 by 0.015 in. in cross section and a minimum of 0.150 in. in length, and are positioned on 0.050-in. centers.   These packages can be mounted on both sides of a printed-circuit board. In this way one of the standard 4 by 5 by 0.060-in. boards can accommodate 320 flat packages.

TO-5 packages, on the other hand, can be mounted only on one side of a printed-circuit board because of their plug-in nature.   Hence a single board will accept only 130 packages.   (The major diameter of the TO-5 package is 0.362 in.)   We have noted that there are some variations in the designed size of both packages, and in order to compare volume packing density it would of course be necessary to specify all dimensions.   However, as a rule of thumb it is usually considered that the flat package gives advantage in compactness of 5 or 6 to 1.

15-1   Package Sealing

A wide variety of materials which could be considered for package fabrication are in themselves sufficiently impervious to moisture and gases to meet the most stringent requirements.   (Unfortunately, most plastic materials are not among these.) Still there remains the problem of joining these materials in truly hermetic fashion. Metals can be joined to other metals by soldering, brazing, and hot or cold welding (see Sec. 14-3).   Glasses can be sealed to each other by fusing them at high temperatures, or by cementing them with a lower melting glass.   Glasses and metals can also be joined successfully, but the problem is more difficult.   Basically this is true because most ordinary glasses have low coefficients of expansion and are poor thermal conductors, whereas most ordinary metals have large coefficients of expansion and are good conductors.   Hence the heating rates of the glass and metal portions tend to be unequal, and the expansion coefficient mismatch causes trouble.   However, the development of alloys with low expansion coefficients has made it possible to fabricate matched seals even with comparatively *hard* glasses (those with high melting points).

Matched Seal with Oxide Buffer.   A widely used type of glass-to-metal seal employs a metal-oxide layer as a buffer between the glass and the metal.   This thin, controlled layer is formed on the metal parts before sealing the glass to them.   During the sealing operation the outer surface of the metal-oxide layer dissolves into the glass surface, forming a continuous transition from metal, to metal oxide, to metal oxide dissolved in glass, to glass.   In this way the metal-oxide buffer makes possible a continuous gradation in composition from metal to glass.   This situation is shown schematically in Fig. 15-2.   Since metal oxides are more porous to gases than the metals themselves, the thickness of the oxide layer must be kept small.   If the layer is too thin, however, it may dissolve in the glass, eliminating the buffer and producing a leaky seal.   Hence the oxide-layer thickness is a critical matter.

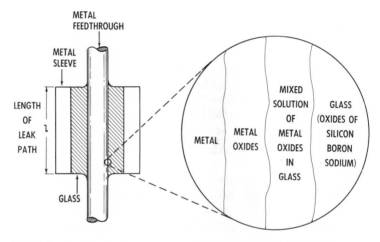

Fig. 15-2   A schematic representation of a glass-to-metal seal, showing the continuous transition from metal, to metal oxide, to metal oxide dissolved in glass, to glass.

Solder-glass Seal.   Where sealing temperatures must be kept below 700°C, a *soldering* technique is usually used.   This technique involves the use of another material (a special-composition glass with a low melting point) sandwiched between the parts to be joined.   Upon heating, this special glass melts and wets the two surfaces, much as solder wets and joins two pieces of metal.   Because of this analogy, such glasses are called *solder glasses*.

There are several types of solder glasses but the *devitrifying* type such as Pyroceram* solder glass is normally preferred for integrated circuit packaging.   Such a glass wets and seals to glass, metals, and ceramics.   It produces seals at temperatures below 500°C and has high mechanical strength.   It is an excellent electrical insulator but still has good thermal conductivity.   And it produces hermetic seals capable of passing all environmental tests now required for integrated circuit packaging.

*Pyroceram is a trade name of Corning Glass Works.

The devitrifying solder glass might be compared to a thermosetting plastic because the glass, after heat treatment during sealing, may be reheated to a reasonably high temperature without melting. This type of glass is available with a wide range of expansion coefficients to match a greater range of glasses, ceramics, and metals than do the vitreous glasses. It also has much greater strength through the combined effects of the glassy matrix and the dispersed crystalline phase which results from the heating process.

When a devitrifying solder glass is heated to accomplish sealing, it first goes through a molten glassy stage and flows well, wetting ceramics or other glasses and metal leads. This of course contributes to a strong seal. On further heating, the glass begins to devitrify, or crystallize. Crystallite size depends on time and temperature; size increases as time and temperature are increased.

A devitrified seal owes its strength to this crystalline structure. With such a seal it is possible to bend the leads more violently without failure than with a vitreous (glassy or noncrystalline) seal. Such treatment of a vitreous seal produces cracks which establish a continuous leak path through the glass. But corresponding treatment of a devitrified seal causes *shaling,* or the generation of microcracks which terminate on crystallites and do not pass entirely through the seal.

By regulating the crystalline content of the solder glass through time and temperature adjustment, it is also possible to regulate its coefficient of expansion. The coefficient of expansion is of course the relative change in length per centigrade degree. In the glass-to-metal-seal industry it is customary to quote as the coefficient of expansion for a given material the average value exhibited by the material in the range from 0 to 300°C. The starting glass in the seal discussed below in connection with the flat package has a coefficient between 80 and $90 \times 10^{-7}/C°$, whereas the final glass can be made to fall anywhere from 40 to $120 \times 10^{-7}/C°$. Thus the coefficient for solder glass can be adjusted to fall between those of the materials being joined, yielding an optimum seal.

As indicated above, the devitrifying solder glass is strongly favored for integrated circuit work, but at least two other types should also be mentioned. One of these is the vitreous solder glass. This is simply a glass with a low melting point which can be applied to a junction between a metal and a high-melting-point glass to effect a seal at moderate temperatures. It is necessary for the metal and glass to be well matched in expansion coefficient in order to join them successfully with a vitreous solder glass. Further, the resulting seal is comparatively weak.

A third solder glass is the conductive type. This is a devitrifying glass recently developed by the Kimble Glass Company. It is intended to provide both a seal and a low-resistance electrical path between component parts. The processing of this glass is quite critical, but good seals can be obtained if sufficient care is exercised.

15-2 The Flat Package

Developed specifically for integrated circuit applications, the flat package has proved to be efficient and reliable. Figure 15-3 shows an assembled view and an exploded view of one version having 14 leads. This may be compared with the assembled view of the 10-lead version shown in Fig. 15-1a. Typically the flat

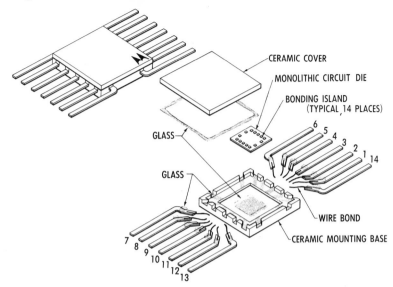

Fig. 15-3 Exploded view of the 14-lead version of the flat package, showing the various components as well as the completed flat package.

package consists of a square or rectangular enclosure made of an alumina ceramic. Typically this material contains 94 per cent Al_2O_3, with the rest being MgO and SiO_2. The enclosure is fitted with peripheral ribbonlike leads made of a low-expansion metal such as Kovar* alloy, which consists primarily of iron, nickel, and cobalt, or Sealmet* alloy, which consists primarily of iron, nickel, and chromium. The sealing agent for bonding the leads to the body and for final closure is a solder glass of the devitrifying type. (Sealing the leads with hard glass is also possible, but this choice poses additional technical problems.) Table 15-1 gives the composition of a typical solder glass which may be used for this purpose.

Flat-package Assembly. At the initial assembly stage the flat package (Fig. 15-3) consists of only three parts, and this fact greatly facilitates the assembly operation. The leads are all common initially by virtue of a surrounding frame (not shown). This one-piece lead clip is of course stamped out of alloy sheet. The lower portion or body of the ceramic enclosure is castellated so that the lead clip fits it in self-jigging fashion.

The solder glass is in a powdered form and is suspended in a liquid carrier for ease and accuracy of application. It is applied to the recesses in the body, the clip is dropped into place, and a little more solder glass is applied on top of the lead. Sealing can be accomplished by heating the assembly in air, oxygen, nitrogen, argon, or helium. A typical schedule calls for 440°C for one hour.

It was noted above that the expansion coefficient of the solder glass can be regulated through adjustment of the time-temperature schedule. Ideally it should be

---

* Kovar is a trade name of Westinghouse Electric Corporation, and Sealmet is a trade name of Allegheny Ludlum Steel Corporation.

made to fall between that of the ceramic body ($79 \times 10^{-7}/\text{C}°$) and that of the lead metal (Sealmet alloy, for example, is $89 \times 10^{-7}/\text{C}°$).

The next step in flat-package fabrication is lead trimming, which eliminates the surrounding frame. The leads then have the appearance presented in the assembled views (Figs. 15-1 and 15-3). At this point the package is ready to receive an integrated circuit.

Monolithic Die and Lead Attachment. A monolithic circuit is attached within the ceramic body by means of the same solder glass used for lead sealing. The coefficient of expansion of silicon is 76×10^{-7} versus $79 \times 10^{-7}/\text{C}°$ for the ceramic, and this close matching aids in the formation of an extremely adherent bond. Tests show that the silicon or ceramic will shatter before the devitrified solder glass will fail.

There are several methods for establishing contact from the package leads to the silicon integrated circuit. One of the most widely used involves simply stitch-bonding (see Sec. 14-2) a one-mil aluminum wire from the terminal bonding island or pad on the circuit to the inner end of the corresponding package lead. Note in Fig. 15-3 that the package body has a shelf for supporting the inner ends of the package leads during wire bonding.

In an alternative approach, the package leads are made slightly longer internally so that they lap over the silicon die. The package leads are then bonded directly to the integrated circuit. This is sometimes called the "contact-bond" system.

Both the wire-bond and contact-bond arrangements are facilitated by providing the package leads with aluminum-clad inner ends. This has been achieved in very satisfactory fashion by rolling an aluminum wire under appreciable heat and pressure down the center of the virgin metal strip from which lead clips will later be punched. This kind of operation is known in the metal-parts industry as *cladding*. In this way an all-aluminum bond system is generated for either the wire-bond or the contact-bond arrangement, and purple plague is avoided (see Sec. 14-2).

Hybrid Die and Lead Attachment. The devitrified-solder-glass method of die attachment is usually not applicable for hybrid dice. It can be seen in Part 2 of this volume that one usually has to make electrical contact to the back surface of a hybrid die. For this reason, for hybrid applications a pattern of metallic bonding islands and interconnections is placed on the inner bottom of the ceramic body.

A useful metallizing material is a suspension of powdered molybdenum and manganese in a liquid vehicle. This can be permanently bonded to the ceramic in a firing operation—typically 30 min at 1475 to 1525°C in hydrogen. This metallizing procedure is known in the industry as the *moly-manganese* technique.

Table 15-1   Composition of a Representative Solder Glass

	Per cent
PbO	58
B_2O_3	12
SiO_2	20
ZnO	8
Other	2

Once fired, the metallic pattern is plated by the electroless gold technique; dice are then attached by a gold-eutectic brazing procedure. (The gold-germanium eutectic alloy is usually preferred for such operations.)

At this point the integrated circuit, whether monolithic or hybrid, is checked electrically. Finally, then, the ceramic cover is attached with the devitrifying solder glass by firing in a controlled atmosphere. In this manner the flat package is hermetically sealed.

Finally, the external leads are plated with an electroless gold solution developed especially for this package. Standard electroless and electrolytic gold-plating procedures attack the seal in a way that sometimes causes leaks. The special procedure employs a weakly acidic aqueous solution and produces a fine hard-gold finish. This operation completes the fabrication of an integrated circuit in the flat package.

15-3 The TO-5 Package

The 10-lead TO-5 integrated circuit package is an adaptation of the well-developed TO-5 transistor package. The transistor package has three or four leads positioned on a 0.200-in.-diameter pin circle. For the integrated circuit application this diameter has been increased to 0.230 in. to accommodate 10 leads.

Figure 15-4 presents an exploded view of the 10-lead TO-5 package and integrated circuit. The package consists of ten 0.019-in.-diameter leads each 0.750 in. long, a glass preform, an eyelet with 10 holes, and a can with a weld flange. Typically the leads and eyelet are made of Kovar alloy, and the can is made of Kovar alloy, nickel, or german silver (an alloy of copper, zinc, and nickel). The preform is made of Corning 7052 glass, which is in the borosilica family.

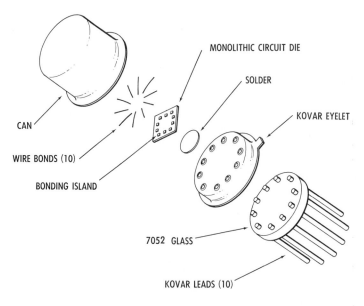

Fig. 15-4 Exploded view of the 10-lead TO-5 package and integrated circuit.

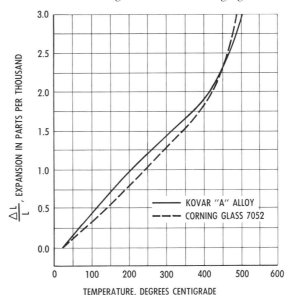

Fig. 15-5 Thermal expansion curves for Kovar "A" alloy and Corning 7052 glass. (*Courtesy of The Carborundum Company.*)

A glass and a metal are considered compatible if the difference in their coefficients of expansion does not exceed $4 \times 10^{-7}/C°$. The expansion coefficient of Kovar alloy is 47×10^{-7} and that of Corning 7052 glass is $46 \times 10^{-7}/C°$, and so these materials are indeed well matched. Figure 15-5 presents thermal expansion curves for these two materials in the range from room temperature to 500°C.

The oxide-buffer principle, described in Sec. 15-1, is applied here to accommodate the slight remaining difference in expansion rates and ensure a good hermetic bond. To this end, the Kovar alloy is preoxidized in a controlled manner before the sealing operation. Control is exercised through weight-gain measurements and by sealing in a neutral atmosphere. Sealing is done with a graphite boat or jig at a temperature of approximately 1000°C.

After sealing, the *header,* as the lead and eyelet assembly is known, is cleaned. Then the leads are clipped to the desired length. The outer lead length is normally 0.300 in. The inner post height will depend on the number of circuits to be placed in the package. As Fig. 15-1*b* suggests, the height of the can employed is varied according to need. Sometimes as many as four circuits, suitably mounted on ceramic wafers, are placed in a single TO-5 package in a stacked arrangement. Finally, the header is plated with gold. Normally this is done electrolytically in a cyanide bath to a plating thickness of 100 μin.

Die and Lead Attachment. Monolithic circuits are normally brazed to the header with a gold-eutectic preform. Circuit-to-header-lead connections are then made with 0.0007-in.-diameter gold wire by one of the thermocompression bonding methods described in Sec. 14-2. Figure 5-1 shows a monolithic circuit on a TO-5 header, complete except for final closure.

In the hybrid case, a thin alumina or beryllia ceramic wafer is attached to the header first. Before mounting, the wafer is metallized with moly-manganese by means of a process described above for the flat package. This provides mounting islands for the hybrid dice and suitable interconnections of these islands. Normally the wafer is also metallized on its bottom surface so that it can be mounted readily on the header, again by brazing with a gold-eutectic alloy. Figure 14-6 shows a TO-5 header with a metallized ceramic wafer in place.

Once the metallized wafer has been mounted on the header, hybrid dice are brazed in position, again with a gold-eutectic material. All remaining interconnections are completed by thermocompression wire bonding, and the circuit is checked electrically. Figure 5-2 shows a completed hybrid assembly on a TO-5 header, ready for final closure. The integrated circuit, monolithic or hybrid, is then closed by resistance-welding a can in place in a controlled atmosphere, and this completes its fabrication.

15-4   Package Testing

Packages in process must be tested in order to monitor their integrity and reliability. The tests outlined below are described for the flat package. Analogous tests (and in some cases such as leak checking, identical tests) are applicable to the TO-5 package; since the TO-5 is an older package whose properties are quite generally known, we have chosen to place emphasis here on flat-package testing.

For testing purposes, samples are extracted from the line at various stages of package assembly processing. For example, samples of the incoming ceramic boxes are assembled empty and are checked for leaks. Identical tests are also performed on sample quantities of completed integrated circuits. Though some of the tests are nondestructive it is not common practice to do 100 per cent testing, because it is not economically justifiable in view of the comparatively low failure rates which have been achieved.

Hermetic Seal. The metals, glasses, and ceramics used in integrated circuits packaging are for practical purposes impervious. The same cannot be said, however, of the junctions or seals between these materials. Hence we apply quantitative interpretation to the word *hermetic,* which in everyday language means airtight in an absolute way. According to one quantitative definition, a good hermetic seal will not permit more than one cubic centimeter of helium gas to leak through a seal in 30 years, with an applied pressure difference of one atmosphere. This is slow leakage indeed, and hence special techniques have been developed to meet testing needs.

One such technique employs the helium leak detector, which is basically a mass spectrometer set to maximum sensitivity for the detection of helium. The package under test is immersed in helium under a pressure of 60 psi for one hour and helium is permitted to leak *into* the package. The package is then transferred to a mass spectrometer chamber which is then evacuated. If helium has leaked into the package during the pressure cycle, some of it will now leak out of the package into the spectrometer vacuum chamber where it can be detected and measured. To make this requirement seem more feasible we may note in passing that the leak rate just named (1 cm^3 per 30 years) corresponds to 10^{-8} cm^3/sec or 3 billion atoms/sec!

A second test employing a radioactive tracer is somewhat similar to the helium test. It uses a gaseous radioactive compound, or radioactive krypton gas. The package is immersed in the radioactive medium, again under a pressure, and is removed after an interval; the exterior is washed free of absorbed radioactivity. The package is then placed in a radiation detector where the radiation count it produces is a measure of the amount of radioactive material leakage.

In a third method, the dye test, the package is immersed in a dye solution under pressure, after which the exterior is washed free of excess solution. Examination then reveals any cracks and holes where the dye may have become trapped.

Each technique has its advantages and limitations. The helium leak test, for example, is nondestructive in that any helium remaining inside a package will have no effect on the device. The radioactive gas and dye tests could have an adverse effect on the device, even if the amount of gas or dye that enters the package is acceptable from the standpoint of leakage. Very large leaks, on the other hand, may be overlooked in the helium test if they are large enough to permit rapid evacuation of *all* the helium in the package during the evacuation period.

Thermal Shock. Temperature is changed quickly from room temperature to 125°C and is held there for at least 15 min, permitting the package to achieve thermal equilibrium. The package is then returned to room temperature and is held there for not more than 5 min. It is then taken to −55°C and held there for at least 15 min, and then returned to room temperature for not more than 5 min. Fifteen such cycles are completed. After this, the normal leak checks are carried out to see whether the seals have suffered in this process.

Lead Fatigue. The package leads are deflected approximately 45° by a force of 8 ± 1 oz. This is done three times, and once again the package is checked for leaks.

Soldering. The device must withstand the immersion of the leads for 10 sec in molten metal to a point 0.015 in. from the body of the device. No flux can be used. The temperature of the molten metal must be 260 ± 5°C.

Other Tests. There are "brute force" tests of seal and package integrity. In one, a 0.200-in.-diameter point is pressed against the top or bottom of the package which is mounted on a flat plate, and force is increased until the package breaks. The stress at failure, translated into equivalent uniform loading, should be in the 300- to 800-psi range.

In another test, air pressure is suddenly applied to a peak of 80 psi. This is gauge pressure, and in view of the fact that the package interior is well below atmospheric pressure, the effective stress value on the package is about 90 psi. Ceramic flat packages withstand this test very well, though some of the older kinds of flat packages did not.

Finally, the package is inspected visually for satisfactory general appearance. The gold plating on the leads is particularly scrutinized. It must show no peeling or blistering, and there must be no evidence of corrosion on the body of the lead. Then there are certain specific requirements on the plating which go beyond satisfactory general appearance:

The package leads must be gold-plated from the ends to within 0.010 in. from the device body. The plating must have a minimum thickness of 50 μin. and must be at least 99.5 per cent gold composition by weight.

15-5 Thermal Design Considerations

The problems associated with adequate thermal design for systems utilizing integrated circuits are basically the same problems that exist in systems employing conventional components. Heat is dissipated by the circuit elements and must be transferred to some ultimate sink without excessive temperature rises. The integrated circuit manufacturer establishes the maximum allowable internal temperatures based on performance and reliability considerations. These maximum temperatures along with the system thermal resistances, total heat load, and ultimate sink temperature establish the boundary conditions for the overall thermal design. As an introduction to these problems, it will be worthwhile to review briefly some of the basic physical factors involved in them. For those who want additional basic information, general treatises are available[1-3] as well as more specialized discussions.[4-14]

Heat-transfer Fundamentals. Heat may be transferred by three mechanisms: conduction, convection, and thermal radiation. Conduction is the transfer of heat by direct molecular communication without appreciable displacement of the molecules. It involves transfer within some medium—gas, liquid, or solid. It is the only mechanism of heat transfer within opaque solids. Convection is the primary means of heat transfer between a solid surface and a fluid in contact with it. The term *convection* is a catch-all for the combined action of fluid conduction, energy storage, and mixing which actually occurs. Thermal radiation is energy transfer by means of electromagnetic radiation falling in the wavelength region from 0.1 to 100 microns. Radiation is the only mode of heat transfer between bodies separated by a vacuum. Almost every real heat transfer situation involves at least two of these foregoing modes.

In general, for a given temperature difference more heat can be transferred by conduction than by any of the other mechanisms. If one were developing a packaging technique that would be most efficient from a thermal standpoint, every effort would be made to utilize conduction as a primary heat transfer mode. This has been done, for example, in the design of power-device packages where large base areas, stud mounts, and other similar techniques are used. The same approach is being taken with integrated circuits.

Table 15-2 Thermal Conductivity of Some Materials Important to Integrated Circuits

Material	Thermal conductivity K_t, watts/$C°$ in.
Copper	9.86
Beryllium oxide	5.28
Aluminum	5.15
Silicon	2.12
Aluminum oxide	0.505
Kovar alloy	0.424
Glass (borosilicate)	0.0277
Epoxy laminate	0.007

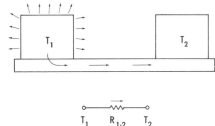

Fig. 15-6 Pictorial analogue of heat flow, depicting thermal resistance.

For each mode of heat transfer, certain material properties and configuration details govern the rate of transfer for any given temperature difference. For conduction the thermal conductivity is the governing property, and typical values for materials of interest are shown in Table 15-2.

Convection processes are predominantly dependent upon fluid properties such as density, viscosity, specific heat, and thermal conductivity. Radiation is basically a surface phenomenon so that the texture, "finish," and configuration of the surfaces control the rate of radiative transfer for a given temperature difference.

An electrical analogy is often used for treating a heat transfer problem. Voltage is analogous to temperature, and current is analogous to heat-flow rate. The ratio of temperature difference to heat-flow rate then is called *thermal resistance*, again by analogy. It is usually expressed in centigrade degrees per watt. One usually deals with a lumped thermal resistance which is the net result of a complex combination of thermal paths in series and parallel. Figure 15-6 presents the analogue pictorially.

Heat Transfer within the Silicon Die. All the heat is dissipated by the active and resistive elements on the top of the silicon die. These heat sources are quite localized, with the exact distribution depending on the particular circuit type. Calculations to date indicate that the intra-die gradients are very small. Silicon is a good conductor so that the dissipated heat is well diffused throughout the die. One example was analyzed with computer techniques for 2 watts dissipated in an area measuring 0.002 by 0.020 in. on a die measuring 0.040 by 0.040 in. The maximum temperature difference within the silicon was 15 C°. On this basis, the entire die can be considered essentially isothermal.

Thermal Resistance of Integrated Circuit Packages. Figure 15-7 represents heat-flow paths schematically for the flat package. Calculation shows that internal free convection and radiation and lead conduction can be neglected. The predominant mode of heat transfer is conduction through the die to the ceramic case. The exact value of the junction-to-case thermal resistance R_{jc} will depend on the die dimensions, manufacturing process and materials, circuit configuration, and the location of the selected case reference point.

At the present time the solder-glass bond between the die and the alumina case has sufficient thickness to cause a very significant thermal resistance. Preliminary calculations for the flat package with die sizes

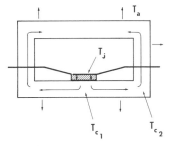

Fig. 15-7 Schematic representation of the heat-flow paths for the flat package.

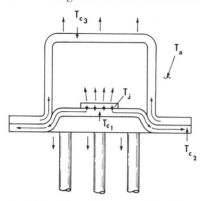

Fig. 15-8 Schematic representation of the heat-flow paths for the TO-5 integrated circuit package.

from 0.025 to 0.050 in. square predict values of AR_{jc}, where A is die area, between 0.125 and 0.500 C° in.²/watt. Limited measurements have been made which provide values of 0.150 and 0.300 C° in.²/watt for a 0.050-in. square die. An examination of the flat-package construction shows that potentially it has good thermal design characteristics since the die is mounted directly on the outer case. An effort will have to be made to reduce the die-to-case thermal resistance.

Figure 15-8 shows a cross section of a TO-5 integrated circuit package with the heat-flow paths schematically indicated. On the basis of uniform dissipation over the top surface of the die, most of the heat is conducted through the die to the header, and then radially through the header to the "lip" or flange and the sides of the package. Again, calculations show that the heat transfer by the internal leads, the internal free convection and radiation heat transfer directly from the die to the case, and the conduction heat transfer through the glass sealing the leads are all negligible. Further calculations based on the die sizes named above in connection with the flat package yield values for AR_{jc} of 0.125 to 0.225 C° in.²/watt for low-power circuitry. The reference point on the case is the lip. Some measurements have been made which provide somewhat lower values in the 0.075 to 0.120 C° in.²/watt range. It should be pointed out that these measurements were made using a calibrated property of a transistor junction (e.g., V_{BE}) as the temperature indicator. The calibrated junction should be in direct proximity to the expected maximum-temperature point, so that the measured R_{jc} will be conservatively based on a hot-spot temperature.

Table 15-3 summarizes representative values for the two packages just treated. One can base approximate calculations on values such as these. A further item of interest in such calculations is the maximum permissible junction temperature, often taken as 175°C.

Table 15-3   Junction-to-case Thermal Resistance Times Die Area, and Temperature Rise of Two Package Types

Characteristic	Flat package	TO-5 package
Typical junction-to-case thermal resistance times die area, C° in.²/watt....................................	0.250	0.200
Junction-temperature rise for typical dissipation (35 mw), C°..	4	3

An Isolated-package Situation. Before discussing a case where many packages have been assembled into a system, let us consider the extreme case of a single isolated package. Simplifying further, let us neglect the leads and consider only the rectan-

gular ceramic box of the flat package and
the cylindrical metal enclosure for the TO-5
package. For an isolated package, external
heat transfer to the surroundings will be only
by radiation and convection from the case.
Figure 15-9 presents surface temperature rise
versus surface power density with altitude as
a parameter. With this chart and with the
package surface areas given in Table 15-4,
one obtains the case-to-ambient-atmosphere
thermal resistance values also given there.
The measured values given in the last column
are lower because of thermal paths contributed by the leads and supports.

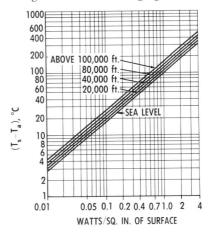

Fig. 15-9 Surface temperature rise versus surface power density with altitude as a parameter.

System Thermal Considerations. Now let
us consider another extreme case wherein
a solid cube is arranged by the closest possible
packing of integrated circuits. Suppose that
these circuits are in flat packages. Figure 15-10 suggests the arrangement. Now
assume that the cube so arranged is itself totally isolated. Once again, heat loss
from its surface will be totally by radiation and convection. Heat transfer from a
package near the center of the cube to the surface of the cube will be almost totally
by conduction, however. Thus the thermal resistance from the case of an inner
package to the atmosphere is a series combination of R_{cs} (cube-center case to surface) and R_{sa} (surface to atmosphere).

Assuming uniform dissipation within the cube, it follows from symmetry that the
temperature at its center T_c will be the maximum temperature existing within the
cube. The case-to-surface thermal resistance R_{cs} (where, of course, case refers to
a package case at cube center) may of course be written as

$$R_{cs} = \frac{T_c - T_s}{P_t} \tag{15-1}$$

where P_t is the total power dissipation within the cube, but it must be realized that
T_s is only approximately constant over the surface, and hence our treatment here is
approximate. Further, it can be shown also in an approximate way that the thermal

Table 15-4   Case-to-atmosphere Thermal Resistance of Two Package Types

Characteristic	Flat package, 0.250 × 0.250 in.	TO-5 package
Surface area, in.²	0.20	0.33
Case-to-atmosphere thermal resistance R_{ca}, C°/watt:		
From Fig. 15-8 (sea level).	800	485
Measured.	250–300	90–150
Case-temperature rise for typical dissipation (35 mw), C°	9–11	3–5

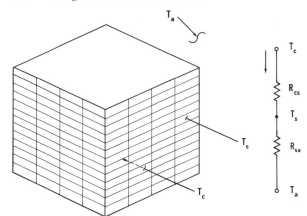

Fig. 15-10 An isolated cube made up of many flat packages arranged in a closest packing configuration, indicating the thermal resistances and temperatures.

resistance from a point near the center of a uniform cube to its surface may be approximated by

$$R_{cs} \approx \frac{0.05}{K_t l} \tag{15-2}$$

where K_t is the thermal conductivity of the material constituting the cube, and l is the length of a cube edge. The surface-to-atmosphere thermal resistance R_{sa} can again be determined from Fig. 15-9.

Numerical Example Pertaining to a System. It will be instructive to carry through a numerical example which emphasizes certain features of this problem. Suppose we treat the case of 2,000 logic circuits in flat packages, each dissipating 35 mw. Using a rule of thumb which allows 100 flat packages/in.^{3}, we have a cube with a volume of 20 in.^{3}. Hence the length l of a cube edge is 2.7 in., and the area of the cube is 44 in.^{2}. Further, the total power dissipation is 2,000 $\times$ 35 mw, or 70 watts. The power density at the cube's surface is therefore 1.6 watts/in.^{2}. From Fig. 15-9 (for sea level) we see that the resulting steady-state temperature difference between the cube's surface and the ambient atmosphere will be in the neighborhood of 130 C$^\circ$.

Now let us look at heat transfer within the cube. The thermal conductivity of the cube has to be an effective value for the composite configuration of alumina, air, leads, etc. Let us take 0.37 watt/C$^\circ$ in. Then from Eq. (15-2), R_{cs} becomes 0.05 C$^\circ$/watt. From Eq. (15-1), then, we find that

$$T_c - T_s = R_{cs}P_t = (0.05 \text{ C}^\circ/\text{watt})(70 \text{ watts}) = 3.5 \text{ C}^\circ \tag{15-3}$$

Hence it is clear that the center-to-surface temperature difference is far smaller than the surface-to-atmosphere temperature difference for a compact but isolated system.

This example emphasizes that arrangements for heat transfer from the system surface to the ultimate heat sink are of paramount importance, and that intra-system temperature rise will not be a serious problem in cases such as low-level logic systems, even for fairly large aggregations of circuits.

Fortunately the most rudimentary external heat sink arrangements represent a vast improvement over the isolated-system example considered above as a worst case.

Further, a metallic cold plate at a face of the cube can drop the center-to-ultimate-sink temperature difference by a factor of 10 to 20.

Practical System Situations. By calculations like these supported by experimental measurements, one can arrive at a junction-to-ultimate-sink thermal resistance R_{ju}. For the ceramic flat package in a system of moderate size, a representative value is 200 C°/watt. For the TO-5 package, a corresponding value is 95 C°/watt. In typical low-power digital integrated circuit situations one encounters an overall temperature rise $(T_j - T_u)$ of the order of 20 C°. As a practical matter, integrated circuits can be operated with an ultimate sink temperature as high as 100°C.

15-6   A Glimpse of Future Integrated Circuit Packaging

With but few exceptions, today's discrete semiconductor devices as well as integrated circuits are packaged in "boxes." They are safely and neatly sealed inside some kind of more-or-less empty container. When we can do away with the container safely and generally, we will of course have a new set of ground rules. A new order of compactness and reliability will again be possible. Problems of interconnection, heat flow, optimum circuit and subsystem size and complexity will all have to be reconsidered. Piece parts will be eliminated in the process, an always-welcome tendency toward simplification with its accompanying increase in system reliability. The contact-bond scheme mentioned in Sec. 15-2 provides an example of piece-part elimination; in that case the bonded wires were eliminated. Similar changes will probably come in the joining of monolithic circuits to each other and to thin-film circuits. The multiphase monolithic procedure described in Chap. 6 in itself has "packaging" ramifications. In short, we still have a way to go before ultimate barriers stop us in the art of integrated circuit and system packaging.

REFERENCES

1. Jakob, M.: "Heat Transfer," vols. I and II, John Wiley & Sons, Inc., New York, 1957.
2. McAdams, W. H.: "Heat Transmission," 3d ed., McGraw-Hill Book Company, 1954.
3. Brown, A. I., and S. M. Marco: "Introduction to Heat Transfer," 3d ed., McGraw-Hill Book Company, New York, 1958.
4. Baum, J. R.: Thermal Design Considerations in Thin-film Microelectronics, *Electro-Technol., New York,* vol. 68, no. 1, pp. 92–94, July, 1961.
5. Early, J. M.: Speed, Power and Component Density in Multi-element High-speed Logic Systems, Digest of Technical Papers, International Solid-State Circuit Conference, pp. 78–79, Philadelphia, Feb. 10–12, 1960.
6. Keonjian, E. (ed.): "Microelectronics," McGraw-Hill Book Company, New York, 1963; Wallmark, J. T.: Heat Considerations, Sec. 2.3, pp. 32–61.
7. Stern, S.: Cooling Power Transistors, *Electron. Ind.,* vol. 18, pp. 77–82, September, 1959.
8. Burke, F. P., Jr.: Dissipating Heat From Transistors, *Electron. Equipment Eng.,* vol. 7, pp. 57–59, July, 1959.
9. Baum, J. R.: Thermal Considerations in the Use of Power Transistors, *Electron. Design,* vol. 7, pp. 56–59, June 10, 1959.
10. Maloff, I. G.: Heat Transfer in Power Transistors, *Electron. Ind.,* vol. 16, p. 54, December, 1957.

11. Luft, W.: Design of Fins for Cooling of Semiconductors, *Elec. Mfg.,* vol. 60, no. 5, pp. 98–103, November, 1957.
12. "Motorola Power Transistor Handbook," Motorola Inc., 1961.
13. Bureau of Ships: Guide Manual of Cooling Methods for Electronic Equipment, *Navships* 900,190.
14. Mark, M., and Stephenson, M.: Design and Performance of Air Cooled Chassis for Electronic Equipment, *IRE Trans. Component Parts,* vol. CP-3, no. 2, pp. 38–44, September, 1956.

Appendix *A*

THE SYMMETRICAL JUNCTION
AT EQUILIBRIUM

The starting point for analysis of the junction at equilibrium is Poisson's equation. In MKS units we may write it as follows:

$$\nabla^2 \psi = -\frac{Q_v}{\kappa \epsilon_o} \tag{1}$$

where Q_v is charge per unit volume. Assuming complete ionization of the impurities and taking account of both carrier charge and ionic charge, we can write Poisson's equation for the case at hand as follows:

$$\nabla^2 \psi = -\frac{q}{\kappa \epsilon_o}(p - n + N_D - N_A) \tag{2}$$

From Eqs. (2-29) through (2-42), it is apparent that p and n can be related very simply to potential by means of the Boltzmann factor; the simplest form of the Boltzmann factor is obtained by choosing the zero of potential at the Fermi level in this equilibrium situation. Thus

$$p = n_i e^{-q\psi/kT} \tag{3}$$
$$n = n_i e^{+q\psi/kT} \tag{4}$$

Hence Eq. (1) can be rewritten* as

$$\nabla^2 \psi = \frac{2qn_i}{\kappa \epsilon_o}\left(\sinh \frac{q\psi}{kT} + \frac{N_A - N_D}{2n_i}\right) \tag{5}$$

The coefficient is sometimes written in terms of an intrinsic Debye length L_i which is defined thus:

$$L_i \equiv \left(\frac{\kappa \epsilon_o kT}{2q^2 n_i}\right)^{\frac{1}{2}} \tag{6}$$

*W. Shockley, The Theory of p-n Junctions in Semiconductors and p-n Junction Transistors, *Bell System Tech. J.*, vol. 38, pp. 435–489, July, 1949.

One might think that the current balance equations mentioned in Sec. 2-3 would facilitate the solution of the junction problem being addressed here. However, they are individually implicit in Eq. (5). That is, equating hole drift and diffusion, for example, provides a differential equation whose solution is the Boltzmann relation, Eq. (3) [given the Einstein relation, Eq. (2-5)].

Equation (5) cannot be solved in closed form, although numerical solutions are, of course, possible and some special cases have been treated.[*] For analytical treatment, certain approximations are conventional. For example, well away from the junction it is considered that mobile charges approximately balance ionic charges, and quasi-neutrality prevails. Thus

$$\nabla^2 \psi = 0 \tag{7}$$

and Poisson's equation reduces to Laplace's equation. In the vicinity of the junction, the mobile charges are treated as negligible in comparison to ionic charge, so that

$$\nabla^2 \psi = \frac{q}{\kappa \epsilon_o} (N_A - N_D) \tag{8}$$

In many cases it is further assumed that a sharp boundary exists, separating the neutral region where Eq. (7) is valid from the ionic-charge region where Eq. (8) applies. This assumption is the basis of the solutions generated in Chap. 2, and as pointed out there, the results agree well with experiment for a wide range of situations.

[*] R. B. Adler and R. L. Longini, "Introduction to Semiconductor Physics," John Wiley & Sons, Inc., New York, 1963.

Appendix B

BUFFERED ETCH (NH$_4$F/HF)

1. Mix eight (8) parts by weight of NH$_4$F to fifteen (15) parts by weight of deionized water. Stir until dissolved and then filter extraneous material.

2. Add HF to the NH$_4$F solution in the volume ratio of $4:1$ NH$_4$F:HF and stir.

3. Store in clean, tightly capped polyethylene bottles.

Appendix *C*

SAFETY CONSIDERATIONS

In modern semiconductor processes a variety of very toxic, corrosive, and explosive materials are routinely employed. Potassium cyanide, hydrofluoric acid, hot sulfuric acid, hydrazine, and hydrogen are a few of these hazardous materials. A number of the precautions required in connection with these materials will be named. Each new material encountered in laboratory work must be carefully studied to determine its hazards. Often a material by itself will not be very dangerous to handle, but will become so if it is allowed to come in contact with certain other materials in the laboratory.

Perhaps the most widely used dangerous material in the industry is hydrofluoric acid (HF). Chemically speaking, HF is characterized as a weak acid. However, HF in contact with the skin can cause severe burns, whose onset is very slow and whose duration is extremely long. It is for this reason that HF is much more dangerous than the common acids which produce immediate reaction. Thus, it is possible for the presence of HF on the skin to go unnoticed for some time, at which point it is too late to do anything about it. In addition to personal hazards, HF poses a potential hazard to equipment because it attacks so many different substances. In practice, HF should be used only in a special polyvinyl chloride (PVC) hood, with adequate protection for the exposed parts of the body, such as the hands and the eyes.

In addition to HF, the more common acids such as HNO_3, H_2SO_4, and HCl are also used in great quantities. These acids produce an immediate burning reaction and so are easy to detect. The same precautions pointed out above apply to these materials. Also, the addition of water to certain concentrated acids results in explosive reactions which can spatter acid for a great distance. This reaction is increased at higher temperatures.

Finally, it should be pointed out that certain acids react with potassium cyanide to evolve cyanide gas, which is a lethal substance. It is important to remember this when planning hoods and drains. Never use cyanide and acid in the same hood or dump them into a common drain system, because minute quantities of HCN are sufficient to cause death. In addition, potassium cyanide itself, widely used in the laboratory for the removal of gold wastes from evaporator parts, is extremely poisonous if ingested.

Liquid nitrogen and other liquefied gases are frequently used in both the experimental and production situations in the semiconductor industry. Liquid nitrogen is commonly transported in open Dewar flasks which have been filled from a large Dewar system. Whenever filling and transporting such vessels of liquid gas, it is imperative that gloves and eye shields be used. A quantity of liquid nitrogen splashed in the eye will freeze and destroy the tissue, resulting in partial or total blindness. Extended exposures of other portions of the body to liquid gas can result in frostbite. Safeguards should also be provided for protection against implosion of the large Dewar vessels used to handle the liquid nitrogen.

In addition to these hazards, the use of arsenic, antimony, and phosphorus derivatives in the diffusion and epitaxial laboratories constitutes a major health hazard. These materials may appear in the form of vaporized liquids or solids, or they may be derived from certain gaseous compounds contained in high-pressure tanks. Substances whose lethal concentration is as low as 0.01 part per million in air are in current use in the industry! Tanks of such materials must be handled with great care and only by trained personnel.

These and other potentially dangerous situations are constantly present. However, common sense and extreme caution combined with adequate training on potential hazards will make semiconductor processing safe, as many firms have demonstrated.

INDEX